Fluid Catalytic Cracking

ACS SYMPOSIUM SERIES 375

Fluid Catalytic Cracking
Role in Modern Refining

Mario L. Occelli, EDITOR
Unocal Corporation

Developed from a symposium sponsored by
the Division of Petroleum Chemistry, Inc.,
at the 194th Meeting
of the American Chemical Society,
New Orleans, Louisiana,
August 30–September 4, 1987

American Chemical Society, Washington, DC 1988

Library of Congress Cataloging-in-Publication Data

Fluid catalytic cracking: role in modern refining
Mario L. Occelli, editor

Developed from a symposium sponsored by the Division
of Petroleum Chemistry, Inc., at the 194th Meeting of the
American Chemical Society, New Orleans, Louisiana,
August 30–September 4, 1987.

p.   cm.—(ACS symposium series, ISSN 0097–6156;
375).

Papers presented at the Symposium on Advances in
FCC, held in New Orleans, La., Aug. 30–Sept. 4, 1987.

Bibliography: p.

Includes index.

ISBN 0–8412–1534–0

1. Catalytic cracking—Congresses.

I. Occelli, Mario L., 1942–   . II. American Chemical
Society. Division of Petroleum Chemistry.
III. Symposium on Advances in FCC (1987: New Orleans,
La.) IV. Series.

TP690.4.F57   1988
665.5′33—dc19   88–22151
                                                CIP

PRINTED IN THE UNITED STATES OF AMERICA

ACS Symposium Series

M. Joan Comstock, *Series Editor*

1988 ACS Books Advisory Board

Foreword

The ACS SYMPOSIUM SERIES was founded in 1974 to provide a medium for publishing symposia quickly in book form. The format of the Series parallels that of the continuing ADVANCES IN CHEMISTRY SERIES except that, in order to save time, the papers are not typeset but are reproduced as they are submitted by the authors in camera-ready form. Papers are reviewed under the supervision of the Editors with the assistance of the Series Advisory Board and are selected to maintain the integrity of the symposia; however, verbatim reproductions of previously published papers are not accepted. Both reviews and reports of research are acceptable, because symposia may embrace both types of presentation.

Contents

INDEXES

Preface

FLUIDIZED CRACKING OF PETROLEUM FRACTIONS is still the main process for large-scale gasoline production even 40 years after its introduction. Worldwide cracking-catalyst sales in 1987 amounted to about $457 million and represented 48% of the total catalyst sales to the petroleum industry.

In response to recent federal and local environmental concerns (e.g., industrial emission controls and lead phase-out) and to the growing interest of refiners in cracking residual fuels, researchers have generated new families of cracking catalysts. There is now a need to review the merits of these newly developed materials. This volume contains contributions from researchers involved in the preparation and characterization of cracking catalysts. Other important aspects of fluid catalytic cracking, such as feedstocks and process hardware effects in refining, have been intentionally omitted because of time limitations and should be treated separately in future volumes.

This volume focuses on the use of novel materials (zeolite beta, pillared clays, or S scavengers) and novel compositions (e.g., those containing lanthanide-free faujasite crystals, shape-selective zeolite, or metal scavengers) in meeting the challenges of lead-free gasoline production, the increasingly stringent S-emission regulations, and the cracking of residual and metal-contaminated oils. Modern spectroscopic techniques, such as nuclear magnetic resonance spectroscopy, X-ray absorption and X-ray photoelectron spectroscopy, laser Raman spectroscopy, and electron microprobe measurements, have been used to characterize extraframework Al in zeolites and to elucidate metal–surface interactions in cracking catalysts. The applied aspects of cracking are discussed in chapters dealing with heavy oils, hydrotreated feedstocks, catalyst demetalation, and catalyst development for resid upgrading.

In concluding, I would like to acknowledge the help received from D. L. Hilfman in chairing the symposium from which this volume was developed and to express my gratitude to colleagues at Unocal Corporation and elsewhere for acting as technical referees. I am also particularly grateful to Unocal for permission to participate in and complete this project and to G. Smith for her invaluable secretarial help. The views and conclusions expressed herein are those of the authors, whom I sincerely thank for their time and effort in presenting their research at the symposium and in preparing the camera-ready manuscripts for this book.

MARIO L. OCCELLI
Unocal Science & Technology Division
P.O. Box 76
Brea, CA 92621

March 9, 1988

Chapter 1

Recent Trends in Fluid Catalytic Cracking Technology

Mario L. Occelli

Unocal Science & Technology Division, Unocal Corporation,
P.O. Box 76, Brea, CA 92621

In the United States, approximately one-third of all
processed crude oil, amounting to about 5×10^6
bbl/day, is catalytically converted over fluidized
catalysts. Over 500 tons of catalyst are required
daily, yielding sales that in 1987 were estimated at
~250 million dollars (1). Thus, in terms of catalyst
usage and product value, catalytic cracking is still
the most important unit operation of the petroleum-
refining industry. This year, the worldwide sales of
catalysts to the petroleum, petrochemical, and
chemical industry are expected to exceed 2.4 billion
dollars, and catalyst producers are preparing
themselves for the turn of the century when catalysts
are projected to become a 5 billion dollars per year
global business (2).

In the United States, the catalytic cracking of petroleum fractions
is believed to have begun in 1936 with the Houdry fixed-bed process
employing a solid regenerable catalyst. E. Houdry observed that
the performance of racing cars could be improved by using
high-octane gasoline obtained from cracking heavy petroleum
fractions over acid-treated montmorillonites or halloysites (3).
Today, catalytic cracking is still the major process for gasoline
manufacture.
   Prior to 1938, gasoline was obtained from thermal-cracking
plants; then the Houdry fixed-bed catalytic cracking process led to
the development of a fluidized-bed process by Standard Oil for the
catalytic production of motor fuels (4-8). Acid-treated clays of
the montmorillonite type were the first fluid-cracking catalysts
widely employed by the industry. However, the ever greater demand
for aviation fuels during the 1939-1945 period prompted the search
for more active and selective catalysts. Research on novel catalyst

0097–6156/88/0375–0001$06.00/0
© 1988 American Chemical Society

formulations thus began, and by the end of World War II, clays were abandoned in favor of synthetic silica-alumina, silica-magnesia, alumina, or even phosphate catalysts (9). The beginnings and early developments of the (FCC) process have been reviewed in detail by Marshall (9).

Amorphous aluminosilicates were used as cracking catalysts for over twenty years; then, in the early sixties, the catalytic properties of synthetic faujasite were discovered, and zeolites rapidly came to dominate the petroleum-refining industry (10,11). The introduction of rare earth-exchanged zeolites X or Y in cracking catalyst preparations was a most important breakthrough because zeolitic catalysts afforded a large increase in cracking activity and gasoline make while minimizing light gases and coke generation. As a result, these new types of catalysts were quickly accepted by refiners.

In 1976, the first African fluid cracking unit became operational in Nigeria, and since then, all of the catalytic cracking units in North America and the USSR employed zeolites. In the years that followed, catalyst manufacturers dedicated a large part of their research efforts to provide refiners with cracking catalysts for processing sweet U.S. and Middle-Eastern crudes. Aluminosilicate matrices, clay minerals (kaolin), and zeolites (with the faujasite structure) were manipulated to yield cracking catalysts capable of satisfying the refiner's special needs (12,13). Research work was then directed mainly toward the generation of FCC with improved physical properties (such as attrition resistance, density, thermal and hydrothermal stability) and gasoline selectivity.

In 1973, the Arab oil embargo and the sudden escalation in crude oil prices (Figures 1,2) and availability placed refiners under great economic pressures to process more abundant, less expensive, metals-contaminated crude oils and residuum feedstocks. The need for metals-resistant FCC became apparent, and work on understanding metal-catalyst interactions became an area of intense research in industrial laboratories and in the academic community.

When in 1984 the Environmental Protection Agency (EPA) proposed the lead phaseout from gasoline, the emphasis on FCC research shifted toward the generation of octane-selective catalysts. Environmental concerns have also proposed limits on sulfur emissions from FCC units, thus initiating research on on catalysts capable of sorbing S-impurities in the regenerator and releasing them as H_2S in the reactor side from where they can be easily adsorbed.

Political events, oil supply and costs, technological breakthroughs, and environmental concerns have influenced, and will probably continue to influence, the petroleum and, therefore, the catalyst manufacturing industry. Thus efforts to understand possible trends in future catalyst activities and research directions must proceed with the understanding of the aforementioned factors.

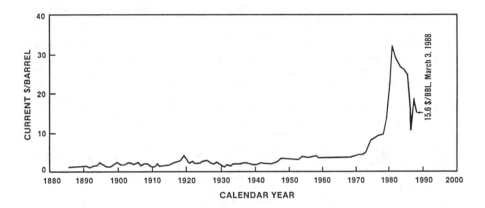

Figure 1   Annual average price (in terms of current dollars) of
             U.S. oil. On March 3, 1988, West Texas crudes traded
             for $15.60/bbl.

Oil Supply, Demand, and Utilization

In response to oil price increases and to structural changes in the economy caused by conservation efforts and by the rapid development of coal, nuclear, and hydroelectric power, oil demand and consumption in industrialized and developing countries have changed considerably. Between 1981 and 1985, refinery capacity in the United States shrunk by almost 3.5 million bbl/d owing to the closing of over 100 refineries (14) and it is expected to remain fairly constant and near the present level in the future. Even in the event of a new oil embargo, excess capacity is available to carry out all essential refining operations provided an adequate crude oil inventory is maintained (14). Simultaneously with an overall capacity reduction, an increase in conversion capacity (as measured by considering fluid catalytic cracking, hydrocracking, residual HDS, and coking capacity) has occurred, Figure 3. The remaining U.S. refineries are the most modern units with the highest conversion capabilities in the world and are expected to successfully compete in the world market well into the 1990's (15).

Use of oil products as transportation fluids will respond only slightly to lower crude prices, and some of the uses for oil may have been irreversibly lost (16). Projections of expected liquid fuels consumption in the United States is shown in Figure 4. Demands for midbarrel (diesel and jet fuels) and residual fuels products will probably remain strong. As a result of more gasoline-efficient vehicles, demand for gasoline is expected to remain near the present level. However, lower crude prices could encourage driving; in one report, demand for gasoline has been projected to grow at an average rate of about 0.5% per year (17). Gasoline consumption will probably continue to depend on crudes' availability.

Even before the 1986 price collapse, U.S. oil imports were expected to rise during the 1980-1990 period. The present decline in oil price, together with windfall profit taxes, will likely discourage exploration in the continental United States resulting in even faster and larger growth in oil imports in the near future; in 1986, oil imports climbed by almost one million bbl/d above 1985 (15). Fluctuations in oil prices are expected and U.S. Department of Energy (DOE) workers have made projections about U.S. oil imports based on "low" and "high" oil price values (15); see Figure 5. The lower oil price case is based on $15/bbl until 1990, after which the oil price will gradually increase to about $22/bbl by 1995. The higher oil price case is based on a $23/bbl oil price until 1990 and on $25/bbl in 1995 (15). These price fluctuations will cause oil imports to fluctuate between 10 and 8 million barrels of oil in 1995; see Figure 5. Because almost 100% of the world's current excess oil production capacity (as well as about 75% of the known oil reserves) is in OPEC, it is likely that future U.S. oil imports will continue to depend strongly on the availability of crudes from Persian Gulf states (15).

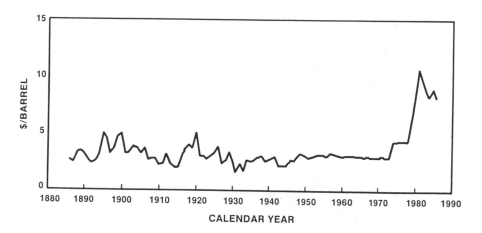

Figure 2   Annual average price of U.S. oil for the 1886-1986
period corrected for inflation (18).

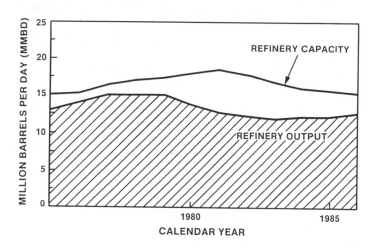

Figure 3   U.S. oil refining capacity and output (15).

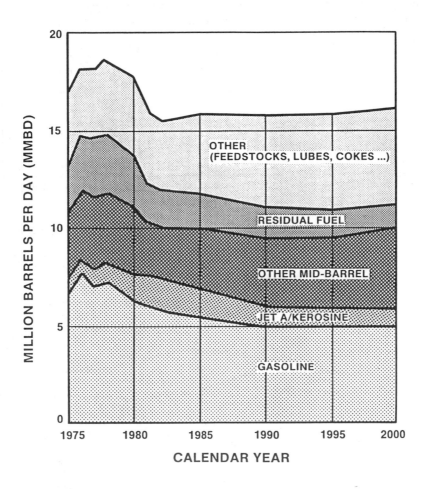

Figure 4   Projected trends in U.S. liquid fuels demands.

A perspective on the historical pricing of crudes is shown in Figure 1 (18). If the same annual average price of U.S. crudes is corrected for inflation (i.e., expressed in terms of 1967 constant U.S. dollars), it can be seen that the real price of crudes rose almost fourfold during the 1972-1980 period; see Figure 2 (18). The data in Figures 1-2 project that (in a free market system) oil prices in the future should stabilize near 11.50-16.50 current dollars/bbl. Middle-East politics make return to historical oil price ranges unlikely and higher oil prices are expected. With about 10 million bbl/d of excess oil capacity and somewhat flat oil demand, world oil prices will more than likely stabilize in the 15-25 U.S. dollars/bbl range.

Octane Catalysts

In little more than a decade, unleaded gasoline (that is gasoline containing less than 0.05 gr Pb/gal) usage has increased from zero to represent (in 1986) more than 68% of all the gasoline sold in the United States (19). Since most of the vehicles using leaded gasoline are pre-1975 car and truck models, unleaded gasoline consumption is expected to increase with the replacement of old vehicles with newer models. The United States replaces approximately 10% of its automotive stock each year (20). Refiners have two main options to increase the octane number from FCC units. They can change operating variables and/or use octane-enhancing cracking catalysts.

Gasoline octane from FCC units is very sensitive to operating conditions. Increases in riser temperature, together with reductions in catalyst/oil contact times, will decrease hydrogen transfer reactions (and minimize secondary cracking), thus generating olefin-rich gasolines with improved octane numbers. The choice of feedstocks rich in naphthenes and aromatics will also help in producing gasoline high in octane (21). However, gas oil aromaticity can reduce the catalyst octane enhancing properties and increase coke generation. Octane cracking catalysts minimize H-transfer reactions and favor the secondary cracking of hydrocarbons in the gasoline boiling range with formation of butanes and other low molecular weight gases, at the expense of gasoline yields. Since these reactions are endothermic, the use of octane-boosting catalysts increases the heat of reaction in commercial FCC units (22). Higher catalyst circulation will increase the coke burned in the regenerator and bring the unit back into heat balance (22). Thus, the judicious choice of operating variables can help minimize octane losses owing to tetraethyl lead phaseout and problems associated with octane catalyst usage.

In the early 70's, FCC formulations containing 10-40% CREY (calcined rare-earth exchanged Y zeolites) were widely employed because these catalysts offered improved chemical as well as thermal and hydrothermal stability over FCC compositions containing equivalent amounts of (low sodium) HY crystals (23-25). The presence of lanthanide ions in the zeolite increased hydrogen transfer reactions like those in which easily cracked olefins and naphthenes are transformed into more refractory products (olefins + naphthenes = aromatics + paraffins), thus increasing gasoline yields (26). However, since octane losses from olefins saturation are greater than octane gains from aromatics generation, hydrogen transfer reactions will have to be minimized now that octane-boosting lead compounds can no longer be used. As a result, CREY has been replaced by siliceous HY (ultrastable HY,USY) crystals in most octane FCC. Since the Environmental Protection Agency (EPA) first proposed lead phaseout from gasoline in late 1984, production of USY more than doubled; an estimate of catalyst usage in catalytic cracking (and in other refining processes) is given in Table 1. To compensate in part for hydrothermal stability losses due to rare-earth ions removal, FCC containing REHY or both CREY and HY crystals have now become available, thus restoring to the refiner the flexibility needed to confront the complexity of a particular operation.

The use of a shape-selective zeolite, such as Mobil's ZSM-5, has attracted the refiner's interest because this zeolite selectively cracks low-octane n-paraffins (and olefins) into higher octane components (27). Gasoline octane is thus increased by a few points, and the light olefins produced can be alkylated to high octane liquids that compensate for gasoline losses. In 1986, Mobil reported the evaluation of ZSM-5 containing FCC in 20 commercial cracking units (28). Nevertheless, to date, refiners' response to ZSM-5 containing FCC has been somewhat guarded, probably due to royalty costs and/or alkylation limitations.

Gasoline octane also strongly depends on the gasoline boiling range used during a certain period. More volatility is needed in winter gasolines for easier cold-engine starting, and less volatility is desirable for summer gasolines to reduce vapor lock problems. For these reasons, refiners may reduce the gasoline final boiling point in winter and raise the initial boiling point in summer, thus affecting octane. The challenge to researchers and catalyst manufacturers is to provide the refiners with versatile, stable, cracking catalysts capable of enhancing the octane number (possibly at constant operating conditions) while producing gasoline with the desired vapor pressure limits.

Metals Resistant Cracking Catalysts

The difficulty of converting more abundant, less expensive, but metals-contaminated, residuum feedstocks (and crude oils) into liquid products by direct catalytic cracking is recognized; nevertheless, there is still an economic incentive justifying efforts to convert these oils into useful products. As a result, metal levels in equilibrium FCC have been steadily increasing regardless of crude prices; see Figure 6. During the last 20 years, V/Ni ratios have not changed appreciably and have remained in the 1.4 to 1.7 range, indicating a fairly stable supply of crudes and crudes selection (28).

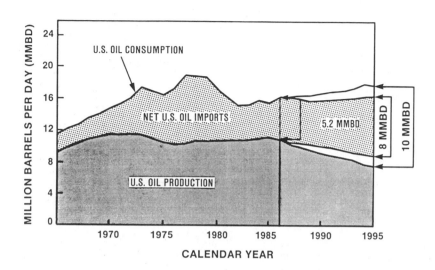

Figure 5   Projections of U.S. oil imports based on low and high
             crude price values (15).

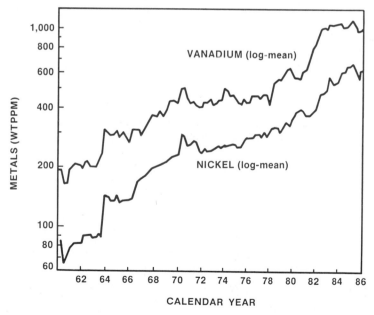

Figure 6   Trends on Metal Levels on Equilibrium Fluid Cracking
             Catalysts (28).

TABLE 1 ESTIMATED REFINING CATALYSTS/USAGE IN 1987

REFINING PROCESSES	CAPACITY MILLIONS OF BPCD	CATALYST CONSUMP., LB/BBL	USAGE, MILLIONS OF LB	UNIT PRICE, $ LB	U.S.	W. EUROPE	OTHERS	WORLD
CAT. CRACKING	4.9	0.2	380	0.70	250	76	131	457
HYDROTREATING	8.4	0.009	28	3.00	84	42	63	189
ALKYLATION, H_2SO_4	0.50	18	3,300	0.03	99	1	6	106
HYDROCRACKING	1.0	0.013	4.7	10.00	47	9	42	98
CAT. REFORMING	3.5	0.0033	4.5	6.50	27	15	21	63
ALKYLATION, HF	0.40	0.15	22	0.70	15	3	5	23
ISOMERIZATION	0.25	0.015	1.4	6.00	8	4	2	14
OLIGOMERIZATION	0.05	-	-	-	-	-	-	-
TOTAL					**530**	**150**	**270**	**950**

Header spanning: "TYPICAL U.S. AVERAGES" spans CAPACITY / CATALYST CONSUMP. / USAGE / UNIT PRICE columns; "CATALYST MARKET (MILLIONS OF U.S. $)" spans U.S. / W. EUROPE / OTHERS / WORLD columns.

SOURCE: Reproduced with permission from reference 1. Copyright 1988 Gulf Publishing Company.

Processing of metals-contaminated feedstocks has been practiced since 1961 by Phillips at Borger, Texas. By 1981, 24 other units were using heavy oils in their FCC operations (29-30). At the present, it is believed that by 1989, 15-20 resid units will be operational and that by 1995, 25-30% of the world's FCC units will be partially operating as resid crackers (2). Refiners without the capability of converting resids and less costly oils into transportation liquids will probably suffer in a most competitive energy market.

Crude oil consists mainly of a mixture of paraffinic, naphthenic, and aromatic hydrocarbons with small amounts of metals-containing heterocyclic compounds. The most abundant metals found in oils are those contained in porphyrin or porphyrin-like complexes (nickel, copper, iron, and vanadium). These organo-metallic compounds can be volatized with relative ease, thus contaminating catalysts used to upgrade the various distillate fractions.

The deactivation of FCC catalysts by feed metals is believed to be caused by a partial or total blockage of the catalyst pore structure, by the irreversible destruction of the zeolite crystallinity (by V and, to a lesser extent, by Cu) and by the great activity that metals like Ni (and Fe), when activated, show toward coke and hydrogen formation. Conventional methods of crude oil demetallization (such as H_2 pretreating) are not economical. It is also possible to contact a contaminated surface with a gaseous HCl-Cl$_2$ mixture and remove metal impurities in the form of volatile chlorides (31-33). Since this procedure could offer corrosion problems and affect the catalyst stability, it is not widely practiced in the industry even though effective.

Resistance to metals (like Ni, V, Cu, and Fe) contaminants on a cracking catalyst surface can be achieved by modifying the composition and the microporous structure of the catalyst or by adding metals like Sb, Bi (34), or Sn, (35) or Sb-Sn combinations (36) capable of forming inert residues on the catalyst surface. Antimony organics have been shown to reduce by 50% gas formation due to metal contaminants, especially nickel (37,38). Vanadium passivation has not been as successful, although tin has been reported capable of reducing the deleterious effects of V-contaminants (39). So far, best results in the laboratory have been obtained with dual-function cracking catalyst (DFCC) systems containing metal scavengers capable of retaining an FCC useful cracking activity even when metal-loaded with as much as 1.0-1.5% vanadium (40,41). The DFCC systems containing natural layered magnesium silicates as a separate distinct particle (40,41) or incorporated into a synthetic mixed oxide matrix (42) could become of particular interest in the preparation of FCC formulations for resid cracker units.

Sulfur and Nitrogen Resistant Catalysts

Gas oils contain sulfur typically in the 0.3-3.0% range, with residual fuels having as much as 4.0% S (and 1.0% N). Most of this S leaves a cracking unit as H_2S with the cracked products from which it is easily removed with amine solutions. The rest (10-20% S) is carried in the regenerator buried in the spent catalyst coke. Following the oxidative decomposition of carbonaceous deposit and catalyst regeneration, sulfur (mostly as SO_3) leave the regenerator with flue gases, thus contributing to atmospheric pollution. Present S-emission standards could probably be met by flue gas desulfurization or by feed desulfurization via hydrotreating. These methods, although effective, require substantial and costly capital investments. The use of additives (to FCC) capable of sorbing S in the regenerator as heat stable sulfates and releasing it as H_2S in the reactor side is probably the most cost effective approach to minimize S-emissions from FCC units (43,44). Although sales in 1985 amounted only to ~$15 million/year, it has been predicted that additives sales will double every year for the next 4 to 5 years (45).

    Alumina, alkaline-earth oxides, mixed oxides (spinels), rare-earth oxides, and lanthanide ores are known additives capable of sorbing S-impurities. The properties of these materials can be manipulated to produce catalysts capable of reducing up to ~80% S-emissions and meet the refiner needs. It is, however, unlikely that these systems will be capable of satisfying the more stringent environmental S-emission standards expected in the future. Details of the reaction mechanism by which additives and promoters catalyze the oxidative sorption of S-impurities and details of catalyst deactivation have not yet been proposed. This work could provide useful information to help design more efficient S-transfer catalysts. The catalytic control of S-emissions from FCC units has been described in detail in two papers appearing in this volume (46,47) and in the references given (59).

    Nitrogen contaminants in the feed, in addition to increasing NOx-emissions from the regenerator, reduce catalyst activity and gasoline selectivity (48). Basic N-compounds neutralize the catalyst acid sites, thus decreasing cracking activity while increasing carbon make (49). An alternative to costly feed pretreatments (such as hydrotreating, solvent extraction, or absorption of N-compounds) is catalyst modification to increase N-resistance (50). Matrix composition and porosity, rare-earth levels, and Si/Al ratio in the zeolite are parameters that deserve studying. Recently, it has been reported that polycarboxylic acids and certain amorphous aluminosilicates can function as N-scavengers and reduce the deleterious effects of N-contaminants on FCC properties (51,52). More such materials are expected to appear in the patent literature in the future.

The Future

Oil shortages have, at the present, disappeared, but refiners are nonetheless under economic pressure to process metals-contaminated residual oils (fractions boiling above 340°, such as ATB, HGO, VGO) to produce nothing less valuable than the feed to the cracking unit (29); see Figure 6. Our dependence on oil from OPEC countries will increase (Figure 5); therefore, instabilities in Middle-East politics could precipitate another oil embargo, forcing refiners to consider processing readily available, but metals-contaminated, crudes from the Americas. Metals on catalysts will probably increase significantly above the levels shown in Figure 6 and dual function cracking catalysts (DFCC) containing metal scavengers capable of withstanding as much as 1.5 wt% V could play an important role in the refining technology of the 1990s. Research on novel (natural and synthetic) metal scavengers will probably continue in an effort to find a more universal catalyst (like a multiple-particle system, MFCC) capable of passivating simultaneously the various impurities (metals, S, N) associated with certain abundant crudes (from Venezuela and Mexico) and residual fuels.

Refining problems resulting from Federal and State environmental regulations will continue to represent great business opportunities for catalyst manufacturers. National and international concern about air pollution from industrial sources should foster the demand for more stringent emissions control standards. Thus, novel, more efficient S and N scavengers, especially for West Coast refineries, will be required. Research on octane-boosting catalysts will continue well into the 1990s, since more lead can be removed from gasoline, and lead phasedown is now beginning also in Europe. As a result of expected federal concerns, in the future gasoline will have lower vapor pressure limits. Therefore, new octane-boosting cracking catalysts that minimize butanes formation will be required. The unique structural characteristics of newly synthesized zeolites and molecular sieves like the aluminophosphates and silicoaluminophosphates reported by Union Carbide workers (53) could provide new additives and components for FCC formulations. New large-pore, shape selective materials (like pillared clays, delaminated clays, and 18-membered ring molecular sieves of the VPI-5 type) (54,55) could be used to selectively crack and transform branched naphthenes and polyalkyl aromatics in the LCGO fractions to BTX (benzene, toluene, and xylenes) components in the gasoline boiling range.

Although gasoline demand is not expected to change greatly, consumption of LCGO, light cycle gas oil, (221°-343°C) has been projected to increase in the future; see Figure 4. This distillate, a major component of No. 2 fuel oil and diesel fuels, is almost as valuable as gasoline and is highly regarded in Europe and in Japan. Pillared and delaminated clays are the only cracking catalysts that have exhibited LCGO-selectivity, probably because their large pore openings (~8 x 15A) afford the cracking of high molecular weight hydrocarbons in the SO, slurry oil, range (>343°C) (56). Large-pore molecular sieves (like VPI-5) (54), amorphous aluminosilicate particles with variable SiO_2/Al_2O_3 ratio and pseudo-bohemite containing materials are other candidates of potential interest in the preparation of LCGO-selective FCC.

Fast deactivation rates due to coking and the limited hydrothermal stability of pillared clays have probably retarded the commercial development of these new type of catalysts and prevented (to date) their acceptance by chemical producers and refiners. However, there is a large economic incentive justifying efforts to convert inexpensive (i.e. $40-100/ton) smectites into commercially viable (pillared clay) catalysts (56). Therefore, it is believed that work on the chemical modification of natural (and synthetic) clays, and work on the preparation and characterization of new pillared clays with improved hydrothermal stability are, and will remain, areas of interest to the academic community, as well as to researchers in industrial laboratories (56).

According to a recent survey (58), catalyst manufacturers offered 45 new catalysts in 1987, bringing to more than 170 the commercially available FCC. Close inspection of these materials indicates that there is, at the present, a trend toward forming customized specialty FCC and several of the new formulations appear to be incremental modifications of existing FCC compositions (58). Bold (high risk) research programs aimed at developing new materials are needed to improve the understanding of the technologies used in making novel FCC formulations. Industry sources have reported that FCC worldwide capacity is 1.5 times greater than actual demand (2). Catalyst producers involved in long-range research will probably be able to develop new and outstanding products capable of generating the technological advantage necessary to survive and prosper in a most competitive future energy market.

Finally, the increasing availability and application of modern characterization techniques such as laser Raman spectroscopy, solid state NMR (MASNMR), x-ray photoelectron spectroscopy (XPS), and extended X-ray analysis of fine structures (EXAFS), together with transmission and scanning electron microscopy (TEM and SEM), will stimulate basic research and encourage fundamental studies of the chemical nature of catalytic surfaces and provide guidance into the mostly empirical approach to catalyst design. Commitment to integrate basic research results and newly synthesized compositions and structures (molecular sieves and supports) with process research will be essential to the successful translation of technological advances into novel catalyst formulations capable of meeting the challenges that await modern refineries.

Acknowledgment

Special thanks is given to Dr. D. Fenton for providing useful information and references.

REFERENCES

1. Hoffman, H. L. Hydrocarbon Processing, p. 41, February 1987.
2. Chemical Week, p. 20, June 24, 1987.
3. Voge, H. H. in "Heterogeneous Catalysis, Selected American Histories," ACS Symposium Series 222, Eds., B. H. Davis and W. P. Hettinger, 1983, p. 235.
4. O'Dell, W. W. U.S. Patent No. 1,984,380, 1934.
5. Hemminger, C. E. U. S. Patent No. 2,303,047, 1942.
6. Brueckmann, F. G. U. S. Patent No. 2,303,680, 1942.
7. Gohr, E. T.; Thompson, W. I. and Martin, H. Z. U.S. Patent No. 2,320,273, 1943.
8. Tyson, C. W. U. S. Patent No. 2,322,075, 1943.
9. Marshall, S. Petroleum Refiner, 31, 9, 263, 1952.
10. Plank, C. J.; Rosinski, E. J. and Hawthorne, W. P. Ind. Eng. Chem., Prod. Res. Dev., 1964, 3, 165.
11. Plank, C. J. and Rosinski, E. J. Chem. Eng. Prog. Symps. Ser., 1967, 73 (63), 26.
12. Magee, J. S. and Blazek, J. J. in Chemistry and Catalysis, J. A. Rabo, Ed., ACS Monograph, 171, 615, 1976.
13. Magee, J. S. Molecular Sieves II, J. R. Katzer, Ed., ACS Monograph No. 40, 650, 1977.
14. Cobb, C. B. Chemical Eng. Progress, p. 1c, April 1987.
15. Energy Security, A Report to the President of the United States; U.S. Department of Energy, March 1987.
16. Abelson, P. H. Science, 232,4747, p. 141, April 1986.
17. Oil and Gas Journal, October 13, 1986.
18. Pferd, J. W. Unocal, private communication, 1986.
19. National Petroleum News, p. 29, June 1986.
20. Starks, L. Oil and Gas. J., December 1987.
21. Magee, J. S.; Ritter, R. E.; Wallace, D. N. and Blazek, J. J. Oil and Gas Journal, p. 63, August 4, 1980.
22. Leuenberger, E. J. and Wilbert, L. J. Oil and Gas Journal, p. 38, May 25, 1987.
23. Rabo, J. A., Pickert, P. E., Stamires, D. N. and Boyle, J. E. Actes 2nd Int. Congr. Catal. Paris, 1960, 1961, 2, 2055.
24. Rabo, J. A., Angell, C. L. and Schomaker, V., Proc. Int. Congr. Catal. 4th Moscow, 1968, p. 135 (Akademiai, Budapest, 1971), Vol. II.
25. Letzsch, W. S., Ritter, R. E. and Vaughan, D. E. W., Oil Gas J., 1971, 69 (47), 130.
26. Venuto, P. B. and Habib, E. T. in "Fluid Catalytic Cracking with Zeolite Catalysts," M. Dekker, Inc., 1979.
27. Anderson, C. D. et al., Iberoamerican Symp. Cat., Lisbon, Portugal (1984).
28. Ushiba, K. and Dautzenberg, F., California Cat. Soc. Fall Meeting, Los Angeles, CA, October 22, 1987.
29. Murphy, J. R. and Logwinuk, A. K. NPRA Annual Meeting, AMSI-29, 11, 1981.
30. Ritter, R. E. et al., NPRA Annual Meeting, AM81-44, 1-4 1981.

31. Gooth, E. et al., _Am. J. Sci._, VII, 41,371, 1899.
32. Havens, J. and Way, L. _Am. J. Sci._, VII, 41,219, 1899.
33. Suggitt, T. and Paull, R. U.S. Patent No. 4,013,546, 1977.
34. McKay, D. L. U.S. Patent No. 4,153,536, 1979.
35. Readal, T., McKinney, J. D. and Titmus, R. U. S. Patent No.
     3,977,963, 1976.
36. Mitchell, B. and Swift, H. E. U.S. Patent No. 4,101,417, 1978.
37. Murphy, J. R. in "Sym., Prod., Character., Process of Heavy
     Oils, etc.," University of Utah, 5, 1981.
38. Gall, J. W. et al., NPRA Annual Meeting, AM82-50, 5, 1982.
39. English, A. R.; Kowalczyk, D.C. _Oil & Gas J._ July 16, 1984,
     127.
40. Occelli, M. L. this volume.
41. Occelli, M. L. and Stencel, J. M. this volume.
42. DeJong, J. I. U.S. 4,519,897, 1985.
43. McArthur, D. P.; Simpson, H. D.; Baron, K., 1981, _Oil Gas J._,
     79, (8), 55.
44. Hemler, C. L.; Vermillion, W. L. _Oil Gas J._, Nov. 5, 1973, 88.
45. _Chemical Week_, p. 26, June 26, 1985.
46. Hirschberg, E. H. and Bertolacini, R. J., this volume.
47. Rheaume, L. and Ritter, R. E., this volume.
48. Dallhoff, R. A. _Oil Gas J._, Feb. 22, 1982, 137.
49. Voltz, S. E.; Nace, D. M.; Jacob, S. M.; Weekman, Jr. V. W.
     Inq. Enq. Chem. Process Des. Dev., 1972, 11, 263.
50. Scherzer, J. and McArthur, D. P. _Oil and Gas J._, Oct. 27, p.
     76, 1986.
51. Occelli, M. L. U.S. Patent No. 4,708,786, 1987.
52. Occelli, M. L. and Aitken, E. J. U.S. Patent No. 4,731,174,
     1988.
53. Flanigen, E. M. et al., "New Developments in Zeolite Science
     and Technology," Stud. Surf. Sci. Catal., 28, p. 103,
     Elsevier, Amsterdam, 1986.
54. Davis, M. E.; Saldarriaga, C.; Montes, C.; Garces, J. and
     Crowder, C. _Nature_, 331, 698, 1988.
55. _Chem. and Enq. News_, p. 22, March 21, 1988.
56. Occelli, M. L. _I&EC Prod. Res. and Dev. J._, 22,4,553, 1983.
57. Occelli, M. L. in "Keynotes in Energy Related Catalysis," S.
     Kaliaguin, Ed., Elsevier, p. 101, 1988.
58. _Oil and Gas J._, p. 41, Oct. 5, 1987.
59. Bhattacharyya, A. A., Woltermann, G. M., Yoo, J. S., Karch, J.
     A. and Cormier, W. E., ACS Div. of Fuel Chemistry, Vol. 32, No.
     4, p. 397, 1987.

RECEIVED June 27, 1988

Chapter 2

Tetrahedral and Octahedral Extraframework Aluminum in Ultrastable Y Zeolites

Implications in the Cracking of Gas Oil

A. Corma[1], V. Forneś[2], A. Martiñez[1], and J. Sanz[2]

[1]Instituto de Catalisis y Petroleoquímica, CSIC, Serrano, 119, 28006–Madrid, Spain
[2]Instituto de Ciencia de Materiales, CSIC, Serrano, 115 bis, 28008–Madrid, Spain

It is shown by ^{27}Al MAS-NMR that, besides tetrahedral framework Al ($\sim$60 ppm), extraframework pentacoordinated or tetrahedrally distorted Al ($\sim$30-40 ppm), and octahedral extraframework aluminum ($\sim$0 ppm), tetrahedral Al in amorphous silica-alumina is formed during the dealumination of Y zeolite, either by steam or by $SiCl_4$ treatment. This silica-alumina shows characteristic hydroxyl groups at 3600-3610 cm^{-1}, with acid strength higher than that of zeolite framework hydroxyls. By mild acid or basic treatments it is possible to change the proportion of the different types of aluminum that affect the cracking of gas-oil. It has been found that in highly steam-dealuminated HY zeolites a radical cracking mechanism increases the formation of C_1 and C_2 on HY zeolites with less than 5 Al per unit cell.

Despite the fact that many zeolites have been synthesized in the last 20 years, zeolite Y remains the active zeolitic component in most commercial cracking catalysts.

Different procedures can be used in practice to activate the zeolite, and the choice of a particular method will depend on the catalytic characteristics desired. If the main objective is to prepare a very active cracking catalyst, then a considerable percentage of the sodium is exchanged by rare earth cations. On the other hand, if the main purpose is to obtain gasoline with a high RON, ultrastable Y zeolites (USY) with very low Na$^+$ content are prepared. Then a small amount of rare earth cations is exchanged, but a controlled steam deactivation step has to be introduced in the activation procedure to obtain a controlled dealumination of the zeolite. This procedure achieves a high thermal and hydrothermal stability of the zeolite, provided that silicon is inserted in the vacancies left by extraction of Al from the framework (1). The commercial catalysts so obtained have framework Si/Al ratios in the

0097–6156/88/0375–0017$06.00/0
© 1988 American Chemical Society

range of 5 to 9. When the "fresh" catalyst is introduced in a
cracking unit, further dealumination takes place during regeneration
of the catalyst. Therefore, the zeolite in the equilibrium catalyst
can have an average framework Si/Al ratio as high as 80. It is
possible to extract part of the extraframework aluminum (EFAL)
generated during the activation procedure by a chemical treatment,
or even to dealuminate the zeolite, leaving practically no EFAL on
it (2). However, the EFAL generated during catalyst regeneration
accumulates in the zeolite outer surface (3,4). This extraframework
aluminum can either play a positive role such as converting bottoms,
or can act negatively, catalyzing undesired reactions. Therefore
the formation of EFAL should be performed in such a way that its
positive effects could be preserved, while the negative ones are
avoided or minimized. It should be possible by using different
dealumination methods to produce different EFAL levels as well as
control the nature of the EFAL generated.

   We have characterized HY zeolites dealuminated by different
procedures and at different levels and have shown that the
proportion of the different types of EFAL can be controlled.
Furthermore, all the zeolite modifications clearly influence the
product distribution during gas-oil cracking.

Experimental
Materials

The starting NaY zeolite was an SK-40 from Union Carbide with a
framework Si/Al ratio of 2.4. Ultrastable HY zeolites (HYUS) were
prepared by steam-calcination of partially ammonium exchanged
zeolites at atmospheric pressure and 550-750 °C during 3-20 hours.
After dealumination they were exchanged twice with an NH_4^+ solution
at 80 °C for one hour and then calcined at 550 °C for 3 hours. In
this way dealuminated samples containing less than 2% of the
original Na^+ were obtained. One of these (HYUS-8) was subjected to
different treatments: (1) washed with a solution of citric acid or
HCl (pH=3) at 25 °C for one hour (samples HYUSAC and HYUSl,
respectively); (2) washed with a solution 0.1 M of NaOH at 40 °C
for one hour (HYUSN), and (3) washed with a 38% v/v solution of
acetylacetone in ethanol at 20 °C for 2 hours (HYUSA).
   The $F_6Si(NH_4)_2$ dealuminated sample (HYF) was obtained following
the procedure described in the patent literature (2). Samples
dealuminated with $SiCl_4$ were prepared following Ref. 5, working
at temperatures of 400, 450 and 500 °C (HYD-T). The characteristics
of the zeolite samples are given in Table I. The gas-oil was a
vacuum gas-oil whose physicochemical properties are described
elsewhere (6).
   The unit cell constant of the zeolites were determined by X-ray
diffraction using CuKα radiation and following ASTM procedure
D-3942-80. The estimated standard deviation was $\pm$ 0.01 Å. The
crystallinity of the samples were calculated by comparing the peak
height of the (5,3,3) peak, and considering the reference NaY SK-40
as representing 100% crystallinity.
   The ^{27}Al Magic Angle Spinning (MAS)-NMR spectra were obtained
in a Bruker MSL-400 spectrometer (ν_{Al}=104.25 MHz). A 2 s pulse
(30° degree) was used with a repetition time of 2 s between pulses
in order to avoid saturation effects. Zircona cylindrical sample

TABLE I

STRUCTURAL AND CHEMICAL CHARACTERISTICS OF DEALUMINATED HY ZEOLITES

Zeolite	Si/Al[a]	u.c. (Å)	Si/Al[b]	Al/u.c.	Cryst. %
HYUS-6	2.9	24.48	5.9	28.0	85
HYUS-8	2.8	24.42	8.1	21.1	90
HYUS-14	2.8	24.34	14.2	12.6	90
HYUS-141	2.3	24.24	141.0	1.4	70
HYD-400	4.0	24.31	21.2	8.6	90
HYD-450	10.4	24.22	--	~0	90
HYD-500	10.2	24.20	--	~0	30
HYUSAC	4.2	24.40	9.2	18.8	100
HYUS1	3.2	24.42	8.1	21.1	100
HYUSN	2.3	24 39	9.9	17.6	95
HYUSA	2.9	24.37	11.0	16.0	95
HYF	5.2	24.43	7.7	22.1	100

[a] From chemical analysis

[b] Calculated from Fichtner-Schmittler equation

spinners with 5 mm inner diameter were used and the spinning frequency was in the range 4-4.5 KHz. Cross polarization and proton decoupling were not used. The number of accumulations was 400. All measurements were carried out at room temperature with $Al(H_2O)_6^{+3}$ as standard reference; the mean error in the measured isotropic chemical shift was 0.5 ppm. ^{27}Al spectra were obtained using a spectral width of 50 KHz and data acquired in 2K points of memory. The background signal from the probe was negligeable, special attention was paid to remove from the Free Induction Decay (FID) the points associated with the radio frequency pulse that are the origin of ficticious broad components in the spectra. In order to prevent the quantitative relation between peak intensities, no mathematical procedures for data treatment (such as multiplication of the FID by an exponential function) were used. Spectra deconvolution was carried out assuming a gaussian profile for each component; the intensity of each component was obtained by integration over the corresponding curve and normalization to a hundred for the intensity of the spectra.

Infrared spectroscopic measurements were carried out in a conventional greaseless IR cell. Wafers of 10 mg.cm^{-2} were pretreated overnight at 400 °C and 1.33 x 10^{-3} Pa of dynamic vacuum. The spectra in the 4000-3300 cm^{-1} region were recorded at room temperature in a Perkin Elmer 580 B spectrophotometer equipped with Data Station. For the pyridine adsorption experiments, 6.66 x 10^{2} Pa of pyridine was introduced into the cell at room temperature. After equilibrium the samples were outgassed at temperatures in the range of 250-400 °C under vacuum, and the spectra were recorded at room temperature.

Gas-oil cracking was carried out in a fixed bed tubular reactor at atmospheric pressure and 482 °C. Average yields of the different products -diesel, gasoline, gases (methane, ethane, ethylene, C_3, C_4), and coke- were measured at different levels of conversion by varying the catalyst to oil ratio in the range 0.025-0.40 g.g^{-1}, but always at 60 sec on-stream. The operational procedure has been detailed elsewhere (6).

Results and Discussion

^{27}Al NMR Characterization

The ^{27}Al NMR spectra of three steam-dealuminated HY zeolites are shown in Figure 1. They show one intense line centered at ~60 ppm (tetrahedral aluminum, Al^{IV}) and two more lines at ~30 ppm and ~0 ppm (octahedral aluminum, Al^{VI}). A line at ~30 ppm, observed in hydrothermally treated amorphous silica-alumina (7) and HY zeolites (7,8), has been assigned to a pentacoordinated (7) or to strongly distorted tetrahedrally coordinated nonframework aluminum nuclei (8). Figure 1 clearly shows that the percentage of aluminum related to the ~30 ppm line increases as the severity of the treatment increases. On the other hand, spectrum 1c is very similar to that reported for steamed amorphous silica-alumina (7). Moreover, if we take into account the intensity of the framework Al^{IV} (34%), it becomes difficult to understand a value of 140 for the zeolite framework Si/Al ratio obtained from the unit cell size value (24.24 Å). This effect also appears in the spectra of the two samples dealuminated by $SiCl_4$, HYD-450, and HYD-500 (Fig. 2). These

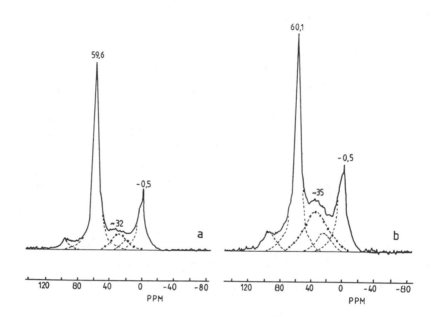

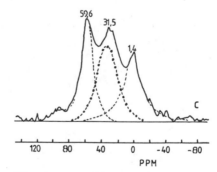

Figure 1. ^{27}Al MAS–NMR spectra of steamed samples.
a. HYUS–8 sample
b. HYUS–14 "
c. HYUS–141 "

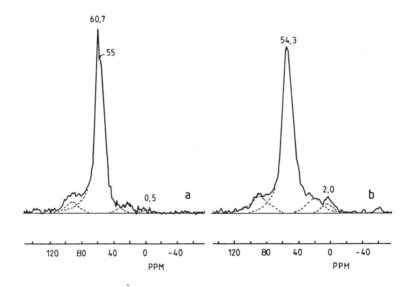

Figure 2. ^{27}Al MAS–NMR spectra of SiCl$_4$ treated samples.
a. HYD–450
b. HYD–500

two samples show a quite intense ^{27}Al NMR line at ~60 ppm, while the unit cell size values are 24.22 and 24.20 Å. The spectrum of sample HYD-450 (Fig. 2a) shows two types of Al^{IV}, one at ~60 ppm and another at ~54 ppm. However, in the spectrum of sample HYD-500 (Fig. 2b), only one type of Al^{IV} remains at 54.3 ppm.

These results show that it is difficult in any of the highly dealuminated samples studied here to prove that the Al^{IV} observed corresponds only to framework aluminum of the zeolite, since two very different types of Al^{IV} are observed. On the other hand, Al^{IV} is observed at ~56 ppm in amorphous silica-alumina (7,9). Thus one could safely conclude that during dealumination by steam and by $SiCl_4$, besides the Al^{IV} (~60 ppm), Al^{VI} (~0 ppm), and tetrahedrally distorted or pentacoordinated EFAL (~30 ppm) in the zeolite framework, there exists aluminum that is tetrahedrally coordinated in an amorphous silica-alumina. This amorphous silica-alumina has probably been formed in the case of steam HY zeolites by reaction of some of the silica coming up from destroyed zeolite and part of the EFAL. In the $SiCl_4$ dealuminated sample, the silica needed to form the amorphous silica-alumina should proceed from both the $SiCl_4$ and the destroyed zeolite.

The HYF zeolite dealuminated with $(NH_4)_2F_6Si$ only shows lines at 0 ppm and 60 ppm, even after deep bed calcination; the lines at ~30 ppm and ~54 ppm are not visible.

IR Characterization

The IR spectra in the OH region of the sample HYF deep bed calcined at 450 and 550 °C (Fig. 3) and HYUS-8 (Fig. 4) are different. Indeed the HYF sample calcined at 450 °C (Fig. 3a) shows only two bands at 3557 (LF) and 3636 cm^{-1} (HF). The band at 3750 cm^{-1}, related with silanol groups and consequently with structural breaking, is very small. This shows that a very good substitution of aluminum by silicon has been achieved by this procedure without damage to the structure. Moreover, when pyridine was adsorbed and desorbed at 250 °C (Fig. 3b), all the OH appearing at 3636 cm^{-1} and most of those at 3557 cm^{-1} interacted with pyridine. The pyridine adsorption bands (Fig. 3c) indicate that a very small amount of pyridine coordinated to Lewis sites (1450 cm^{-1}), while the amount of pyridinium ions (1550 cm^{-1}) is high. This observation suggests that probably only very small amount of Lewis acid sites, i.e., $AlOH^+$ type species (or even amorphous or crystalline alumina) are present and that practically acidity is mainly of the Brönsted type. However, after the HYF sample was calcined at 550 °C (Fig. 3d) its IR spectrum changed. The two OH bands described above are not clearly resolved and other OH bands appear, while the intensity of the band corresponding to the silanol groups increases. The 3636 and 3557 cm^{-1} hydroxyl groups can interact with pyridine but bands appearing at ~3615 and ~3690 cm^{-1} do not (Fig. 3e). However, the difference spectrum indicates that some hydroxyls at 3600-3610 cm^{-1} also retain pyridine strongly (Fig. 3f). The hydroxyl groups at ~3615 and ~3690 cm^{-1} do not interact at all with pyridine, even without degassing. This indicates that these hydroxyls are not accesible to pyridine, or they are non-acidic in nature. The spectrum of adsorbed pyridine shows that a quite high Lewis acidity

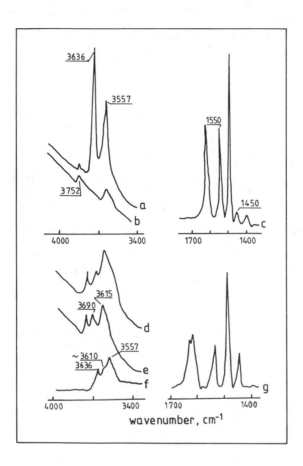

Figure 3. IR spectra of HYF sample treated at different temp.:
Hydroxyl and pyridine region.
        a. Hydroxyls of HYF deep bed calcined at 450°C
        b. "a" after adsorption of pyridine and desorption at
           250 °C and vacuum
        c. IR bands of pyridine adsorbed on HYF "b"
        d. Hydroxyls of HYF after deep bed calcination at
           500 °C
        e. "d" after adsorption of pyridine and desorption at
           250 °C and vacuum
        f. Difference spectrum "d" minus "e"
        g. IR bands of pyridine adsorbed on HYF "d"

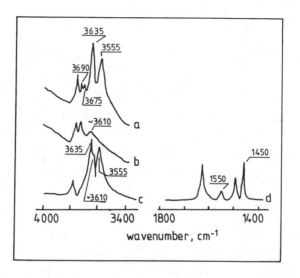

Figure 4. IR spectra of HYUS-8 sample before and after pyridine adsorption.

        a. Hydroxyls of HYUS-8
        b. "a" after pyridine adsorption and desorption at
           250 °C and vacuum
        c. Difference spectrum "a" minus "b"
        d. IR bands of pyridine adsorbed on HYUS-8, and
           desorbed at 400 °C and vacuum

has developed (Fig. 3g). Together with the fact that the unit cell size of the zeolite sample has decreased by 0.07 Å after calcination at 550 °C, this shows that some dealumination has occurred during calcination and that the hydroxyl groups identified with the 3615 and 3690 cm^{-1} bands and at least a part of acidity observed in the calcined sample, is attributed to the generation of EFAL.

The above interpretation can also explain the IR spectra of the HYUS samples. Indeed, the HYUS-8 sample shows two bands at 3555 and 3635 cm^{-1}, a considerable amount of silanol groups, and hydroxyl vibrating at ~ 3675 and ~3695 cm^{-1} (Fig. 4a). After pyridine is adsorbed the bands at 3555 and 3635 cm^{-1} disappear, while the other two bands remain and a new band at 3615 cm^{-1} is now clearly visible (Fig. 4b). If the difference spectrum is obtained a band at 3600-3610 cm^{-1} (Fig. 4c) again indicates the presence of strongly acid hydroxyl groups.

The acidic hydroxyl groups appearing at 3600-3610 cm^{-1} are clearly visible in $SiCl_4$-dealuminated HY zeolites. For instance, Figure 5a (the difference spectrum after pyridine desorption at 250 °C in vacuum for a HYD zeolite with an unit cell size of 24.31 Å) clearly shows the presence of these acidic hydroxyls together with the HF and LF ones. After desorption of pyridine at 400 °C and 1.33 x 10^{-2} Pa, only the hydroxyls at ~3610 cm^{-1} retain pyridine. Therefore these hydroxyls are more acidic than the framework HF and LF hydroxyl groups. A hydroxyl group at ~3610 cm^{-1} has been observed in amorphous silica-alumina, with an acid strength higher than that of other hydroxyl groups present in amorphous silica-alumina (10). Thus, the observed acidic hydroxyl groups at ~ 3610 cm^{-1} can be associated with the amorphous silica-alumina formed during the dealumination process (11).

In conclusion, ^{27}Al MAS-NMR and IR results show the formation of amorphous silica-alumina during dealumination. It shows stronger acidity than the hydroxyls attached to zeolite framework aluminums. This silica-alumina can account for the superacidity observed by some authors in steamed zeolite samples (12,13).

In order to study the Lewis acidity of the samples, the intensity of the 1450 cm^{-1} pyridine band was also measured. Sample HYUS-8 shows a high amount of Lewis centers (Fig. 4d), relative to the HYD-400 sample (Fig. 5c). This agrees with the absence of Al^{VI} as observed by ^{27}Al MAS-NMR for HYD samples. However, chemical analysis (Table I) indicates that there is more aluminum in this sample than in that from the unit cell constant measurements. These differences could be explained considering that ^{27}Al MAS-NMR does not detect octahedral EFAL because of the low symmetry of its environment (14). If this is so, it is remarkable that this EFAL does not show Lewis acidity as measured by pyridine adsorption. On the other hand, if indeed there is a small amount of Al^{VI}, then the EFAL should be present as Al^{IV} outside the zeolite framework. In this case it should be present as amorphous silica-alumina.

The HYUS-8 sample treated with different chemicals has been studied by ^{27}Al NMR and the results are given in Figure 6. The citric acid treatment eliminates the signal appearing at ~30 ppm and strongly decreases the Al^{VI} (~0 ppm) but the Al^{IV} signal remains unaffected (Fig. 6a and Table I). The HCl treatment eliminates some of the aluminum at ~30 ppm but the line at ~0 ppm becomes sharper,

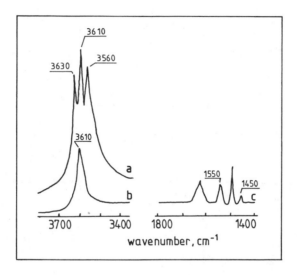

Figure 5.   Difference spectra of hydroxyl groups of HYD-400, between the spectra before and after pyridine adsorption and desorption at:
        a. 250 °C
        b. 400 °C
        c. IR bands of pyridine adsorbed on HYD-400 and
           desorbed at 400 °C and vacuum

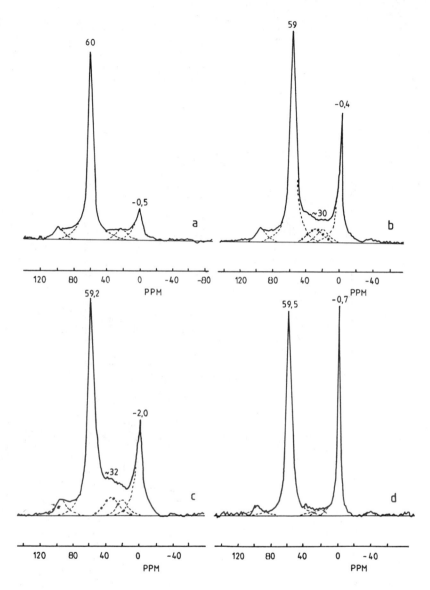

Figure 6. ^{27}Al MAS–NMR spectra of HYUS–8 treated with different chemicals:

            a. HYUSAC, citric acid
            b. HYUSl, hydrochloric acid
            c. HYUSN, sodium hydroxyde
            d. HYUSA, acetylacetone

probably indicating that less polymerized species of Al^{VI} are formed
(Fig. 6b). The acetylacetone treatment does not change the relative
intensity of the component in the ^{27}Al NMR spectrum (Fig. 6c). In
contrast, the NaOH treatment (Fig. 6d) eliminates the ~ 30 ppm
signal, in agreement with previous work (7), and also strongly
increases and sharpens the line at ~ 0 ppm. These results clearly
show that it is possible, by simple treatments, to modify the
proportion of the different types of aluminum present on a steam
treated zeolite.

Cracking Behaviour of Steam-Dealuminated HY Zeolites

In Figure 7 the selectivity to methane, ethane, ethylene, gases,
gasoline (210°C), diesel (310°C), and coke at 65% level of
conversion have been plotted for HYUS zeolites with 28, 21, 12, and
2 Al per unit cell for cracking gas-oil. It is apparent from the
figures that the selectivity to C_1 and C_2 products decreases with
a decreasing number of aluminum, up to 10-20 Al per unit cell. With
further dealumination the selectivity to C_1 and C_2 products
increases again.

The formation of methane and ethane can be explained by the
protolytic cracking of an alkane (15) (specially branched alkanes)
on very strong Brönsted sites. However, it would be difficult to
explain by acid catalysis the formation of ethylene, because this
would involve the formation of primary carbenium ions. On the other
hand, after ~ 30 Al per unit cell have been removed from the
framework, one should not expect large changes in the acid strength
of the sites by further dealumination. Therefore changes in
selectivity due to differences in acid strength should not be
expected. Thus it is difficult from the point of view of acid
catalysis to explain the large increase in the selectivity for C_1
and C_2 observed with strongly dealuminated zeolites. Therefore we
propose that the observed increase in the C_1 and C_2 fraction,
together with the decrease in the i-C_4/n-C_4 ratio, can be explained
by considering that on highly steam dealuminated HY zeolites radical
cracking (cracking via radical intermediates) becomes very
important. A cracking of this type will give more C_1 and C_2 and less
branched products than ionic cracking. This is exactly what is
experimentally observed.

In conclusion, we believe that cracking of gas-oil is taking
place on zeolites via carbonium, carbenium ions and radicals. In
the case of steam dealuminated samples, when more than 5 Al per unit
cell (Si/Al<30) are present in the framework of the zeolite, the
ionic mechanism is much more important than the radical one. When
the framework aluminum decreases and the number of defects
increases, the radical mechanism becomes operative and eventually
dominant when practically no aluminum is present in the zeolite
framework and superacid Brönsted sites (at ~ 3610 cm^{-1}) are not
present.

In heavily steam-dealuminated zeolites, most of the activity
should come from the EFAL that is concentrated on the external
surface (3,4). We believe that Lewis acidity, which can stabilize
radicals, can play an important role in the radical cracking
observed with strongly steam-dealuminated HY zeolites. Furthermore,

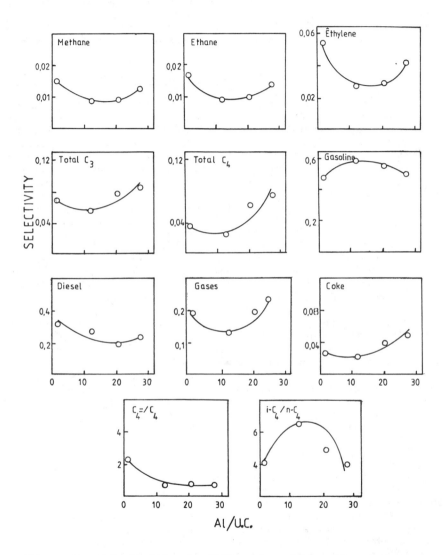

Figure 7. Selectivities to different products of gas–oil cracking on HYUS catalysts, as a function of the number of Al per unit cell.

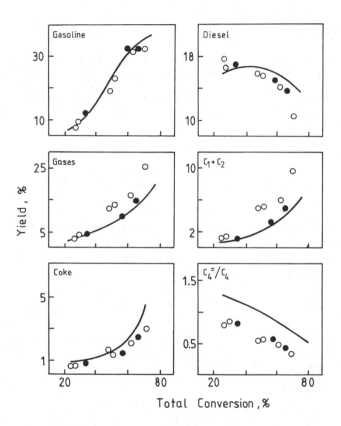

Figure 8.   Yields to different products of gas-oil cracking for different samples, as a function of level of conversion.
continuous line HYUS-8
○ ...... HYUSAC
● ...... HYUSN

coke formation follows the same trends as C_1 and C_2 make when changing the Al per unit cell in the zeolite. This in turn brings up the hypothesis that cracking could occure via a radical mechanism.

Finally, the variation of the yields of gasoline and diesel versus Al per unit cell allow us to conclude that highly steam-dealuminated HY zeolites behave, from the point of view of gas-oil cracking, like a well-dispersed active alumina.

Catalytic Behaviour of "leached" Steam-Dealuminated Zeolites

When the steamed HY zeolites are treated with citric acid or NaOH, the EFAL giving a ^{27}Al NMR line at ~30 ppm disappears. However, the signal of the Al^{VI} at ~0 ppm increases and becomes very sharp. On the other hand, after these treatments gases and diesel yields increase and the selectivities to gasoline and coke decrease slightly (Fig. 8).

Conclusions

We can conclude that amorphous silica-alumina is formed in steamed and SiCl$_4$-dealuminated zeolites. If the treatment is not too severe, the amorphous silica-alumina has hydroxyl groups at 3610 cm^{-1} which are strongly acidic and active in catalytic cracking (superacid Brönsted centers). In the case of highly steam-dealuminated (~5 Al per unit cell) HY zeolites, a radical cracking mechanism becomes important. Then, as with active alumina, gas and coke are produced in higher amounts. Finally, it is possible by mild acid or basic treatment, to modify the population of the different EFAL species, thus changing product selectivity for gas-oil cracking.

Acknowledgments

This work was supported by the Comisión Asesora de Investigación Científica y Técnica (CAICYT, project 999/070).

Literature Cited

1. Scherzer, J. ACS Symp. Ser. 1984, 248, 157.
2. Breck, D.W.; Blass, H.; Skeels, G.W. U.S. Patent 4503023, 1985.
3. Dwyer, J.; Fitch, F.R.; Nkang, E.E. J. Phys. Chem. 1983, 87, 540.
4. Corma, A.; Fornés, V.; Pallota, V.; Cruz, J.M.; Ayerbe, A. J. Chem. Soc. Chem. Comm. 1986, 333.
5. Beyer, H.K. and Belenkaya, I. "Catalysis by Zeolites" Ed. B. Imelik et al. Elsevier, Amsterdam, 1980, p. 203.
6. Corma, A.; Juan, J.; Martos, J.; Molina, J. Proc. 8th Int. Congr. Catal. 1984, II, 29.
7. Gilson, J.P.; Edwards, G.C.; Peters, A.K.; Rajagopalan, K.; Wormsbecher, R.F.; Roberie, T.G.; Shatlock, M.P. J. Chem. Soc. Chem. Comm. 1987, 91.
8. Samoson, A.; Lippmaa, E.; Engelhardt, G.; Lohse, D.; Jerschwitz, H.G. Chemical Physics Letters 1987, 134, 589.

9. Thomas, J.M.; Klinowski, J.; Wright, P.; Roy, R. Angew. Chem. Int. Ed. Engl. 1983, 22, 614.
10. Borovkov, U.; Yu,   ;Alexeev, A.A., Kazanski, V.B. J. Catal. 1983, 80, 462.
11. Garralón, G.; Corma, A.; Fornés, V. J. Chem. Soc. Chem. Comm. (Submitted for publication).
12. Mirodatos, C.; Barthomeuf, D. J. Chem. Soc. Chem. Comm. 1981, 39.
13. Lago, R.M.; Haag, W.O.; Mikovsky, R.J.; Olson, D.H.; Hellring, S.D. Proc. 7th Int. Zeolite Conf. 1986, 677.
14. Thomas, J.M. and Klinowsky, J. Adv. Catal. 1985, 33, 271.
15. Corma, A.; Montón, J.B.; Orchillés, A.V. Ind. Eng. Chem. Prod. Res. Dev. 1984, 23, 404; Appl. Catal. 1985, 16, 59.
16. Fichtner-Schmittler, H.; Lohse, V.; Engelhardt, G.; Patzelova, V. Crys. Res. Technol. 1984, 19 (1), k1-k3.

RECEIVED February 25, 1988

Chapter 3

Hydrocarbon Cracking Selectivities with Dual-Function Zeolite Catalysts

K. Rajagopalan and G. W. Young

Davison Chemical Division, W. R. Grace & Company, 7379 Route 32, Columbia, MD 21044

High yield of C_6 to C_8 aromatics was obtained with thermally treated ZSM-5 (with a SiO_2 to Al_2O_3 ratio of 47) during n-hexadecane cracking in a fixed bed reactor. After steam treatment, yield of C_5 to C_7 olefins increased at the expense of aromatics. The effect of the addition of a small concentration (1 Wt.%) of ZSM-5 to a rare earth Y fluid cracking catalyst during cracking of a commercial gas oil was investigated by measurement of yields of gasoline range hydrocarbons. The addition of either thermally treated or steam treated ZSM-5 to the catalyst reduced the concentration of normal and monomethyl paraffins in the product gasoline, thus enriching olefins and aromatics. No evidence of preferential reduction of straight chain paraffins compared to monomethyl paraffins was observed. Experiments using a catalytically cracked gasoline as feedstock suggest that ZSM-5 cracks paraffin precursors (carbonium ion or olefin intermediates) and prevents formation of gasoline range paraffins. These changes in gasoline composition due to ZSM-5 in the dual zeolite catalyst are probably responsible for increased gasoline octane number observed with that catalyst.

Synthetic Y faujasite zeolites have been used commercially as cracking catalysts over the past two decades (1) and more recently dual zeolite fluid cracking catalysts containing faujasite and ZSM-5 were discovered to increase the octane number of the product gasoline during catalytic cracking of gas oil (2). This concept, where ZSM-5 constitutes only a small fraction (about 1 weight percent) of the cracking catalyst, has been tested commercially in Europe (3) and in the United States (4). Cracking of paraffinic and olefinic hydrocarbons by ZSM-5 catalysts have been studied by several investigators (5-11) over a range of temperatures (350 to 540°C). These investigators used either nearly pure ZSM-5 or a catalyst containing 50 Wt.% ZSM-5 in a silica matrix. The

0097–6156/88/0375–0034$06.00/0

mechanism of octane enhancement with the dual zeolite catalyst was investigated by examining the effect of addition of 1 Wt.% ZSM-5 to the cracking catalyst composition on product selectivity during catalytic cracking of a commercial gas oil at 500°C. Changes in composition of product gasoline (paraffins, olefins, naphthenes and aromatics) caused by ZSM-5 were measured. A model paraffin compound and a gasoline obtained by catalytic cracking were used as feedstocks in certain experiments. Since commercial cracking catalysts undergo continuous high temperature regeneration in the presence of steam (1), the effect of hydrothermal treatment of ZSM-5 was also investigated.

Experimental Methods

Catalysts and Pretreatment. ZSM-5 was prepared in our laboratory and was determined to be crystallographically pure by X-ray diffraction. H-form of the zeolite was obtained by ion exchanging with NH₄NO₃ solution followed by calcination to reduce the sodium content below 500 ppm. The designation ZSM-5 will be used in this manuscript to denote the H-form of the zeolite. The SiO_2 to Al_2O_3 ratio of the zeolite was analyzed as 47 and average particle size was about .2 µm. Catalysts were prepared by a thorough mixing of zeolite with a silica-alumina sol binder and kaolin clay diluent followed by drying. The binder and clay component of the catalyst will be referred to as the "matrix". Two catalysts containing 1 Wt.% and 25 Wt.% ZSM-5 in the matrix were prepared. A "pure" matrix catalyst that did not contain any zeolite was also prepared so that the effect of the matrix in the ZSM-5 catalysts could be taken into account. Commercially available Super-D, which contains rare earth exchanged Y zeolite (REY) in the matrix and is manufactured by the Davison Chemical Division of W. R. Grace & Co., was used as the REY catalyst.

Steam pre-treatment of fluid cracking catalysts has been conventionally employed to represent the deactivation occurring in a commercial FCC unit. Appropriate steam pre-treatment methods have been developed so that the activity and selectivity of the steam pre-treated catalyst is equivalent to a commercially deactivated catalyst (12). However, a unique steaming method may not be suitable for catalysts of varying compositions (12). Two steaming methods designed to simulate deactivation in a commercial unit of the two types of catalysts used in this work were employed. Super-D was treated for 8 hours at 732°C with a steam pressure of 2 atmospheres. The catalysts containing ZSM-5 were treated for 12 hours at 827°C with a steam partial pressure of 0.2 atmosphere. In addition to the above pre-treatments, the ZSM-5 containing catalysts were also thermally treated for 3 hours at 704°C in static air to represent the effect of freshly added ZSM-5 in a commercial FCC unit.

Dual zeolite catalysts were prepared by physically blending Super-D with the catalyst containing 25 Wt.% ZSM-5 so as to achieve 1 Wt.% ZSM-5 in the physical blend. Two blends, one containing steam treated Super-D and thermally treated ZSM-5 catalyst and the other containing steam treated Super-D and steam treated ZSM-5 catalyst were prepared. Each of the blends was then intimately mixed.

Feedstocks and Reactor. Feedstock for the experiments was chosen
from among a gas oil with properties described in Table I, a
gasoline obtained by catalytic cracking with the composition
described in Table VI and 99% pure n-hexadecane from Aldrich
(Milwaukee, WI). A fixed bed reactor described in ASTM D3907 was
employed for catalytic testing. Experiments were carried out at a
reactor temperature of 500°C, Weight Hourly Space Velocity of
16 and catalyst residence time (13) of 75 seconds. Material
balance for the reactor runs ranged from 95 to 102 weight percent.

Table I.   Properties of a Commercial Gas Oil

Mass Spectral Analysis
>   Paraffins, Vol.%   :   14.5
>   Cycloparaffins (1, 2, and 3 ring), Vol.%   :   33.1
>   Aromatics, Vol.%   :   52.4

Boiling Point Distribution (ASTM: D-1160)
>   Initial   :   187°C
>   10 Vol.%   :   339°C
>   50 Vol.%   :   437°C
>   90 Vol.%   :   544°C

>   Specific Gravity at 16°C   :   .912

>   UOP "K" Factor   :   11.78

>   Sulfur, Wt.%   :   .39

>   Nitrogen, Wt.%   :   .11

Product Analyses. Liquid product from the reactor was separated
into its components and analyzed with the aid of a Hewlett-Packard
(HP) 5880A gas chromatograph using a 50m Dimethyl Silicone Fluid
capillary column and a flame ionization detector. A column
temperature program ranging from 15°C to 280°C was used to
enable adequate resolution. The components were identified using a
HP 5990A GC/MS System. Light hydrocarbons (C_1 to C_5) were
collected in a gas bag and analyzed on a HP 5710 gas chromatograph
with a 20% Dibutylmaleate packed column maintained at 22°C and a
flame ionization detector. Hydrogen in the gas bag was analyzed by
a Gow-Mac thermal conductivity detector connected to a 13X molecular
sieve packed column. Coke on spent catalyst was measured by Carbon
Determinator WR-12 (Leco Corporation, St. Joseph, MI).

Results and Discussion

Effect of Steam Treatment. X-ray diffraction analyses indicated
that ZSM-5 retained in excess of 90% of its crystallinity after the
steam treatment described in the methods section. Unit cell
constant of the REY zeolite in Super-D declined from 24.65Å to
24.38Å due to the steam treatment. Independent measurements

indicated that RE ion exchange results in a lattice expansion of
0.04Å. Thus, the unit cell shrinkage due to steaming cannot be
fully explained by postulating rare earth migration outside the
zeolite. It is reasonable to infer that dealumination of the
faujasite framework occurred during the steam pretreatment. Unit
cell shrinkage of faujasite has also been observed during use in a
commercial unit (14).

The effect of steam treatment of ZSM-5 on its cracking activity
and selectivity was measured with experiments using n-hexadecane
feed. With the thermally treated ZSM-5 catalyst, concentration of
the unconverted n-hexadecane in the product was not measurable while
50% of the feed was unconverted with the steam treated ZSM-5
catalyst (Table II). The lower limit of conversion with the
thermally treated catalyst corresponding to detection limit of
n-hexadecane is 99.99%. This lower limit suggests at least an order
of magnitude reduction in apparent first order rate constant of the
ZSM-5 catalyst upon steam treatment. The small reduction in
crystallinity upon steaming cannot fully explain the dramatic
activity loss. Loss of active sites due to dealumination of ZSM-5
can be postulated to explain the reduction in activity.

TABLE II.   Effect of Steam Treatment of ZSM-5 Catalyst[1] on
            Product Selectivity During n-hexadecane Cracking

Pretreatment:	3 Hours at 704°C in Static Air	Steaming for 12 Hours at 827°C with Steam partial pressure = .2 atm.
Yield ÷ Fractional Conversion, Wt.% Feed		
Paraffins Plus Olefins		
C_1 :	0.17	0.10
C_2 :	5.1	1.4
C_3 :	26.7	19.8
C_4 :	26.9	29.4
C_5 :	14.2	22.0
C_6 :	2.7	10.0
C_7 :	1.3	3.2
C_6-C_8 Aromatics :	11.5	0.6
Olefin/Paraffin Ratio		
C_3 :	0.4	3.0
C_4 :	0.3	1.8
C_5 :	0.3	1.8
C_6 :	0.2	1.5
C_7 :	0.3	0.7
Conversion, Wt.% :	100	50
H_2, Wt.% Feed :	0.12	0.01
Coke, Wt.% Feed :	1.10	0.10

[1] 25 Wt.% ZSM-5, 75 Wt.% matrix

Observations regarding activity and selectivity of steam treated
ZSM-5 in this work could thus apply to dealuminated ZSM-5.
     For the sake of brevity, the yield data for all the individual
components are not reported in Table II and subsequent tables. The
yield of unreported components (usually C_8+ olefins and
naphthenes) can be calculated as 100 minus percentage yield of the
reported components. Results shown in Table II indicate that
thermally treated ZSM-5 produced a high yield of C_6 to C_8
aromatics, C_3 and C_4 hydrocarbons. Steam treatment of ZSM-5
reduced cracking activity and increased the selectivity for C_5 to
C_7 aliphatics at the expense of aromatics. The olefin to
paraffin ratio in the product also increased upon steaming.
Olefins have been suggested to be intermediates during formation of
aromatics with ZSM-5 (6). Hence, as the activity of ZSM-5 was
reduced through steam treatment, consumption of olefins to form
aromatics did not take place. These results are thus consistent
with observations of Anderson et al. (6).

Gas Oil Cracking by the Dual Zeolite Catalyst. After the steam
pre-treatment, the gas oil cracking activity of REY was about 100
times greater than the activity of the "pure" matrix catalyst.
Thus, the dominant contributor of cracking selectivity of Super D
is expected to be the REY zeolite present in the catalyst. Yields
of C_5 to C_7 paraffin isomers measured during the cracking of
the gas oil at 500°C by the steam treated REY catalyst are
shown in Table III. The yield of branched paraffins was generally
five to ten times higher than the yield of normal paraffins and the
major (>50%) portion of the branched paraffin yield consisted of
monomethyl paraffins.

Table III.   Yield of Paraffin Isomers During Cracking of
               the Gas Oil by the REY Catalyst

Catalyst Pretreatment	:	Steam treated for 8 hrs at 732°C Steam pressure = 2 atmospheres.
Wt.% Conversion	:	55.8
Product Yields (Wt.% Feed)		
n–Pentane	:	.20
Isopentane	:	1.2
n–Hexane	:	.32
2–Methylpentane	:	1.7
3–Methylpentane	:	1.1
2,3–Dimethylbutane	:	.33
n–Heptane	:	.23
2–Methylhexane	:	1.5
3–Methylhexane	:	1.1

Table IV.   Cracking of the Gas Oil by Dual Zeolite Catalysts

Catalyst Description :	REY Catalyst[1]	REY Catalyst + 1% Thermally Treated[2] ZSM-5	REY Catalyst + 1% Steam Treated[3] ZSM-5
Conversion, Wt.% :	55.8	54.4	50.3
Product Yields, Wt.% Feed			
H_2 :	.04	.04	.04
Methane :	.33	.32	.33
Ethane + Ethylene :	1.1	1.5	.67
Propylene :	2.2	6.1	2.4
Propane :	.9	2.2	.9
C_4 Olefins :	2.6	4.1	2.7
C_4 Paraffins :	3.6	6.0	3.7
C_5^+ Gasoline :	43.2	31.9	37.4
C_5-C_{12} Paraffins :	18.8	11.5	15.6
Coke :	2.1	2.4	2.2
Gasoline Composition, Wt.%			
n-hexane :	.92	.97	.83
Methylpentanes :	7.9	5.9	7.3
2,3 Dimethyl Butane :	.94	.73	.86
n-heptane :	.65	.64	.63
Methylhexanes :	7.3	4.1	6.8
n-C_8-C_{12} :	2.7	2.9	2.5
Total Paraffins :	43.4	36.0	41.6
C_5-C_7 Olefins :	7.2	8.4	8.0
C_6-C_8 Aromatics :	11.9	16.2	12.2
C_9-C_{11} Aromatics :	20.9	21.8	20.8

[1] Steam treated for 8 hours at 732°C.
   Steam pressure = 2 atmospheres.

[2] Heat treated for 3 hours at 704°C in static air.

[3] Steam treated for 12 hours at 827°C.
   Steam partial pressure = .2 atmosphere.

The effect of adding 1% ZSM-5 to the REY cracking catalyst on
product yields is described by the data in Table IV. Two cases
where ZSM-5 was either thermally treated or steam treated were
considered. Consistent with earlier findings (2, 3), addition of
1% ZSM-5 to the cracking catalyst increased the yield of C_3 and
C_4 hydrocarbons at the expense of C_5^+ gasoline. Analysis of
the gasoline composition indicated that the addition of ZSM-5 to
the catalyst enriched olefins and aromatics (especially C_6 to
C_8 aromatics) in the gasoline at the expense of paraffins. With
1% thermally treated ZSM-5, about 20% reduction in the
concentration of paraffins was observed in the product gasoline.
The reduction in the yield of gasoline range paraffins (as a per
cent of feed) due to 1% thermally treated ZSM-5 was about 40%.
Paraffin yield reduction to a lesser extent was observed with the
steam treated ZSM-5. Thus, enrichment of olefins and aromatics in
the gasoline occurred with the addition of either thermally treated
or steam treated ZSM-5.
    The data in Table IV and Figure 1 indicate that most of the
paraffin concentration reduction took place in the C_6 to C_9
range and involved monomethyl paraffins. The blending octane
numbers for 2-methyl and 3-methyl hexanes are reported as 40 to 56
by ASTM (15) and are lower than the blending numbers for light
(C_5 to C_7) olefins and C_6 to C_{11} aromatics. Thus,
reduction in concentration of these branched paraffins is expected
to improve the research octane number of the gasoline.

Table V.   Cracking of the Gas Oil by 1% ZSM-5 Catalyst

Catalyst Description	:	1% ZSM-5 99% Matrix	100% Matrix
Catalyst Pretreatment	:	3 hours at 704°C in Static Air	
Conversion, Wt.%	:	34.5	24.1
Product Yields, Wt.% Feed			
C_1-C_4	:	11.5	7.5
n-hexane	:	.39	.10
Methylpentanes	:	.16	0
2,3 Dimethylbutane	:	.06	0
n-heptane	:	.40	.16
Methylhexanes	:	0	0
n-C_8-C_{12}	:	.72	.80
Total Paraffins	:	2.3	1.5
C_5 Olefins	:	2.2	.25
C_6 Olefins	:	1.5	.54
C_7 Olefins	:	.47	.45
C_6-C_8 Aromatics	:	5.7	1.8
C_6-C_{11} Aromatics	:	10.0	6.4

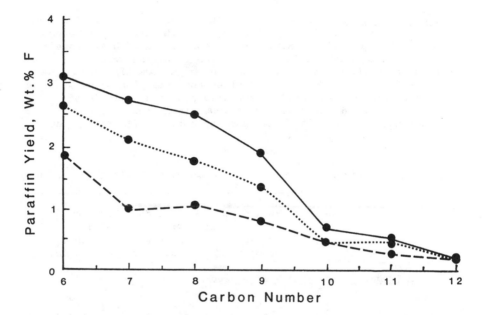

Figure 1.   Paraffin yield as a function of carbon number for
three catalysts during gas oil cracking.
————   REY Catalyst
– – –   REY Catalyst + 1 Wt.% thermally
treated ZSM–5
· · · · ·   REY Catalyst + 1 Wt.% steam treated ZSM–5

To clarify the mechanism by which gasoline composition is changed (reduction in concentration of the paraffins and an increase in concentration of olefins and aromatics) by ZSM-5 in the dual zeolite catalyst, experiments were carried out on catalysts containing only ZSM-5 dispersed in the matrix. The catalyst containing 1 Wt.% ZSM-5 was used in order to duplicate the concentration of ZSM-5 in the dual zeolite catalyst studied earlier. Experiments with the "pure" matrix catalyst were used to define the contribution of ZSM-5.

Gas Oil and Gasoline Conversion by ZSM-5. Results obtained during cracking of the gas oil indicated that 1 Wt.% thermally treated ZSM-5 exhibited a higher activity for conversion of heavy paraffins (C_{20}^+) than 10 Wt.% REY (Figure 2). The paraffins were converted mainly to C_6 to C_{11} gasoline range aromatics and light hydrocarbons (Table V). Smaller concentration of n-paraffins and light olefins (C_5 and C_6) were also produced. Yields of monomethyl branched paraffins were lower than that of the corresponding n-paraffin unlike results obtained (Table III) during cracking with the REY catalyst.

Table VI. Conversion of Components in Gasoline by 1% ZSM-5 at 500°C

Description	:	Feed Catalytically Cracked Gasoline	Product with Matrix Catalyst	Product with 1% ZSM-5 in Matrix Catalyst
Feed or Product Composition, Wt.% Feed				
Methane	:	0	.09	.09
Ethane + Ethylene	:	0	.33	1.8
C_3 Olefin	:	0	.92	4.2
C_3 Paraffin	:	0	.03	.43
C_4 Olefin	:	.60	.68	1.4
C_4 Paraffins	:	.32	.24	.27
C_5-C_7 Olefins	:	12.3	8.8	2.4
C_5-C_{12} Paraffins	:	33.5	30.5	27.9
C_5-C_7 Naphthenes	:	6.2	6.0	5.4
C_6-C_8 Aromatics	:	12.5	13.5	15.2
C_9-C_{11} Aromatics	:	17.5	19.3	19.1
Coke, Wt.% F	:	--	.5	.4

Matrix catalyst as well as the catalyst containing 1% ZSM-5 were pretreated for 3 hours at 704°C in static air.

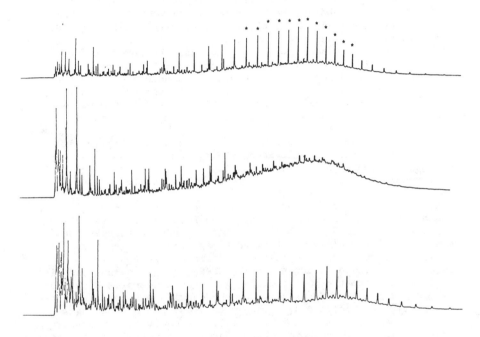

Figure 2.   Gas chromatographs of products from gas oil cracking
with three catalysts: 100% matrix catalyst (above),
1 Wt.% ZSM–5 in the matrix (middle) and 10 Wt.% REY
in the matrix (below).   Peaks marked with * indicate
heavy (C_{20}^{+}) paraffins.

The composition of the gasoline obtained by catalytic cracking
and used as a feedstock for the ZSM-5 catalyst is given in
Table VI. Product analyses, also given in Table VI, show that 80%
of the olefins and less than 10% of the paraffins are converted by
the ZSM-5 catalyst with about 30% of the olefin conversion
attributable to the matrix present in the catalyst. This is not
surprising due to the well-known higher reactivity of olefins.
Light hydrocarbons (C_1 to C_4) and aromatics (mainly C_6 to
C_8) were produced by ZSM-5 due to the the conversion of olefins
and paraffins. Thus, these results provide evidence for cracking of
olefins, paraffins and cyclization of olefins by ZSM-5 at
500°C. The steam deactivated ZSM-5 catalyst exhibited reduced
olefin conversion and negligible paraffin conversion activity.

Isomerization of linear olefins to branched olefins by ZSM-5
has been observed under certain conditions (3). An analysis of the
distribution of C_5 and C_6 olefin isomers in the feed gasoline
as well as the product from steam deactivated ZSM-5 show no strong
evidence for deactivated ZSM-5 to produce branched olefins from the
α-olefins (Table VII). The distribution of isomers obtained with
the catalyst containing 1% steam deactivated ZSM-5 in a matrix was
equivalent to that obtained with the "pure" matrix catalyst.

Discussion. Fixed bed cracking reactors as well as commercial
moving bed reactors operate under steady state or pseudo-steady
state conditions (13). Observed selectivity (eg., ratio of yield
of branched to n-paraffin) in a steady state catalytic reactor is
independent of space velocity (16, 17). The selectivity depends on
intrinsic rate constants and diffusivities of the reacting species
which depend on temperature. Thus, the selectivity observations
reported here are applicable to commercial FCC units operating at
space velocities different from that employed in this study.

A comparison of the yield of gasoline range (C_5-C_{12})
paraffins obtained during gas oil cracking using the dual zeolite
catalyst with that obtained during gasoline conversion with the
single zeolite (ZSM-5) catalyst can be carried out for both fresh
(thermally treated) and aged (steam treated) ZSM-5. When gas oil
was cracked with the dual zeolite catalyst containing thermally
treated ZSM-5, approximately 40% reduction in the yield of gasoline
range paraffins compared to the faujasite catalyst was observed
(Table IV). However, when the gasoline obtained by catalytic
cracking was fed to a catalyst containing thermally treated ZSM-5
(no REY) under the same conditions, only 10% reduction in the yield
of paraffins was observed (Table VI). Steam treated 1% ZSM-5
catalyst did not produce any measurable reduction in the yield of
paraffins during gasoline cracking. However, a significant
reduction in the yield of paraffins due to 1% steamed ZSM-5 was
observed during gas oil cracking with the dual zeolite catalyst.
Thus, paraffin yield reduction observed with the dual zeolite
catalyst cannot be fully explained by reactivity of ZSM-5 to
gasoline range paraffins.

A mechanism that postulates prevention of paraffin formation
during gas oil cracking with the dual zeolite catalyst can explain
the above data. Such a prevention could take place by more than
one route. ZSM-5 present in the catalyst could prevent certain
secondary reactions that lead to the formation of gasoline range

Table VII.   Yields of Olefin Isomers During Gasoline Conversion
by 1% ZSM-5 at 500°C

Description	:	Feed Catalytically Cracked Gasoline	Product with Matrix Catalyst	Product with 1% ZSM-5 in Matrix Catalyst
Feed or Product Composition, Wt.% Feed				
Pentene Isomers				
1-Pentene	:	.27	.21	.29
2-Pentenes	:	1.8	1.0	1.2
Methylbutenes	:	2.1	2.5	2.6
Cyclopentene	:	.20	.17	.19
Hexene Isomers				
1-Hexene	:	.57	.55	.63
2 & 3-Hexenes	:	1.6	.85	1.0
Methylpentenes	:	2.3	2.4	2.4
2,3-Dimethyl 2-butene	:	.62	.69	.75

Matrix catalyst as well as the catalyst containing ZSM-5 were
steamed for 12 hours at 827°C with steam partial pressure = .2
atmosphere.

paraffins. These secondary reactions include the chain transfer
reaction involving a carbonium ion suggested by Gates, et al. (18)
and the hydrogen transfer reaction involving an olefin, suggested
by Thomas and Barmby (19). Both chain transfer and hydrogen
transfer have been suggested to occur readily over faujasite
leading to the formation of gasoline range paraffins. ZSM-5 could
prevent these bimolecular hydrogen and chain transfer reactions by
preferentially catalyzing the monomolecular cracking of the
carbonium ion or olefin intermediate to produce light (C_2 to
C_4) hydrocarbons. These intermediates are more reactive than the
paraffins and can also be cracked by steam deactivated ZSM-5.
Thus, this mechanism can explain the reduction in paraffin yield

(Table IV) attributable to 1% steam deactivated ZSM-5 – a catalyst that had negligible activity for cracking gasoline range paraffins at 500°C. This mechanism can also explain the increased yield of light hydrocarbons (C_2 to C_4) when the dual zeolite catalyst containing either thermally treated or steam deactivated ZSM-5 is employed.

The concentrations of both normal and monomethyl paraffins in the product gasoline were reduced by the addition of ZSM-5 to the REY catalyst, but preferential reduction of n-paraffins was not observed. This result can be explained by the concept of constraint index (5), which is the ratio of rate constant for conversion of a straight chain paraffin to that for conversion of a branched paraffin of the same carbon number. The constraint index of ZSM-5 was found to be independent of crystal size over a range spanning two orders of magnitude (9). It is thus considered to be a measure of shape selectivity which describes the apparent pore opening of the zeolite (9). The constraint index of ZSM-5 declined with temperature (5) from nearly 10 at 365°C to nearly unity at 500°C. High constraint index is expected to result in preferential conversion of straight chain molecules (carbonium ions, olefins) and preservation of branched molecules. When the constraint index is near unity, both types of molecules have equivalent reactivity and conversion will be determined by concentration (or availability) of molecules. Monomethyl paraffins are produced at an order of magnitude higher concentration than n-paraffins by the REY catalyst (Table III). Thus, addition of ZSM-5 to the catalyst resulted in a significant reduction of monomethyl paraffins in the product gasoline.

The results on olefin isomers (Table VII) can also be explained by the observation that the constraint index of ZSM-5 is approximately unity under the conditions of this study. Shape selectivity or preferential conversion of straight chain olefins by ZSM-5 cannot be expected at 500°C. Thus, under the conditions of this study, olefin isomer distribution was not significantly affected by deactivated ZSM-5. At temperatures lower than that employed in the present study, it is conceivable that distribution of olefin isomers could be altered by steam deactivated ZSM-5.

Conclusions

C_5 to C_7 olefins are intermediates during conversion of C_{16}^+ n-paraffins to aromatics by ZSM-5. Addition of 1 Wt.% (thermally treated or steam treated) ZSM-5 to a REY fluid cracking catalyst results in an increase in the yield of C_3 and C_4 hydrocarbons at the expense of C_5 to C_{12} hydrocarbons (gasoline). The gasoline produced from the dual zeolite catalyst has a lower concentration of normal, monomethyl paraffins and a higher concentration of olefins and aromatics compared to the gasoline produced from the REY catalyst. Preference of the dual zeolite catalyst to monomolecular cracking of paraffin precursors (carbonium ions and olefins) at the expense of bimolecular reactions like hydrogen transfer and chain transfer contributes to the paraffin reduction. ZSM-5 exhibits nearly equivalent reactivity for straight chain and monomethyl branched paraffin precursors at 500°C. Observed enhancement of gasoline octane number (2, 3) with the use of a small concentration of ZSM-5 (either fresh or steam deactivated) is probably due to the reduction in concentration of paraffins (normal, monomethyl) and resultant enrichment of olefins and aromatics in the gasoline. The same mechanism can be used to explain the changes in gasoline composition with either fresh or steam deactivated ZSM-5.

Acknowledgments

The authors thank Dr. M. G. Sanchez for his valuable contributions to this work which included preparation of ZSM-5 and discussion of the experimental methods. We thank Ms. C. R. Petr, Mr. A. L. Wadsworth and Ms. G. B. Lundquist for their experimental work. We also acknowledge helpful discussions with Dr. A. W. Peters and Mr. J. E. Creighton.

Literature Cited

1. Venuto, P. B.; Habib, Jr., E. T. Fluid Catalytic Cracking with Zeolite Catalysts; Marcel Dekker, Inc.: New York, 1979.
2. Rosinski, E. J.; Plank, C. J.; Schwartz, A. B. U.S. Patent 3 758 403, 1973.
3. Anderson, C. D.; Dwyer, F. G.; Koch, G; Niiranen, P. Proc. Ninth Iberoamerican Symposium on Catalysis, Lisbon, 1984.
4. Dwyer, F. G.; Schipper, P. H.; Gorra, F. NPRA Annual Meeting, AM 87-63, San Antonio, March, 1987.
5. Chen, N. Y.; Garwood, W. E. J. Catalysis 1978, 52, 453.
6. Anderson, J. R.; Foger, K; Mole, T.; Rajadhyaksha, R. A.; Sanders, J. V. J. Catalysis 1979, 58, 114.
7. Abbot, J.; Wojciechowski, B. W. Can. J. Chem. Eng. 1985, 63, 462.
8. Corma, A.; Monton, J. B.; Orchilles, A. V. Applied Catalysts 1985, 16, 59.
9. Frillette, V. J.; Haag, W. O.; Lago, R. M. J. Catalysis 1981, 67, 218.
10. Wang, I.; Chen, T-J.; Chao, K-J.; Tsai, T-C. J. Catalysis 1979, 60, 140.
11. Borade, R. B.; Hegde, S. G.; Kulkarni, S. B.; Ratnasamy, P. Applied Catalysis 1984, 13, 27.
12. Magee, J. S.; Blazek, J. J. In Zeolite Chemistry and Catalysis; Rabo, J. A., Ed.; ACS Monograph 171, p. 615. American Chemical Society, Washington, D.C., 1976.
13. Weekman, Jr., V. W. Ind. Eng. Chem. Proc. Des. Dev. 1968, 7, 90.
14. Ritter, R. E.; Creighton, J. E.; Roberie, T. G.; Chin, D. S.; Wear, C. C., NPRA Annual Meeting, AM 86-45, Los Angeles, CA, March, 1986.
15. ASTM Special Technical Publication No. 225, Knocking Characteristics of Pure Hydrocarbons, ASTM, Philadelphia.
16. Satterfield, C. N. Mass Transfer in Heterogeneous Catalysis; M.I.T. Press: Cambridge, MA, 1970.
17. Wheeler, A. Advan. Catalysis 1951, 3, 249.

18. Gates, B. C.; Katzer, J. R.; Schuit, G. C. A. <u>Chemistry of Catalytic Processes</u>; McGraw-Hill: New York, 1979.

19. Thomas, C. L.; Barmby, D. S. <u>J. Catalysis</u> 1968, <u>12</u>, 341.

RECEIVED March 17, 1988

Chapter 4

Zeolite Beta: Structure, Activity, and Selectivity for Catalytic Cracking

A. Corma[1], V. Fornés[2], F. Melo[1], and J. Pérez-Pariente[1]

[1]Instituto de Catálisis y Petroleoquímica, CSIC, Serrano, 119,
28006–Madrid, Spain
[2]Instituto de Ciencia de Materiales, CSIC, Serrano 115 bis,
28008–Madrid, Spain

A series of Beta zeolites have been synthesized in the
presence of tetraethylammonium hydroxide (TEA). Samples
with Si/Al ratio in the 7-100 range have been characterized
by X-ray powder diffraction, I.R. spectroscopy, and pyridine
adsorption. The fraction of TEA which is compensating the
charge of the framework aluminum is removed at temperatures
higher than those required to remove "occluded" TEA. Three
hydroxyl bands are observed at 3740 cm^{-1} (silanol groups),
3680 cm^{-1} (extraframework Al) and 3615 cm^{-1} (acid hydroxyl
groups interacting with pyridine).
Comparison of the catalytic properties of H-Beta and H-Y
zeolites for cracking n-heptane and gasoil shows that
zeolite Beta should have more than one type of channel with
different dimensions. For gas-oil cracking, zeolite Beta is
less active and produces more coke and less gasoline than
zeolite HY.

The beneficial effect of adding small amounts of medium-pore zeolites
to cracking catalysts has recently been shown (1). However, the main
zeolitic component of these catalysts remains the Y zeolite. To crack
large molecules such as those present in vacuum gas-oil residues,
the larger pore opening of the zeolite is needed to increase the
accesible active surface. On the other hand, in the case of Y zeolite
a high framework Si/Al ratio increases its thermal and hydrothermal
stability. Unfortunately, NaY zeolite as synthetized has a framework
Si/Al ratio up to 2.8. Consequently, it must be dealuminated during
the activation step, with a corresponding loss of crystallinity.
Therefore, it would be desirable to synthesize large-pore zeolites
within a wide range of framework Si/Al ratio. Beta zeolite can be
synthesized with silicon to aluminum ratios in the range of 5 to 100
(2,3). Moreover, this zeolite has large pores of 12-member rings (4)
accesible to large molecules.
In this paper we present some structural and acid properties of

0097–6156/88/0375–0049$06.00/0
© 1988 American Chemical Society

Beta zeolite with different framework Si/Al ratios and their influence on activity and selectivity for cracking of n-heptane and vacuum
gas-oil.

Experimental

The tetraethylammonium-Beta (TEA-β) zeolites used in this work have
been synthesized following the procedure described in the literature
(5). Samples with Si/Al ratios between 7 and 106 (as measured by
chemical analysis) and crystallite sizes in the range of 0.2-0.9 μm
(as measured by scanning microscopy) were obtained. The H-form of
these zeolites was prepared in the following way: the TEA-β samples
were heated at 550°C for 3 hours by slowly increasing the calcination
temperature (5°C min^{-1}), with one-hour intermediate steps at 350 and
450°C. After this treatment all TEA molecules had been removed from
the zeolite (as monitored by IR spectroscopy). In a second step, the
zeolite was exchanged with 1 M ammonium acetate solution and then
heated at 550°C for 3 hours as described.
    X-ray powder diffraction patterns of samples heated at tempera-
tures between 20 and 500°C were recorded in situ by using a Philips
instrument equipped with vacuum camera (5x10^{-3} Pa). Heating rates
of 5°C min^{-1} and CuK$_\alpha$ radiation were used. Infrared spectra were
obtained using a conventional greaseless IR cell; the procedure and
sample preparation have been described elsewhere (6). ^{27}Al MAS-NMR
spectra were recorded using a 400 MHz Brüker instrument.
    Catalytic experiments were performed in a fixed bed glass tubu-
lar reactor at atmospheric pressure and at reaction temperature of
450 and 482°C for n-heptane and gas-oil, respectively. Details on
the experimental procedure have already been published (7).

Results and Discussion

IR spectroscopy. The IR spectra of an as-synthesized TEA-β (Si/Al =
10) in the 4000-1300 cm^{-1} range is shown in Figure 1a. Broad bands
centered at 3400 and 1640 cm^{-1}, corresponding to adsorbed water are
clearly visible, together with bands appearing at $\sim$3000 cm^{-1} and
1500-1350 cm^{-1} corresponding to organic material. In the low wavenum-
ber region bending vibrations at 1485 cm 1395 cm^{-1} indicate the presence of CH_2 and CH_3 groups, respectively, corresponding to the
ethyl groups of the TEA cation incorporated into the zeolite during
synthesis. When the sample is outgassed at 1.33x10^{-2} Pa (Figure 1b)
the band at 1640 cm^{-1} dissapears, indicating the removal of the
water adsorbed in the zeolite, and a broad band centered at 3450 cm^{-1}
appears. The intensity of this band can be slightly decreased by
heating at 100°C, and a new band centered at 3700 cm^{-1} develops.
When the outgassing temperature is increased to 200°C, a shift of
the 3450 cm^{-1} band to 3500 cm^{-1} is observed, and a small band appears
at 3745 cm^{-1} that has been assigned to silanol groups in zeolites
(8). On the other hand, the intensity of the bands corresponding to
the organic groups decreased slightly. The heating of the sample at
300°C dramatically decreases the amount of organic material (Figure
1c), and in the sample heated at 350°C bands corresponding to NH_4^+
cation at 3200 and 3075 cm^{-1} are observed. This behavior clearly
indicates the progressive decomposition of the TEA cation to volatile

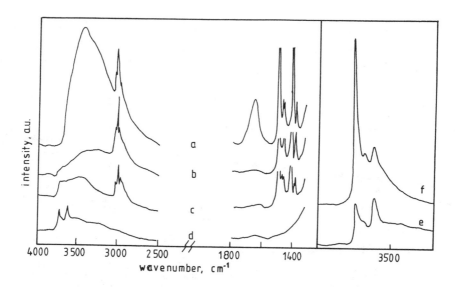

Figure 1. IR spectra of Beta zeolites (Si/Al=10). (a) TEA-β;
(b) Sample a outgassed at 1.33 x 10^{-2} Pa; (c) Sample b heated
at 300°C and 1.33 x 10^{-2} Pa; (d) Sample c heated at 400°C and
1.33 x 10^{-2} Pa; (e) Spectrum of sample c in the OH region;
(f) Spectrum of β-zeolite (Si/Al=7.5), outgassed at 1.33 x 10^{-2}
Pa and 400°C.

compounds (ethylene and amines which are released by the zeolite) and ammonium cation. This process has been studied in the case of TEA containing ZSM-5 (9).

Despite the partial decomposition of the organic cation, no acidic hydroxyl groups appear in the ~ 3600 cm^{-1} region, but the intensity of the 3745 cm^{-1} band increases. When the treatment temperature is raised to 400°C, the organic material is fully removed from the zeolite. Only a sharp band centered at 3745 cm^{-1} and two bands at 3680 cm^{-1} (very low intensity) and 3615 cm^{-1}, both corresponding to hydroxyl groups, are visible (Figure 1d). The band at 3680 cm^{-1} is visible in figure 1e corresponding to figure 1d expanded in the region of 4000-3200 cm^{-1}. However, the intensity of this band is maxima for a Beta zeolite with a Si/Al ratio of 7.5, heated in the same conditions (Figure 1f).

The observed changes in the IR spectra of the sample as a function of the outgassing temperature indicate that in the TEA-β zeolite there are two types of organic species: The occluded TEA, which is removed below 300°C, and the TEA remaining at this temperature, which compensates part of the negative charge due to the presence of aluminium in the framework. The removal of the latter TEA species generates the appearance of framework hydroxyl groups at 3615 cm^{-1}.

The exact nature of the occluded organic cation is more difficult to determine. The increased intensity of the silanol band as this type of TEA is removed strongly supports the presence of the SiO$^-$-TEA$^+$ species, which has been claimed to be present in as-synthesized ZSM-5 (10). On the other hand, the presence of the broad band centered around 3450 cm^{-1} (see figure 1a) could correspond to OH$^-$ acting as counterions of TEA cations. The removal of this organic material would take place through a Hoffman elimination (9):

$$OH^- (N(C_2H_5)_4)^+ \xrightarrow{\Delta T} H_2O + N(C_2H_5)_3 + C_2H_4$$

The presence of water and amines at high temperatures may produce a process equivalent to a shallow bed calcination, and this could explain the formation of silanol groups by partial breaking of the Si-O-Al bonds in the zeolite framework. Probably, both types of occluded TEA exist in the zeolite.

When the IR spectra of Beta samples with the Si/Al ratio increasing from 10 to 35 are compared, several trends can be observed (Figure 2b). Before outgassing, the intensity of the bands assigned to organic groups increases with increasing Si/Al ratio of the zeolite. In contrast, the intensity of bands corresponding to adsorbed water decreases (Figure 2a), indicating that the zeolite becomes more hydrophobic as the Al content decreases. Moreover, the amount of TEA remaining in the samples after heating in vacuum at 300°C decreases, while the intensity of the silanol band increases (Figure 2b). After heating in vacuum at 400°C all the organic material is lost, and the intensity of the silanol band increases significantly. Band intensity of framework hydroxyls (3615 cm^{-1}) decreases with the crystal aluminum content (see Figure 2c). These results suggests that occluded TEA increases and that charge compensating TEA ions decrease as the zeolite becomes poorer in aluminum. This conclusion is in good agreement with the results of thermal analysis (5).

The presence of a small band at ~ 950 cm^{-1} assigned to the stret-

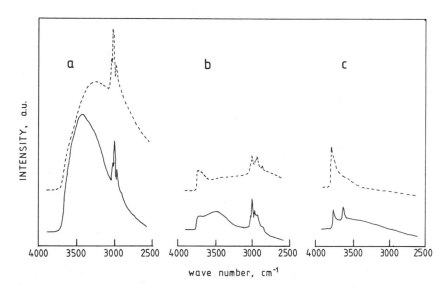

Figure 2.   IR spectra of Beta zeolites of Si/Al=10 (continuous lines) and Si/Al=35 (dashed lines); (a) before outgassing; (b) and (c) after outgassing at 300°C and 400°C, respectively.

ching vibration of Si-O⁻ group (11) further supports the presence of
these groups in the as-synthesized zeolite. This band is clearly visible for samples with Si/Al>13, and its intensity increases by increasing the Si/Al ratio of the zeolite.

X-ray Powder Diffraction. The variation of the area under the main
peak ($2\theta=22.4$) in the X-ray patterns (taked as a measure of the crystallinity of the sample) of a Beta sample with Si/Al=10 has been
plotted in Figure 3 as a function of the outgassing temperature. Two
mains steps of crystallinity loss are observed: the first one takes
place between 200 and 300°C, and the second one from 300 to 400°C,
the loss of crystallinity in the latter step being more important
than in the former. These two steps correspond closely to the temperature ranges where the decomposition of the organic material takes
place, as determined by IR spectroscopy. This correlation strongly
suggests that the loss of crystallinity is induced by the process
involved in the elimination of the TEA cations from the zeolite pores. This process partially breaks the zeolite structure and could
contribute to the increase of silanol groups. Furthermore, the decrease in the area of the main peak after heating at 500°C is more
pronounced for zeolites with low aluminum content.

The aluminum content of the as-synthesized zeolites also influences their X-ray powder diffraction pattern. The height of the main
peak in the patterns decreases with decreasing Si/Al ratio in the
zeolite, but their width increases simultaneously so that the area
remains practically constant for all samples. On the other hand, the
d_{hkl} distance corresponding to the diffraction peak at 43° of 2θ correlated linearly with the aluminum content of the zeolite (Figure
4). However, the lack of knowledge of the crystal structure of Beta
zeolite makes it impossible to correlate the Al content and unit
cell parameters.

Acidity. Pyridine adsorption on samples of Beta zeolite with Si/Al
ratio between 7 and 40 allow us to determine the acidic nature of
the hydroxyl groups and their evolution as a function of its aluminum
content.

For samples with Si/Al ratio lower than ∿10, three hydroxyl
stretching bands appear after heating in vacuum at 400°C: 3745 cm⁻¹,
3680 cm⁻¹, and 3615 cm⁻¹, figure 1f. The band at 3745 cm⁻¹ corresponds to silanol groups and its intensity increases when the Si/Al
ratio increases. Adsorption pyridine and further desorption at 150°C
only slightly decreases the intensity of this band, indicating its
very weak acidic character.

The OH stretching band appearing at 3680 cm⁻¹ has a very low intensity, making it difficult to follow its evolution with the Si/Al
ratio or with the pyridine adsorption. However, the intensity of
this band decreases for decreasing Al content, and becomes invisi-
ble for Si/Al ratios higher than ∿10. A similar band has been observed in ZSM5 (12,13) and assigned to nonacidic OH groups (13). In
contrast, Jacobs et al. (14) did not detected this band in well-
crystallized ZSM-5 samples. The intensity of this band does not
change by adsorption of pyridine, indicating that it corresponds to
nonacidic hydroxyl groups. The variation of the band intensity with
the Al content suggests that it could be related to OH groups associated with nonframework aluminum produced by dealumination. These

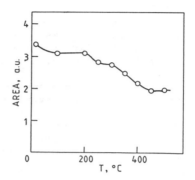

Figure 3. Area of the X-ray diffraction peak at 22.4 of 2θ vs. the outgassing temperature.

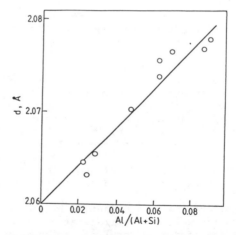

Figure 4. Influence of the aluminum content on the d_{hkl} value corresponding to the diffraction peak appearing at 43.5-43.9 of 2θ.

groups are partially removed when the sample is heated to temperatures higher than 300°C and disappear completely at 700°C.

The band centered at 3615 cm^{-1} disappears by adsorption of pyridine and further outgassing at 150°C, thus confirming its assignment to stretching vibration of acidic OH groups. For samples with a different Si/Al ratio, a direct correlation is observed between the intensity of this band and that of protonated pyridine at 1540 cm^{-1} (Table I).

However, the plot of the intensity of the hydroxyl bands as a function of the Al fraction (Figure 5) shows a maximum for samples with Si/Al ratio ∿10, indicating that extensive dealumination has taken place during activation of aluminum-rich crystals.

Table I.   Influence of the aluminum content on the intensity of the hydroxyl and adsorbed pyridine bands.

			*Pyridine retained at 350°C	
Al/(Al+Si)	I_{3750}	I_{3625}	I^B_{1540}	I^L_{1450}
.114	.52	.06	.08	.25
.104	.40	.09	.10	.19
.088	.45	.14	.12	.25
.053	.55	.08	.08	.20
.032	.65	.07	.07	.12

* The 1540 and 1450 cm^{-1} bands correspond to pyridine adsorbed on Brønsted and Lewis sites, respectively.

^{27}Al MAS-NMR spectra of as-shynthesized samples of Si/Al 10 and 30 show a peak at 54-56 ppm corresponding to tetrahedral aluminum (15). After calcination in air, a peak centered at ∿0 ppm corresponding to octahedral aluminum (15) appears in the spectrum of the sample with the lowest Si/Al ratio. When the samples are exchanged two times with NH$_4^+$ ions and calcined again, the octahedral aluminum signal also appears in the spectrum of the zeolite with Si/Al=30. This treatment enhances the intensity of the octahedral aluminum signal for the low Si/Al ratio. Table II shows the percentage of Al corresponding to tetrahedral and octahedral coordination in each case.

These results indicate that dealumination by thermal treatment seems easier for zeolites with a low Si/Al ratio, in good agreement with the behavior of the acidic hydroxyl groups shown in Figure 5.

It is generally accepted that Lewis acidity in zeolites is due mainly to extraframework aluminum (16,17,18). Consequently, Lewis acid sites measured by pyridine adsorption must correlate with extraframework aluminum. In Table I, the amount of pyridine coordinated to Lewis sites decreases for samples with the lowest Si/Al ratio, showing that, after thermal treatment, the amount of extraframework aluminum decreases with Si/Al ratio of the Beta zeolite.

Table II.   Percentages of Al in tetrahedral and octahedral sites.

| Sample | Al/(Al+Si) | | | |
| | 0.088 | | 0.032 | |
	tetrahedral	octahedral	tetrahedral	octahedral
as-synthesized	100	–	100	–
calcined	91	9	100	–
calcined and exchanged	85	15	85	15

Catalytic Activity. In Figure 6 the activity, for n-heptane cracking, of a series of Beta zeolites with different Si/Al ratios is given and compared with the activity of $SiCl_4$ dealuminated HY zeolites. It appears that Beta zeolite is more active than zeolites HY for n-heptane cracking. However, for gas-oil cracking, Figures 7a-c, the activity is higher for HY zeolites than for the Beta samples. Our results from n-heptane and gas-oil cracking seem to indicate that the Beta zeolite is not unidimensional and that channels of different dimensions are probably present. One type of channel would allow the large molecules of gas-oil to penetrate and react, while the other does not. On the other hand, n-heptane can react in both type of channels.

A very shallow maximum in activity for both n-heptane and gas-oil cracking is observed for Beta zeolites (with nominal framework Si/Al ratio of 20-40), while for Y zeolite a clear maximum is located at values between 10 and 20. In any case, a partial dealumination takes place when the TEA-β zeolites are NH_4^+-exchanged and calcined, Consequently, the activity curve for Beta zeolites should be shifted to higher framework Si/Al with respect to those plotted in Figures 6 and 7a.

Product selectivity curves for gas-oil cracking on a Beta zeolite with a nominal Si/Al ratio of 10 and 27 are compared in Figures 8 and 9 with those for HY zeolites with framework Si/Al ratios of 7.7 and 35, respectively.

At lower Si/Al ratio zeolite Beta produces more coke, probably slightly more gases, less gasoline, and about the same diesel as the Y zeolite. At high Si/Al ratio, zeolite Beta produces more coke and probably slightly more diesel, the same gasoline, and less gases than the corresponding HY sample.

Table III lists the i-butane/n-butane ratio for cracking of n-heptane on Y and Beta zeolites with different aluminum content. The lower ratio obtained on the latter zeolite indicates that the diameter of the 12-membered ring channels of Beta zeolite must be smaller than that of Y zeolite.

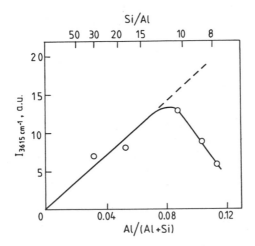

Figure 5.   Intensity of the 3615 cm^{-1} band as a function of the aluminum content of H-Beta zeolites.

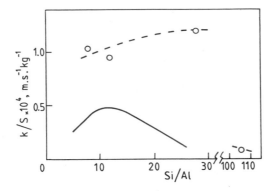

Figure 6.   Comparison between H-Beta zeolites (open circles and dashed lines) and HY zeolites (continuous lines) for n-heptane cracking at different Si/Al ratios.

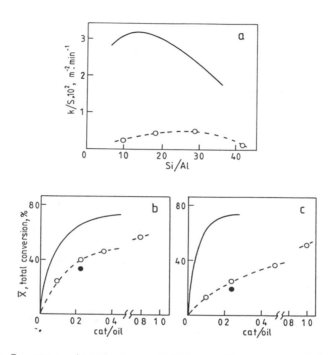

Figure 7. Comparison between H-Beta zeolites (open circles and dashed lines) and HY zeolites (continuous lines) for gas-oil cracking; (a) First-order activity constant by specific surface area vs. Si/Al ratio; (b) and (c) Average total conversion vs. gas-oil ratio for a H-Beta with Si/Al=27 and a HY Si/Al=35, and for a H-Beta with Si/Al=10 and a Hy with Si/Al=7.7 respectively. Solid circles correspond to the H-Beta steamed at 750°C and 1 atmosphere of water pressure.

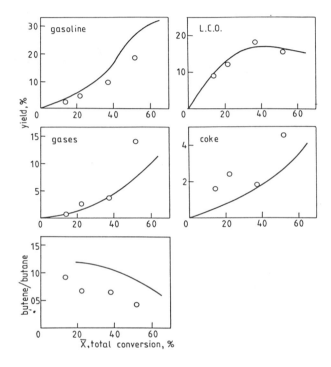

Figure 8.   Comparison of selectivity curves for gas-oil cracking on an H-Beta with Si/Al=10 (open circles) and a HY with Si/Al= 7.7 (continuous line).

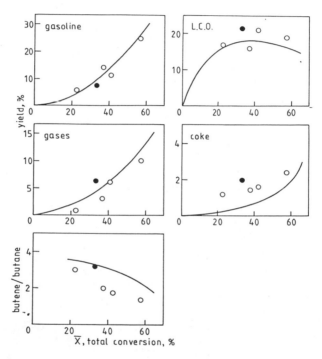

Figure 9. Comparison of selectivity curves for gas-oil cracking on an H-Beta with Si/Al=27 (open circles) and HY with Si/Al=35 (continuous line). The solid circle corresponds to the H-Beta steamed at 750°C and 1 atmosphere of water pressure.

Table III. Isobutane/n-butane for Y and Beta zeolites with
            different aluminum content.

| Y zeolites | | Beta zeolites | |
Al/(Al+Si)	i-butane(n-butane)	Al/(Al+Si)	i-butane/n-butane
0.125	2.93	0.154	2.00
0.091	2.84	0.091	1.86
0.069	2.62	0.036	1.83
0.040	2.27	0.010	1.58

Conclusions

In Beta zeolites synthesized using TEA, only a part of the TEA is
compensating the charge of the framework aluminum, while the other
is "occluded" in the structure. The proportion of the occluded TEA
increases when increasing the Si/Al ratio of the zeolite, and can
be removed at lower temperature than the TEA associated with framework Al.

Calcination of the samples at 500°C causes the formation of
structural deffects and silanol groups. The number of silanols
formed during calcination increases when increasing the Si/Al ratio
of the zeolite.

Hydroxyl bands at 3615 and 3680 cm^{-1} have been observed by I.R.
spectroscopy. The 3680 cm^{-1} OH band has been assigned to extraframework Al, while the 3615 cm^{-1} band corresponds to framework Al and
is acid enough to interact strongly with pyridine.

Beta zeolite is partially dealuminated by deep bed calcination,
and octahedral aluminum is then detected by ^{27}Al MAS NMR. Dealumination is higher when lower the initial framework Si/Al ratio.

H-Beta are more active for n-heptane cracking than HY-zeolites
with the same Si/Al ratio, while for gas-oil cracking the opposite
occurs. Nevertheless we have not looked here to mesoporosity of the
zeolites which may be critical for explaining the activity in gas-
oil cracking. Steaming causes a smaller decreases in activity of
H-Beta than on HY zeolite. H-Beta gives a lower i-C_4/C_4 ratio than
HY in the cracking of n-heptane, while gives more coke and gas, and
less gasoline than H-Y for gas-oil cracking.

Acknowledgments

This work was supported by the CAICYT (project 999/070).

Literature Cited

1. Anderson, D.C.; Dwyer, F.G.; Koch, G. and Nuranen, P.; 9th Ac-
    tas Simp. Iberoam. Catal., 1 (1984) p. 247
2. Wadlinger, R.L.; Kerr, G.T. and Rosirki, E.J. U.S. Pat. 3 308
    069, 1967.
3. Rosinski, E.J.; Plank, C.J. and Rubin, M.K. Eur. Pat. App.
    064 328, 1982.
4. Martens, J.A.; Tielen, M.; Jacobs, P.A. and Weitkamp, J.;
    Zeolites. 1984, 4, 98.
5. Perez Pariente, J.; Martens, J.A. and Jacobs, P.A.; Applied
    Catalysis, in press.

6. Corma, A.; Fornés, V.; Montón, J.B. and Orchillés, A.V.; Ind. Eng. PRD. 1986, 25, 231
7. Corma, A.; Juan, J.; Martos, J. and Soriano, J.M. 8th Int. Congr. Catal. Berlín. Vol. II (1984) p. 239.
8. Ward, J.W. in Zeolite Chemistry and Catalysis, Rabo, J.A., Ed.; American Chemical Soc. Washington, D.C. 1976; Chapter 3.
9. Parker, L.M.; Bibby, D.M. and Patterson, J.E. Zeolites, 1984, 4, 168
10. Dessau, R.M.; Schmitt, K.D.; Kerr, G.T.; Woolery, G.L. and Alemany, L.B.; J. Catal., 1987, 104, 484.
11. Decottignies, M.; Phalippon, J. and Zrzycki, J.; J. Mat. Sci., 1978, 13, 2605.
12. Woorlery, G.L.; Alemany, L.B.; Dessau, R.M. and Chester, A.W. Zeolites, 1986, 6, 14.
13. Topsøe, N.Y.; Pedersen, K. and Derouane, E.G.; J. Catal., 1981, 70, 41
14. Jacobs, P.A. and von Ballmoos, R.; J. Phys. Chem. 1982, 86, 3050
15. Klinowski, J. In Progress in NMR Spectroscopy; Cambridge, 1976. p. 237.
16. Jacobs, P. and Beyer, H.K.; J. Phys. Chem., 1979, 83, 1174
17. Freude, D.; Frøhlich, T.; Hunger, M.; Pfeifer, H. and Scheler, G.; Chem. Phys. Lett., 1983, 98, 263
18. Anderson, M.W. and Klinowski, J.; Zeolites, 1986, 6, 455.

RECEIVED February 25, 1988

Chapter 5

Zeolite ZSM-5 in Fluid Catalytic Cracking: Performance, Benefits, and Applications

P. H. Schipper, F. G. Dwyer, P. T. Sparrell, S. Mizrahi, and J. A. Herbst

Paulsboro Research Laboratory, Mobil Research and Development Corporation, Paulsboro, NJ 08066

The demonstrated performance of ZSM-5 in over 35 cracking units is reviewed. The main features of ZSM-5 are its high activity and stability, favorable selectivity, metals tolerance and flexibility, particularly when used as an additive catalyst. ZSM-5 cracks and isomerizes low octane components in the naphtha produced by the faujasite cracking catalyst. As a result C_3 and C_4 olefins are produced and gasoline compositional changes occur which explain its increased research and motor octanes. A model was developed which predicts ZSM-5 performance in an FCC unit. Discussed is how this model calculates ZSM-5 activity, gasoline research and motor octane increases and catalyst management policies. Also discussed are ways to utilize ZSM-5 and how its use permits reoptimization of not only the FCC unit but the entire refinery.

There have been many advances in catalytic cracking catalysts over the past 25 years starting with the introduction of rare earth exchanged X and Y zeolites (REX, REY) into Thermofor Catalytic Cracking (TCC) and Fluid Catalytic Cracking (FCC) catalysts (1-3). Another significant cracking catalyst improvement was the introduction of CO oxidation promoters (4-6). More recent catalyst improvements have included use of the hydrogen form of Y, ultrastable Y (USY) (7), chemically dealuminated Y and silicon enriched Y zeolites (8). The latest advance in cracking catalysts has been the introduction of ZSM-5 which is the first generic zeolite change in catalytic cracking.
    ZSM-5 is a Mobil-proprietary, shape-selective zeolite which is used commercially in synthetic fuels (methanol-to-gasoline), petrochemicals (xylene isomerization, toluene disproportionation, benzene alkylation) and in petroleum refining (lube and

distillate dewaxing) (9). It has also been used in catalytic
cracking to increase gasoline Research and Motor clear Octane
numbers (RON and MON) and gasoline plus alkylate yield.
    The first full-scale refinery test demonstration of ZSM-5
in catalytic cracking was made in the TCC unit of the Neste Oy
refinery in Naantali, Finland (10). The catalyst used in this
application was a composite catalyst containing both REY and
ZSM-5. This commercial demonstration was a success with RON
increasing up to 4 numbers. Since this initial demonstration,
ZSM-5 has been used in over thirty-five units (both TCC and FCC)
ranging in size from 6,000 to 90,000 barrels per day (BPD).
Table I lists some of the available results from twenty of these
commercial applications. In all cases, ZSM-5 increased both
Research and Motor Octane. The ZSM-5 content in the unit
inventory for these applications ranged from 0.2 to 3 wt %. The
variations in the octane response from a given concentration of
ZSM-5 are due to variations in the base octane (octane without
ZSM-5), gasoline cut point, catalyst makeup rate and regenerator
temperature.
    In FCC applications, ZSM-5 has been used primarily in the
form of a high concentration, separate particle additive, since
this method affords maximum flexibility. However, it has also
been successfully employed as a composite catalyst containing
both ZSM-5 and the faujasitic cracking component in the same
particle (11).
    Detailed results of demonstrations in FCC units belonging
to Oklahoma Refining in Cyril, Oklahoma and EniChem Anic in Gela,
Italy have been published (11-14). These demonstrations have
shown that the target octane can be achieved within 1 to 7 days
by accelerating the initial addition of a ZSM-5 additive
catalyst. In contrast, octane catalysts containing Y zeolites
with reduced unit cell size can generally take several months to
boost octane, since they require significant turnover of catalyst
inventory. Alternative methods, such as increasing riser top
temperature to increase octane, are not as attractive as using
ZSM-5 because the former increases C_2^- ($H_2+CH_4+C_2H_4+C_2H_6$) gas and
coke make and this can potentially limit FCC throughput. Thus,
for a given octane boost, ZSM-5 will produce less wet gas than
raising riser top temperatures. This allows the FCC unit to be
re-optimized so that higher feed rates and/or conversions can be
achieved at constant wet gas, while still improving the overall
pool octane. As a result of these considerations and its
commercial success, ZSM-5 usage has now taken its place among the
least expensive octane enhancement methods available to refiners
(15-17).
    In addition to its octane enhancement ability described
above, ZSM-5 also increases the feed to alkylation, methyl
tertiary butyl ether (MTBE) and tertiary amyl methyl ether (TAME)
units. Since the products from all these processes contain high
Research and Motor Octane components, ZSM-5 provides the refiner
additional flexibility in his downstream processing whenever the
need exists to increase overall gasoline pool octane. In
addition, the overall refinery can be rebalanced to take

advantage of the benefits arising from the use of ZSM-5;
particularly, the higher fraction of reformate and alkylate in
the overall gasoline pool. One example is to reform the FCC
heart cut, i.e., the mid-boiling range, naphtha. ZSM-5 enhances
reforming of an FCC heart cut gasoline by increasing the octane
of the remaining FCC gasoline and also increasing the fraction of
alkylate and reformate in the overall pool gasoline.

In this paper, we discuss how ZSM-5 works to increase
octane in an FCC unit, the development of a model to predict ZSM-
5 performance, and methods to optimize the FCC unit and overall
refinery with ZSM-5.

Table I. Summary of Commercial Performance of ZSM-5
          in Catalytic Cracking

	<---RON--->		<---MON----->		Estimated ZSM-5 in In-
Refinery	Base	Δ	Base	Δ	ventory, wt %
A	91.5	+1.5	79.0	+0.6	2.8
B	93.4	+0.9	80.5	+0.3	2.0
C	91.8	+1.0	79.8	+0.3	0.2
D	86.0	+4.5	77.4	+2.2	2.2
E	87.3	+1.7	78.2	+0.6	0.9
F	87.6	+1.6	77.3	+1.2	0.3
G	89.8	+2.2	N/A	N/A	1.2
H	88.5	+1.5	N/A	N/A	0.8
I	91.5	+1.2	81.5	+0.5	0.5
J	92.6	+1.9	80.3	+0.7	1.5
K	93.4	+0.7	80.3	+0.3	2.4
L	92.5	+0.9	80.5	+1.1	0.2
M	92.5	+1.4	80.6	+0.9	2.2
N	92.5	+1.0	81.5	+0.4	2.4
O	92.0	+1.0	79.9	+0.4	0.2
P	92.5	+0.7	80.2	+0.5	0.2
Q	92.7	+1.2	80.3	+0.5	3.0
R	91.4	+0.8	N/A	N/A	1.5
S	88.6	+1.6	N/A	N/A	2.2
T	91.0	+1.2	79.3	+0.7	2.2

How ZSM-5 Works

ZSM-5 increases octane by catalytically cracking and isomerizing
low octane components in the gasoline boiling range to higher
octane components plus propylene and butylene. ZSM-5
accomplishes this selectively, without increasing coke yield or
C_2^- gas make. In addition, conversion and light cycle oil
(LCO)/main column bottom (MCB) selectivities remain unchanged.
In contrast, increasing octane by raising reactor top temperature
significantly increases C_2^- gas yields which potentially limit
FCC unit throughput or severity.

Several commercial examples of the yield and octane shifts
for ZSM-5 addition are illustrated in Tables II through VI. In

all cases, the same type ZSM-5 additive catalyst was used. Also, operating conditions and feedstock remained constant for each example. In the examples in Table II, the octane gains are accompanied by an increase in C_3 and C_4 olefins (potential alkylate feed) and a decrease in gasoline yield. The increase in potential alkylate more than compensates for the loss in gasoline yield so that overall FCC plus potential alkylate gasoline yield increases. The increase in alkylate increases the refinery pool motor octane because alkylate has a higher motor octane blending number. Table II also illustrates that as the base octane increases, more gasoline plus potential alkylate is produced for approximately the same FCC gasoline octane increase. As shown in the three examples, ZSM-5 does not affect the distillate or bottoms selectivity; nor does it affect C_2^- or coke yield.

We can gain an understanding of the gasoline compositional shifts which occur with ZSM-5 by studying the examples shown in Table III. The gasoline octane increase with ZSM-5 results from a decrease in concentration of the C_7+ paraffins and olefins, and an increase in the concentration of both light olefins and aromatics. The concentration of the light olefins is selectively increased to the single and multiple branched light olefins, all high octane species (Table IV), with an actual reduction in the concentration of linear C_5 and C_6 olefins. A larger increase is observed for single branched olefins when compared to multiple branched olefins.

To understand the reaction pathways, the yield shifts for the three examples illustrated in Table III were calculated on a fresh feed basis (Table V). These data show that the predominant reaction is the loss of C_7+ paraffins and olefins. Approximately 2.5 wt % C_7+ paraffins plus olefins were lost for a +1.5 Research Octane number increase. ZSM 5 is selective to cracking both single branched and linear paraffins, and single branched and linear olefins (9) which have very low Research and Motor Octanes, as illustrated below:

	RON	MON
n-octene	57	58
methyl-hexanes	42-52	46-55

In general, the higher the initial concentration of C_7+ olefins in the gasoline, the larger the rate of cracking of the C_7+ olefins.

The products of the ZSM-5 reaction in the gasoline boiling range are mainly C_5-C_6 single branched olefins which have high Research and Motor Octane, as illustrated below:

	RON	MON
$2M2C_4=$	100	83

The data in Table III show that the concentration of aromatics in the ZSM-5 gasoline fraction increases. As the data in Table V show, the increase is not due to aromatics formation, but rather due to the concentration of the aromatics in a smaller amount of gasoline.

As discussed previously, the ZSM-5 cracking products which occur outside the gasoline boiling range are mainly C_3 and C_4 olefins. The incremental C_4 olefin yield shows a higher percentage of isobutylene, similar to the distributions found in the C_5 and C_6 olefins (Table IV).

% of Incremental C_4 Olefins Using ZSM-5

i C_4=	40
1 C_4=	20
cis-2-C_4=	20
trans-2-C_4=	20

This increase in isobutylene yield increases feed for downstream MTBE processing.

In general, the higher the concentration of C_7+ olefins and paraffins in the base gasoline, the lower is the base Research and Motor Octane. Thus, without detailed information about the gasoline composition, the base octane can be used to characterize the gasoline. As observed in Figure 1, when the base octane (both Research and Motor) is lower, less ZSM-5 is required to achieve a given octane increase. This observation is not surprising because the lower base octane gasolines contain a higher concentration of low octane components. At any given activity, ZSM-5's upgrading rate depends on the amount (concentration) of low octane components available.

In addition, for a given octane boost, the increase in gasoline plus potential alkylate yield also depends on the base octane. As the base octane increases, the formation of gasoline plus alkylate increases (Figure 2). This results from a lower concentration of C_7+ paraffins and olefins in the high base octane gasolines, as these components contribute less to the overall octane. To obtain a 1 number octane increase for an initially high octane gasoline, a greater shift in the C_7+ paraffins and olefins would be required. Consequently, more light olefins for alkylation are produced.

ZSM-5 increases the octane throughout the entire gasoline boiling range (Figure 3). The magnitude of the octane boost depends on the base gasoline composition and the cut point of the gasoline. In the example illustrated in Figure 3, ZSM-5 increases the octane of the 120^+°C gasoline fraction by 2 to 2.5 MON and 2 to 3 RON and the 120^-°C fraction by about 0.5 to 1.0 MON and 1 to 2.5 RON. This gives an overall gasoline octane boost of +1 MON and +1.5 RON. The octane of the 120^+°C fraction increases because the concentration of low octane components (C_7+ paraffins and olefins) decreases. The octane of the front end (120^-°C) fraction increases because the concentration of high octane components, for example, single branched C_5 and C_6 olefins, increases.

In general, the octane boost is greatest in the fraction of the gasoline with the lowest base octane (Table VI). Examples 1 and 3 in Table VI show the base octane to be higher in the lighter portion of the gasoline. In these examples, the boost in octane increases with the gasoline cut point. The base octane in Example 2 is higher in the heavier portion of the gasoline. In this example, the octane boost decreases with gasoline cut point. The base octane in Example 4 is essentially constant with respect to boiling range.

ZSM-5 has been used successfully in commercial operations when processing high boiling range feedstock and resids. This is principally due to its ability to maintain activity despite the presence of a high concentration of feed metals. ZSM-5's excellent metals tolerance has been demonstrated commercially at equilibrium catalyst metals levels up to 10,000 ppm nickel plus vanadium and 6,000 ppm sodium with very little detrimental effect. Laboratory tests show that ZSM-5 is far less affected by metals than Y-zeolite catalysts. Metals were introduced, as follows:

- Nickel: Nickel naphthenate impregnation followed by air calcination.
- Vanadium: Steam treatment in presence of vanadium pentoxide.
- Sodium: Sodium nitrate impregnation.

Essentially no change in octane enhancing performance of the ZSM-5 catalyst was observed after the catalyst was treated with these metals (Table VII).

Table II.   ZSM-5/FCC Performance Examples

Base Octane, RON	87.3	91.5	92.7
MON	78.2	80.6	80.3
Yield Shifts, % Fresh Feed			
C5+ Gasoline, vol %	-1.6	-2.3	-3.7
LCO, vol %	–	–	–
MCB, vol %	–	–	–
iC4, vol %	+0.3	+0.2	+0.3
nC4, vol %	–	–	–
C4=, vol %	+1.1	+1.2	+1.5
C3, vol %	–	+0.1	+0.5
C3=, vol %	+0.8	+1.6	+2.6
C2 Minus, wt %	–	–	–
Coke, wt %	–	–	–
Alkylate (C_3= & C_4=), vol %	+3.2	+4.7	+6.9
Gaso+Potential Alkylate, vol %	+1.6	+2.4	+3.2
Octane Shifts			
FCC Gasoline, RON	+1.7	+1.2	+1.5
MON	+0.6	+0.3	+0.5

Table III. Gasoline Compositional Shifts with ZSM-5

Example	A	B	C
Base Research Octane	92.0	92.7	91.4
Δ RON	+1.5	+1.5	+1.3
Shifts with ZSM-5, wt %			
Paraffins			
C_6-	+1.0	0	-0.7
C_7+	-1.3	-0.9	-2.5
Olefins			
C_6-	+2.0	+2.6	+2.0
C_7+	-5.6	-3.2	-0.6
Naphthenes	+1.3	0	+0.6
Aromatics	+3.4	+1.5	+1.2

Table IV. Light Olefin Distribution Indicates
Increased Branching with ZSM-5

% of Incremental Olefins Increase

Example	B	C
C_5's		
2 and $3M1C_4=$	50	34
$2M2C_4=$	68	80
Straight Chain $C_5=$	-18	-14
C_6's		
Single Branched $C_5=$	75	127
Multiple Branched $C_4=$	0	11
Straight Chain $C_6=$	-175	-38

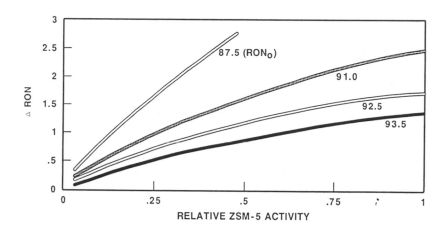

Figure 1. Impact of base octane on ZSM-5 octane boost.

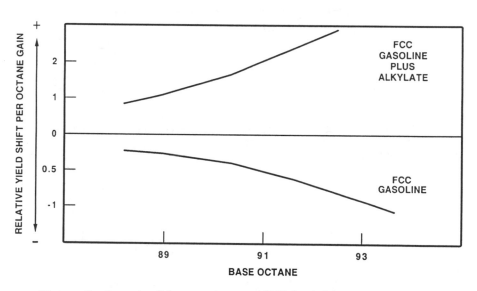

Figure 2. Impact of base octane on ZSM-5 yield-octane response.

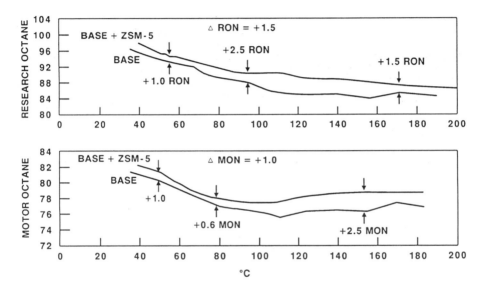

Figure 3. Commercial example. Octane versus cut point.

Table V. ZSM-5 Reactions - Yield Shifts
Based on Fresh Feed

Example	A	B	C
Base Research Octane	92.0	92.7	91.4
ΔRON	+1.5	+1.5	+1.3
Yield Shifts, Wt % Fresh Feed			
Paraffins			
C_6-	+0.1	-0.5	-0.6
C_7+	-0.6	-0.6	-1.7
Olefins			
C_6-	+0.3	+0.4	+0.7
C_7+	-2.2	-2.0	-0.6
Naphthenes	+0.1	-0.2	+0.1
Aromatics	+0.3	-0.1	-0.2
Total	-2.0	-3.0	-2.3
O/P of Base Gasoline	1.5	2.0	0.6

Table VI. Effect of FCC Gasoline Cut Point
and Base Octane on ZSM-5 Octane Boost

Example		Gasoline 90%, °C	Base RON	ZSM-5 RON Boost
	1	91	94.3	+0.5
		170	91.5	+1.5
	2	155	90.4	+2.3
		195	91.5	+1.2
	3	155	94.4	+0.7
		185	93.3	+1.0
	4	155	92.8	+1.7
		195	93.0	+1.5

Table VII. Metals Tolerance of ZSM-5
Laboratory Data

Metal/Content	ΔRON	ΔGasoline, Vol %
Base	+1.2 to +1.6	-2 to -2.5
Ni/2000 ppm	+1.8	-3
V/10000 ppm	+1.7	-2
Na/5000 ppm	+1.0	-1

Predicting ZSM-5 Performance

A model which is consistent with the chemistry described
previously has been developed to predict the performance of ZSM-5
in an FCC unit. Application of this model allows the user to
take full advantage of ZSM-5's flexibility for specific
applications. The model has been used in many commercial
applications to determine the catalyst makeup rate required to
achieve a given octane boost. It has also been used to tailor
the catalyst makeup strategy to obtain a desired octane boost in
a given period of time.

• Model Development

The model is divided into two parts; the calculation of ZSM-5
concentration required to achieve a given activity in the unit
(activity maintenance) and the impact of base gasoline
composition on the gasoline octane boost for ZSM-5 of a given
activity.
    The activity maintenance of ZSM-5 follows the same functional
form as that for normal REY/USY cracking catalysts (18). Using
this format, ZSM-5 activity (the increase in C_3 plus C_4 olefins)
can be expressed in terms of its age, the regenerator temperature
and steam partial pressure according to the following equation:

$$\frac{d\alpha}{dt} = -K_D \, P_W^M \, \alpha^N \qquad \text{where } K_D = K_{Do} \exp(-E_D/RT) \qquad (1)$$

The deactivation order, N, the initial activity, $\alpha_\emptyset$, the
exponent, M, which describes the effect of steam partial
pressure, the activation energy, E_D, and the activity rate
constant, K_{Do}, were determined from both pilot plant and
commercial data.
    In a commercial unit, catalyst is added continuously
resulting in an age distribution of the catalyst in the unit.
Therefore, the overall ZSM-5 activity is a distribution of the
ZSM-5 activities and is related to their relative ages. To
calculate the average ZSM-5 activity, the residence time
distribution and rate expression are integrated over time. The
steady state example is given in the following equation:

$$\bar{\alpha} = \int_0^\infty \left[\alpha_0^{(1-N)} - (1-N) \, K_D \, P_W^M \, t \right]^{(1/1-N)} \frac{1}{\tau} \, e^{-t/\tau} \, dt \qquad (2)$$

where $\bar{\alpha}$ is the average activity per fraction of ZSM-5, f_{ZSM-5}, in
the inventory:

$$f_{ZSM-5} = \frac{M_{ZSM-5}}{M_{ZSM-5} + M_B} \qquad (3)$$

The catalyst residence time, τ depends both on the ZSM-5 and base catalyst makeup rates (M_{ZSM-5}, M_B):

$$\tau = \frac{I}{M_{ZSM-5} + M_B} \qquad (4)$$

The model assumes that the retentions of the base cracking catalyst and ZSM-5 additive catalyst are the same. So, by knowing the activity rate K_{Do}, the regenerator temperature, the ZSM-5 and base makeup rates, the water partial pressure in the regenerator, and the catalyst inventory, the activity can be calculated directly.

We now need to relate the activity of ZSM-5 to the octane boost achievable commercially. As discussed previously, the octane boost at any given ZSM-5 activity depends on the base octane, which is a characteristic of the concentration of low octane olefins and paraffins in the gasoline. Figure 1 illustrates the relationship between octane boost and activity at several different base octanes. As can be seen from the curves, as the gasoline base octane increases, more ZSM-5 activity is required to achieve a given octane increase.

Thus, the potential octane boost which can be obtained from ZSM-5 addition is not only a function of its activity and the fraction of ZSM-5 in inventory, but it also depends on its base gasoline octane (gasoline octane without ZSM-5 addition).

$$\Delta RON = F(\bar{a}, f_{ZSM-5}, RON_\emptyset); \quad \Delta MON = F(\bar{a}, f_{ZSM-5}, MON_\emptyset) \qquad (5)$$

• Parametric Sensitivity of Model

As discussed above, the potential octane boost which can be achieved from ZSM-5 addition is a function of five parameters: the regenerator temperature and steam partial pressure (which determine the activity maintenance); the base and ZSM-5 catalyst makeup rates (which determine the catalyst age); and the base gasoline octane. The sensitivity of the model to these parameters is discussed below.

Table VIII shows the influence of base octane on the relative fractional ZSM-5 replacement rate required to achieve a 1 RON boost. Model estimates show that half as much ZSM-5 is required to achieve a +1 RON/+0.4 MON boost at a base octane of 88 as compared to an application with a base octane of 92.

Table IX shows the effect of regenerator temperature on the relative fractional ZSM-5 replacement rate required to achieve a 1 RON boost. The model prediction shows that ZSM-5 is relatively insensitive to FCC regenerator temperature.

The ZSM-5 addition rate required to maintain a 1 RON boost increases with increasing base catalyst makeup rate, but the increase is less than that which would be estimated due to dilution alone. As the base catalyst makeup rate increases, the catalyst inventory turnover rate increases, causing the average

catalyst age to decrease, and the ZSM-5 catalyst activity to
increase. Since the ZSM-5 catalyst is now more active, a lower
concentration is required to maintain a given octane boost.
Therefore, the activity benefit resulting from the decreased age
partially compensates for the increase in base catalyst makeup
rate. Figure 4 shows as the base catalyst makeup rate increases
from 1 to 1.5, the required relative fractional ZSM-5 addition
rate increases from 1 to 1.25 to maintain the 1 RON increase.
For this example, the relative fractional replacement rate of
ZSM-5 in the inventory decreases form 1 to 0.85.

- Model Verification

The model has been verified by accurately predicting the octane
boost for many different commercial applications. Figure 5 shows
the model predictions versus measured data for two commercial
applications. The objective of the application at Refinery A,
was to increase the Research Octane by 1 number within 1 day.
The base octane for this application was 93.4 and the regenerator
temperature was 1335°F. As the data show, the model matches the
commercial response very well. The objective of the application
at Refinery B, was to increase the Research Octane by 1.5 numbers
within the first week. The base octane for this application was
92.7 and the regenerator temperature was 1275°F. Again, the
model prediction fits the commercial data quite well.

- Catalyst Makeup Strategy Options

One of the main applications of the ZSM-5 performance model is to
determine the optimal catalyst makeup strategy to achieve a
desired octane boost in a required period of time. Since ZSM-5
is used primarily as an additive, the catalyst makeup policy can
be tailored to fit the refiner's needs.
    Figure 6 shows two example makeup strategies to boost the
Research Octane in an FCC unit by 1 number. The first example
shows that the addition rate can be accelerated initially to
achieve the octane boost in one day and then it can gradually be
reduced to maintain the desired octane boost. In this example,
one unit of relative fractional ZSM-5 replacement rate was added
the first day to achieve a 1 RON boost. The addition rate was
reduced to less than 0.2 units by the third day to maintain the
octane boost. The second example shows that the catalyst can be
added more gradually to achieve the desired octane boost within
one week or even longer if desired. In this example, 0.4 units
of relative fractional ZSM-5 replacement rate were added
initially giving a 0.4 RON boost after the first day. The
addition rate was gradually reduced to less than 0.2 units by the
eighth day to maintain the 1 number RON boost achieved after
seven days of ZSM-5 addition.

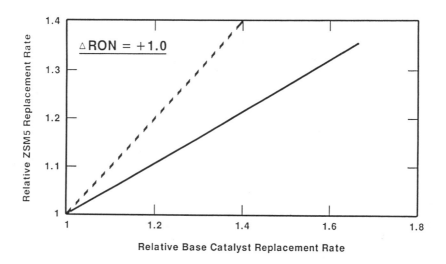

Figure 4. Effect of base catalyst makeup rate.

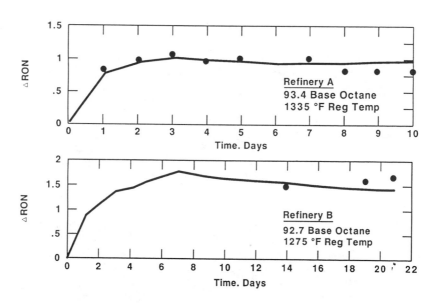

Figure 5. Model fit for commercial trials.

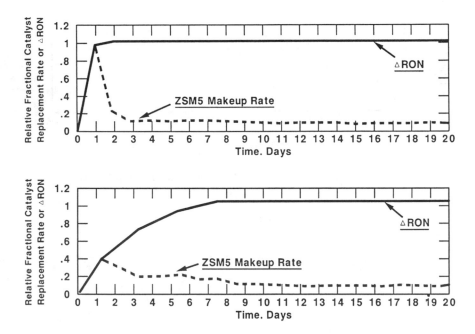

Figure 6. Make up strategies to boost research octane.
Top, rapid octane boost and bottom, gradual octane
boost.

Table VIII.   ZSM-5 Model - Parametric Sensitivity

Effect of Base Octane

$RON_\emptyset$	Relative Fractional ZSM-5 Replacement Rate	ΔRON	ΔMON
88	0.48	+1.0	+0.4
90	0.66	+1.0	+0.4
92	1.0	+1.0	+0.4

Table IX.   Impact of Regenerator Temperature
on ZSM-5 Replacement Rate

Regenerator Temperature	Relative Fractional Replacement Rate of ZSM-5 Required to Achieve a +1 RON Increase
Base	1
Base less 30°C	0.91

Optimization with ZSM-5

- FCC

As mentioned previously, because of its unique chemistry, ZSM-5
produces less wet gas per octane gain than increasing riser top
temperature (Figure 7). This happens because ZSM-5 does not
increase C_2^- yields. Thus, using ZSM-5 allows the refiner to
reoptimize FCC conditions to again reach a wet gas limit.
Several strategies, which allow the refiner to take advantage of
this phenomena, are illustrated below.
   At constant octane, the refiner can:

- Increase FCC feed rate up to the wet gas limit. The
  example in Figure 7 indicates that ZSM-5 provides about 7%
  less wet gas at a constant octane. This translates into
  about 7% additional throughput that could be charged to
  the FCC at constant octane using ZSM-5. This would
  significantly increase the octane barrels produced in the
  refinery.

- Increase FCC conversion by decreasing riser top and preheat temperature (if air blower capacity is available) up to the wet gas limit. Table X gives an example of the yield benefits for using ZSM-5 in this manner.

The refiner can also:

- Increase FCC plus potential alkylate octanes (Motor/Research) at a wet gas constraint by slightly decreasing riser top temperature and increasing preheat (Table XI). Because ZSM-5 increases the fraction of alkylate feed relative to FCC gasoline, the FCC plus potential alkylate gasoline blend has higher octanes.

- Decrease butadiene yield while increasing potential alkylate feed. Unlike increasing riser top temperature, ZSM-5 does not increase butadiene yield with increasing octane (Table XII) (12-14). Butadiene make can negatively impact and ultimately limit downstream alkylation capacity. Thus, C_3 and C_4 products from ZSM-5 can produce more alkylate product at the same effective alkylation unit capacity.

- Refinery

Not only does ZSM-5 increase FCC gasoline Research and Motor Octane and allow for optimization of the FCC operation, its unique chemistry allows for reoptimization of downstream processes to increase pool octane.
Addition of ZSM-5 in a catalytic cracking unit can permit a reduction in reformer severity. At a given pool octane requirement, the higher FCC octane contribution (Research/Motor) allows for lower reformer severity and, consequently, higher reformate yields. At EniChem's Gela FCC unit (12-14), when ZSM-5 was in the FCC, the reformate severity dropped from 95.0 RON clear to 90.0 RON clear while liquid yield increased by 4% vol.
ZSM-5 also significantly enhances the octane gain achievable if a heart cut or mid-boiling range FCC gasoline is reformed. As Figure 8 shows, ZSM-5 increases the Motor Octane throughout the entire gasoline boiling range. However, there is still a minimum in Motor Octane with respect to boiling point. In this example, the minimum occurs at 100°C to 150°C. A heart cut taken in this boiling range (100°C to 150°C) is an attractive feed for reforming since the nitrogen and sulfur levels are low in this boiling range.
LP studies were run to determine the impact on the refinery gasoline pool of adding ZSM-5 to the FCC and then reforming a heart cut of the FCC gasoline. Enough ZSM-5 was added to increase the FCC gasoline octane by +1 RON/+0.4 MON. A 100°C to 150°C heart cut of the FCC gasoline was then reformed, and all additional C_3 and C_4 olefins were alkylated. The impact on the refinery gasoline pool octane was an increase of 0.3 numbers for

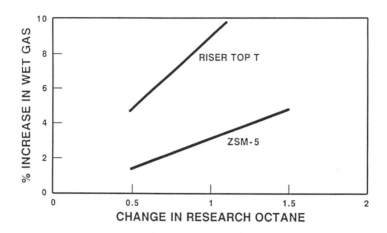

Figure 7. Wet gas increase per octane gain.

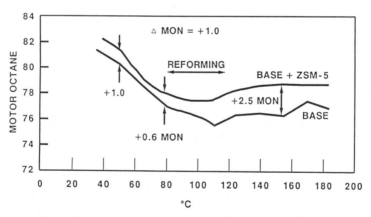

Figure 8. Refinery test scale example. MON clear versus cut point.

both the Research and Motor Octanes. This boost resulted from the combination of: higher FCC gasoline octane, addition of the heart cut reformate to the pool, and an increase in alkylate/FCC gasoline ratio. Although the magnitude of this boost depends on the particular refinery constraints (alkylation, reforming, FCC wet gas capacities), this example illustrates that ZSM-5 can have a significant impact on the overall refinery operation.

Besides alkylate, the products from ZSM-5 reactions outside the gasoline boiling range can be used to increase pool octane. In particular, ZSM-5 increases the percentage of isobutylene and isopentene in the C_4 and C_5 products, which are feedstocks for MTBE and TAME, respectively. Both MTBE and TAME have very high octanes as shown below.

	RON	MON
MTBE	118	101
TAME	112	99

Table X.   ZSM-5 Yield Benefits - Constant Octane
Wet Gas Compressor Constrained

Changes	
Conversion, vol %	+1.3
Gasoline, vol %	+0.3
LCO, vol %	−0.9
MCB, vol %	−0.4
C3+C4's, vol %	+1.7
C2 minus, wt %	−0.4
Potential Alkylate, vol %	+1.9
Preheat Temp., °F	−100
Regenerator Temp., °F	−20

Table XI. FCC/Alkylation Complex

	No ZSM-5	ZSM-5 Spare Alkylation Capacity	ZSM-5 Constrained Wet Gas
FCC Gasoline			
RON	93	94	93.4
MON	81	81.4	81.2
Vol % Fresh Feed	56	54	53
Alkylate			
RON	94	94	94
MON	92	92	92
Vol % Fresh Feed	26.5	31	27.6
Alkylate/FCC Gasoline	0.47	0.57	0.52
Wet Gas (SCF/B)	575	625	575

Table XII. Changes in Composition of Butane/Butene Stream with ZSM-5

	Base Case	+ZSM-5 Δ
FCC Gasoline Octane		
RON	92.6	+1.9
MON	80.1	+0.7
Butane-Butene Composition, vol% of C_4's		
isobutane	33.9	+0.2
N-butane	9.8	−0.6
isobutene	17.1	+2.1
1-butene	14.0	−1.5
2-trans-butene	14.9	+0.1
2-cis-butene	9.9	+0.4
butadiene	0.4	0

Conclusion

The use of ZSM-5 in cracking affords a refiner greater operating flexibility. Ultimately, it permits reoptimization of not only the cracking unit, but the entire refinery. Intrinsic features of ZSM-5 are its high activity, excellent stability, favorable selectivity, versatility, flexibility and metals tolerance.

Commercial experience in over 35 cracking units confirms that ZSM-5:

1) responds rapidly
2) is effective at low concentrations
3) boosts both motor and research octanes
4) increases C_3 and C_4 olefin yields, feed to an alkylation unit
5) increases isobutylene and isopentene, feed to MTBE and TAME
6) does not affect coke, C_2 minus, $450^{\circ}F$ plus or butadiene yields
7) is versatile since it is effective with all types of cracking catalysts and cracking units
8) can be used intermittently
9) is effective with high end point feeds and resids
10) works in the presence of metal passivators such as Sb

The improved performance arising from these benefits ultimately results in economic benefits which depend on refinery constraints and local circumstances.

NOMENCLATURE

E_D	Deactivation Energy, Kcal/mole
f_{ZSM-5}	Fraction of ZSM-5 in inventory
I	Catalyst Inventory, tons
K_D	Deactivation Rate Constant
K_{Do}	Pre-Exponential Term of K_D
M	Water Partial Pressure Effect
M_B	Makeup Rate of Base Catalyst, tons/min
M_{ZSM-5}	Makeup Rate of ZSM-5 Catalyst, tons/min
MON	Motor Clear Octane Number
$MON_{\emptyset}$	Base Motor Octane Number
N	Deactivation Order
O/P	Olefin/Paraffin Concentration in Gasoline
P_W	Water Partial Pressure, KPa
R	Universal Gas Constant
RON	Research Clear Octane Number
$RON_{\emptyset}$	Base Research Octane Number
T	Temperature, °K
t	Time, min
α	ZSM-5 Catalyst Activity
α_o	ZSM-5 Initial Activity
τ	Residence Time, min

Literature Cited

(1)   Elliott, K. M.; Eastwood, S. C. Proceedings of the
        American Petroleum Institute, 1962, 42 (III), pp 272-276.
(2)   Plank, C. J.; Rosinski, E. J.; Hawthorne, H. P. IEC Prod
        Res & Dev. 1964, 3, 165-169.
(3)   Plank, C. J.; Rosinski, E. J. U.S. Patents 3 140 249, 1964;
        3 140 251, 1964; 3 210 267, 1965; and 3 271 418, 1966.
(4)   Chester, A. W.; Hartzell, F. D. National Petroleum
        Refiners Association Annual Meeting, March 25-27, 1979, San
        Antonio, Texas (AM-79-36).
(5)   Chester, A. W.; Schwartz, A. B.; Stover, W. A.; McWilliams,
        J. P. CHEMTECH 1981, 11, 50-58.
(6)   Schwartz, A. B. U.S. Patents 4 251 395, 1981; 4 350 614,
        1982; 4 265 787, 1981; and Re. 32 239, 1986.
(7)   Pine, L. A.; Maker, P. J.; Wachter, W. A. Catalysis 1984,
        85, 466.
(8)   Rabo, J. A.; et al, National Petroleum Refiners Association
        Annual Meeting, March 23-25, 1986, Los Angeles, California
        (AM-86-30).
(9)   Chen, N. Y.; Garwood, W. E. Catal. Rev. 1986, 28(2&3), 185.
(10)   Anderson, C. D.; Dwyer, F. G.; Koch, G.; Niiranen, P.
        Proceeding of the Ninth Iberoamerican Symposium of
        Catalysis, July 1984, Lisbon, Portugal.
(11)   Yanik, S. J.; Campagna, R. J.; Demmel, E. J.; Humphries, A.
        P. National Petroleum Refiners Association Annual Meeting,
        March 24-26, 1985, San Antonio, Texas (AM-85-48).
(12)   Dwyer, F. G.; Gorra, F.; Herbst, J. A. Fourth CCIC
        Technical Symposium, June 9, 1986, Tokyo, Japan.
(13)   Dwyer, F. G.; Schipper, P. H.; Gorra, F. National
        Petroleum Refiners Association Annual Meeting, March 29-31,
        1987, San Antonio, Texas (AM-87-63).
(14)   Dwyer, F. G.; Economides, N. L.; Herbst, J. A.; Gorra, F.
        Petroleum Review 1987, 41, 48.
(15)   NPRA Q&A-1, Oil and Gas Journal March 17, 1986, 77.
(16)   NPRA Q&A-2, Oil and Gas Journal April 14, 1986, 116.
(17)   Corbett, R. A. Oil and Gas Journal November 18, 1985, 127.
(18)   Schipper, P. H.; Sarli, M. S.; Almgren, B. S.; Krambeck,
        F. J.; Tanzio, M. Ninth North American Meeting of the
        Catalysis Society, March 19, 1985, Houston, Texas.

RECEIVED March 30, 1988

Chapter 6

Mechanisms of Product Yield and Selectivity Control with Octane Catalysts

John S. Magee and James W. Moore

Katalistiks International, Inc., 4810 Seton Drive, Baltimore, MD 21215

It is generally accepted that aluminum
deficient structures derived from type Y
zeolite alter the extent of hydrogen transfer
reactions which ordinarily favor the
formation of paraffins and aromatics at the
expense of olefins and naphthenes. This
octane reducing reaction is controlled
principally by the silica/alumina ratio of
the zeolite and its rare earth content(1).
    Furthermore, it has been shown that
octane enhancement occurs through the
formation of different molecular types in
"light" (b.p. 100 to 260°F) versus "heavy"
(bp 260 to 430°F) gasoline(1,2,3). Enhanced
olefins in light gasoline account for
substantial increases in that fraction's
research octane number (RON C) while higher
concentrations of aromatics, for the most
part, improve both RON C and MON C in the
heavy gasoline.
    The present paper describes studies done
which show that the ratio of hydrogen
transfer to cracking (H-t/C) controls product
quality and the presence of non-selective but
catalytically active debris is a contributor
to losses in product yield.

World-wide there is approximately 1000 tons of fluid
cracking catalyst manufactured each day. Of this,
about 35% contains some form of aluminum deficient
zeolite Y, one whose SiO_2/Al_2O_3 ratio exceeds 5.5:1,
and whose performance is generally characterized by
enhanced olefin formation and higher gasoline research
and motor octane number. The aluminum deficient

0097–6156/88/0375–0087$06.00/0

zeolites used in these "octane catalysts" are either
chemical or hydrothermal derivatives of type Y zeolite.
Less commonly used are shape selective molecular sieves
(SSMS), which are derivatives of the pentasils. In
all, some 80-100 tons of aluminum deficient zeolite are
produced each day for consumption in octane catalysts
with a much smaller amount of SSMS being manufactured
for this purpose.

Virtually all the growth in this area has occurred
since 1976 when the first octane catalysts were
commercially used(4). Inspiring this use has been
legislation dictating reductions in lead tetraethyl
usage to the point were its usage is approaching zero
in both the United States and Europe. The resulting
octane debit from the cat crackers contribution to the
gasoline pool is the principal reason for the
outstanding growth in usage of octane catalysts.

Experimental

Catalysts

Five catalysts were used in this study: the predomi-
nately gasoline oriented full rare earth exchanged EKZ-
4, a partially rare earth exchanged gasoline/octane
catalyst SIGMA 300, a competitive USY containing octane
catalyst "COM-USY", Katalistiks' principal octane
barrel catalyst, ALPHA 500, and maximum octane catalyst
BETA 500. Physical and chemical properties are given in
Table I

Catalyst Pretreatment

Prior to evaluation in the pilot plant, all catalysts
were steam treated to simulate equilibrium activity.
The steaming procedure used for all catalysts is as
follows: calcination in nitrogen atmosphere at 1350°F
for three hours followed by steaming at 1350°F for 14
hours with 100% steam at atmospheric pressure.

Catalyst Evaluation

Pilot plant tests were made in a cyclic fixed fluidized
bed unit over a range of conditions. Catalyst-to-oil
ratio was varied from 3 to 5 and WHSV was varied from
32 to 53, inversely. The reactor temperature was held
at 975°F for the cracking and steam stripping cycles,
and at 1200°F for the regeneration cycles. After
regeneration, carbon on catalyst was effectively zero.

Table I.   Catalyst Properties

Catalyst:	EKZ-4	SIGMA-300	"COM-" USY	ALPHA-500	BETA-500
Surface Area, m^2/g	182	157	238	283	278
Pore Volume, cc/g	0.30	0.31	0.32	0.36	0.35
Al_2O_3, wt%	27.8	37.3	34.8	33.9	32.7
Re_2O_3, wt%	4.40	1.46	0.50	<0.10	<0.10
Unit Cell Size, a_o, Å	24.70	24.68	24.51	24.61	24.50
Steamed Properties**					
Surface Area, m^2/g	131	96	166	160	222
Unit Cell Size, a_o	24.50	24.33	24.26	24.26	24.27

* All catalysts except EKZ-4 are believed to contain
   10-20% "free" alumina (i.e. alumina not associated
   with either zeolite or clay components of the
   catalyst). The amount and nature of the "free"
   alumina present does influence gasoline, LCO and
   HCO quality and the quanfication of these
   influences is under study.

**   1350, 14 hours, 100% steam

Two feedstocks were used in this study. The
primary feed was very paraffinic (59.1% C_p, 26.5% C_n
and 14.4% C_A). Selected catalysts SIGMA, ALPHA and
BETA were also run using a moderately aromatic feed
(52.8% C_p, 26.9% C_n and 20.3% C_A). Detailed feed
properties are given in Table II.

Syncrudes from pilot plant runs were fractionated
according to ASTM D2892. Light and heavy gasoline
octanes were determined using a standard ASTM -
Combustion Fuels Research fuel testing engine. The
hydrocarbon type distribution - total paraffins, total
olefins, total naphthenes and total aromatics (PONA) -
of the light and heavy gasoline was determined using a
Hewlett Packard 5880 A gas chromatograph equipped with
a PONA package.

Results and Discussion

Two catalytic reactions appear to control the product
distribution encountered with octane catalysts:
hydrogen transfer (H-t) and cracking (C). Both occur
simultaneously and control of their ratio (H-t/C) gives
the product distributions observed. Generally these
reactions may be illustrated as follows:

Hydrogen Transfer (H-t)

$3C_nH_{2n}$ + C_mH_{2m} ———> $3 C_nH_{2n+2}$ + C_mH_{2m-6}
olefin   naphthene   paraffin   aromatic

Naphthene Cracking (C)

$3C_mH_{2m}$ ———> C_mH_{2m} + $2C_mH_{2m}$
multi-ring   olefin   naphthene
naphthene

A naphthene is used for this illustration as we
believe that the relative amounts of naphthene cracking
versus hydrogen transfer control product distributions
and qualities in octane catalyst systems. Gasoline
selective catalysts favor hydrogen transfer reactions
with these molecules with consequent formation of coke.

Results of the present study at constant
conversion are shown in Tables IIIA and B and IVA and B.
As suggested by the model equations illustrated above
and later in the text we have postulated that the
overall hydrogen transfer reaction forming aromatics
and paraffins from olefins and naphthenes can be
controlled at various intermediate stages. These
stages are characterized by high olefin yields in the
light gasoline with progressively higher concentrations

Table II. Feedstock Properties

	Paraffinic Feed "P"	Aromatic Feed "A"
Gravity, °API	25.9	21.2
Sulfur, wt%	0.53	1.19
Basic Nitrogen, PPM	920	596
Ramsbottom Carbon, wt%	0.59	2.17
Aniline Point, °F	196	186
Pour Point, °F	95	85
Molecular weight	391	390
UOP K Factor	12.0	11.7
Distillation (D1160), °F		
5 vol%	658	615
10 vol%	700	667
30 vol%	782	762
50 vol%	845	825
70 vol%	918	898
90 vol%	1030	1014
Hydrocarbon Type Distribution		
Aromatics (C_A)	14.4	20.3
Naphthenes (C_N)	26.5	26.9
Paraffins (C_P)	59.1	52.8

of heavy gasoline aromatics formed as the SiO_2/Al_2O_3 of
the steam deactivated catalyst increases. Also observed
are measurable quality changes in both the light cycle
(LCO) and heavy cycle oil (HCO).
    In the case of "non-octane" catalysts, H-transfer
is virtually complete and the reaction proceeds
(through aromatic condensation reactions) to coke.
Clear cut control of these stages is related to both
the silica/alumina ratio of the zeolite present (its
unit cell size) and the amount of silica/alumina debris
present. Silica/alumina debris is a reaction product
from the hydrothermal decomposition of the zeolite
present and is calculated by assuming that Al_2O_3 is the
principal degradation product in the conversion from
low to high silica/alumina ratio. Both starting and
product ratios are derived from unit cell measurements
according to the Breck/Flanigen correlation (5a).
    An approximation of the extent of hydrogen
transfer reactions occurring compared to cracking
reactions and the net effect on product distribution
can be initially seen by a consideration of the zeolite
properties of the catalysts tested in the present
study:

Catalyst:	EKZ-4	SIGMA-300	"COM USY"[1]	ALPHA-500	BETA-500
a_o, $\overset{o}{A}$	24.50	24.33	24.27	24.26	24.27
$SiO_2Al_2O_3$[2]	8.8	22	40	46	40
% "Debris"[3]	12	25	29	25	18
# Tetrahedral sites/U.C.[4]	28	10	3.4	2.4	3.4

[1]   Competitive USY-Containing Octane Catalyst
[2]   Calculated. Reference 5a.
[3]   Calculated. Reference 5b.
[4]   Calculated. Reference 6.

        Chemical analysis (Table I) shows that EKZ-4,
SIGMA 300 and "COM-USY" contain rare earth but "COM-
USY" falls in the range associated with a high level of
hydrogen transfer control (low H-t/C) along with ALPHA
and BETA. Data show a large Al(IV) site separation
for "COM-USY", ALPHA 500 and BETA 500 but significantly
different levels of catalytically active but non-
selective "debris" from the de-alumination occurring
during steam deactivation. One of the principal
advantages of the ALPHA and BETA systems is their high

Table III A. Pilot Plant Results at 72 vol% Conversion
Paraffinic Feed, "P"

Catalyst:	EKZ-4	SIGMA-300	"COM-"USY	ALPHA-500	BETA-500
Product Yields, PCT Feed:					
C_2 , wt%	1.4	1.3	1.4	1.3	1.3
C_3 , vol%	2.8	2.2	2.3	1.9	2.0
C_3 , vol%	3.6	4.0	4.6	4.6	5.1
IC_4 , vol%	8.6	8.5	8.5	7.8	8.9
NC_4 , vol%	2.1	1.8	1.7	1.4	1.6
C_4 , vol%	3.4	4.5	5.0	5.1	6.3
C_5 + Gasoline, vol%	61.4	61.5	61.8	62.2	61.0
LCO, vol%	16.0	17.5	17.7	17.7	18.0
HCO, vol%	12.0	10.5	10.3	10.3	10.0
Coke, wt%	4.2	3.8	2.9	3.4	2.4
Light Gasoline Yield, vol%	37.5	36.7	37.1	37.5	37.0
RON	83.8	85.0	87.5	87.2	89.3
MON	78.7	78.4	79.5	79.6	79.8
Heavy Gasoline Yield, vol%	23.9	24.8	24.7	24.7	24.0
RON	88.8	88.0	89.8	90.7	90.7
MON	79.6	78.4	79.8	81.1	81.1
LCO Aniline Pt., °F	42	42	53	55	62
C_4 Alkylate +Gasoline+LCO Vol%	83.5	87.1	88.5	89.1	90.4

Table III B.   Pilot Plant Results at 72 vol% Conversion
Aromatic Feed, "A"

Catalyst:	SIGMA-300	ALPHA-500	BETA-500
Product Yields, PCT Feed:			
C_2 -, wt%	2.9	1.9	2.0
C_3 -, vol%	2.4	2.1	2.2
C_3 -, vol%	5.2	5.8	5.8
IC_4, vol%	7.6	7.1	6.9
NC_4, vol%	1.7	1.4	1.4
C_4 =, vol%	5.2	5.9	6.2
C_5 + Gasoline, vol%	58.0	58.2	58.1
LCO, vol%	18.2	18.6	18.7
HCO, vol%	9.8	9.4	9.3
Coke, wt%	7.1	6.5	6.5
Light Gasoline			
Yield, vol%	34.5	34.2	35.1
MON	86.2	88.6	88.6
MON	80.1	80.7	80.7
Heavy Gasoline			
Yield, vol%	23.5	24.0	23.0
RON	89.3	91.7	92.4
MON	80.6	82.3	83.2
C_4 Alkylate			
+ Gasoline + LCO	85.6	87.4	88.0

Table IV A. Gasoline PONA's at 72 Vol% Conversion
Paraffinic Feed, "P"

CATALYST:	EKZ-4	SIGMA-300	"Com-" USY	ALPHA-500	BETA-500
Light Gasoline:					
Paraffins, vol%	68.9	64.8	61.5	60.6	58.0
Olefins, vol%	12.7	18.1	21.0	21.6	24.2
Naphthenes, vol%	10.0	11.3	10.1	11.5	10.8
Aromatics, vol%	8.4	5.8	7.4	6.3	7.0
Heavy Gasoline:					
Paraffins, vol%	32.5	33.1	30.3	29.4	29.6
Olefins, vol%	2.0	4.4	3.4	6.4	4.3
Naphthenes, vol%	8.3	8.5	9.5	9.0	8.8
Aromatics, vol%	57.2	54.0	56.8	55.2	57.3

Table IV B. Gasoline PONA's at 72 Vol% Conversion
Aromatic Feed, "A"

CATALYST:	SIGMA-300	ALPHA-500	BETA-500
Light Gasoline:			
Paraffins, vol%	62.8	58.7	57.0
Olefins, vol%	17.7	22.0	25.1
Naphthenes, vol%	12.6	12.3	11.4
Aromatics, vol%	6.9	7.0	6.5
Heavy Gasoline			
Paraffins, vol%	24.8	23.5	23.5
Olefins, vol%	1.9	1.9	1.9
Naphethenes, vol%	6.9	6.4	6.2
Aromatics, vol%	66.4	68.2	68.4

hydrothermal stability which retards debris formation
(7). We expect wide site separation (2-3 Al/U.C.) to
increase cracking versus hydrogen transfer if hydrogen
transfer is a two-center reaction like coke formation
(8). Thus more olefinic products are predicted and
higher molecular weight products (more gasoline plus
distillate) due to the wide site separation (greater
distances between locations likely to form carbonium
ions on the carbon chain) is expected. Finally, the
more debris present in these structures the more non-
selective cracking of higher molecular weight products
will occur in zeolites containing the least amount of
Al(IV) sites. Thus, we would expect ALPHA, BETA and COM-
USY to have similarly separated sites but that COM-
USY would show poorer gasoline and coke selectivity due
to the presence of more "debris". A possible mechanism
by which this non-selective cracking may occur is shown
in Figure 1. Here cetane when cracked in the absence
of debris, is influenced by only one active site in the
zeolite supercage and high molecular weight products
are formed*. Debris, when present, effectively reduces
site separation and would be expected to influence
cracking selectivity by reducing product molecular
weight ("overcracking").

Based on the active site properties of the test
catalysts and on the proposed product selectivities
which should result, the observed and predicated
selectivities are virtually identical. For example
product yields change as follows:

Olefins	EKZ4 < SIG-300 < COM-USY < A-500 <B-500
Coke Selectivity	<————— Ditto —————>
C₄ Alky.+ G+D	<————— Ditto —————>
Gasoline**	<————— Ditto —————>
LCO	<————— Ditto —————>
HCO Crack. Ability	<————— Ditto —————>

Our data indicated that LCO yield and quality
improved due to the conversion of HCO molecules
(apparently multi-ring naphthenes) by BETA and, to a

---

* Though ~3 sites/supercage are present (see page 4)
literature reports suggest that only one of three sites is
actually catalytically active (9).
** ALPHA 500 in this instance actually equilibrated at a slightly
lower a₀ (higher SiO₂/Al₂O₃) than BETA 500. By virtue of this we
may expect somewhat higher gasoline selectivity for ALPHA and the
observed product distributions of BETA and Com-USY to be similar.

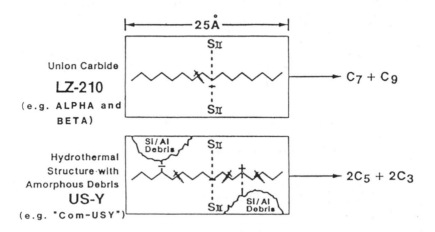

Figure 1. Stylized site placement effects on cetane
cracking in high Si/Al zeolites.

lesser degree ALPHA and COM-USY, into the LCO range. High levels of hydrogen transfer (as in EKZ-4) would probably convert these molecules into aromatics and coke.

Reaction Mechanisms

Possible reaction mechanisms which explain the trends observed in product qualities are illustrated in reactions (1) - (4) below.

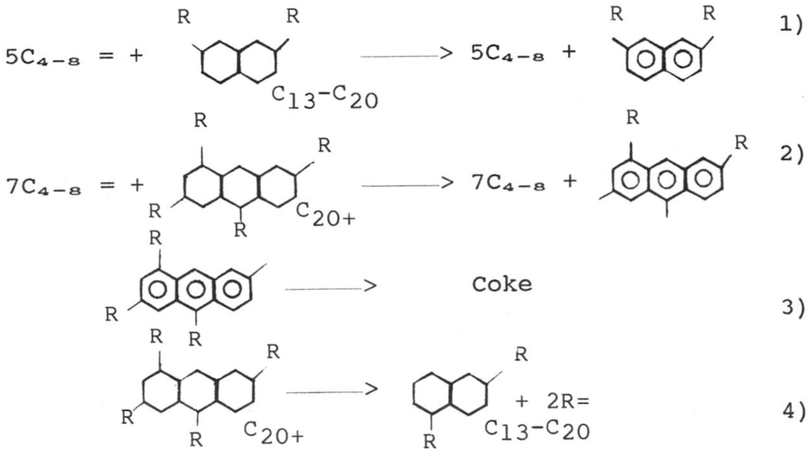

        Reactions (1) and (2) illustrate classical complete hydrogen transfer between light olefins and LCO and HCO range naphthenes. Reaction (3) represents condensation of polynuclear aromatics to coke, while reaction (4) represents zeolitic cracking of heavy gas oil naphthenes into LCO range naphthenes and gasoline range olefins. Based upon these model reactions, the expected effect of decreasing the rate (amount) of hydrogen transfer relative to cracking would be the following:

1. higher gasoline octanes with a significantly higher olefin content,
2. more olefinic LPG, with the potential for increased alkylate production,
3. less aromatic LCO, which would be observed by a higher aniline point,
4. lower coke yield,
5. higher LCO yield at constant conversion.

Observed experimental results are as follows:

Paraffinic Feed

The PONA results at constant conversion (72 vol%) in
the series from EKZ4 to BETA 500 show gasoline olefin
content increased from 8.6 percent to 16.4 percent,
paraffin content decreased from 54.7 percent to 46.8
percent, and naphthene and aromatics contents remained
constant. Research octane increased 4.2 numbers while
motor octane increased 1.2 numbers. The aromatics
content of the LCO as measured by the aniline point
decreased with the aniline point increasing from 42 to
62. LCO yield increased from 16.0 volume percent to
18.0 volume percent, while the coke yield decreased
dramatically from 4.2 percent to 2.4 percent.

Aromatic Feed

The PONA results at constant conversion (72 vol%) for
the series SIGMA 300, ALPHA 500 and BETA 500 show
gasoline olefin content increased from 11.3 percent to
15.9 percent, paraffin content decreased from 47.4
percent to 43.7 percent, naphthene content decreased
from 10.3 percent to 9.3 percent and aromatics content
remained constant. Research octane increased 2.6
numbers while motor octane increased 1.4 numbers. The
LCO yield increased 0.5 volume percent while the coke
yield decreased from 7.1 weight percent to 6.5 weight
percent.

Summary

1. Control of the extent of hydrogen transfer with
respect to cracking (the H-t/C ratio) controls catalyst
selectivity.

As the ratio decreases:
• Gasoline selectivity increases for the paraffinic
    feed
• Coke selectivity improves for both feeds
• LCO selectivity increases for both feeds
• LCO quality improves for the paraffinic feed
• HCO conversion improves for both feeds
• Olefin concentration in light and heavy gasoline
    increases for both feeds
• Aromatic content in heavy gasoline increases
    for the aromatic feed

2. Reduction of the amount of non-selective amorphous
debris present as in ALPHA and BETA catalysts increases
alkylate, gasoline and distillate yields and reduces
the amount of secondary reactions leading to coke and
wet gas.
3. Aside from their demonstrated octane enhancing
capabilities, catalysts with low H-t/C ratios can
effectively lower the yield of HCO while improving both
quality and quantity of LCO.

REFERENCES

1.   Pine, L.A., Maher, P.J. Wachter, W.A., J.Catal., 1984, 85, 466-476 (1984).
2.   Magee, J.S., Cormier, W.E. , Woltermann, G.M., OGJ, 5/27/85.
3.   Andreasson, H.U., Upson, L.L., Katalistiks 6th Annual Symposium, May 22-23, 1985.
4.   Magee, J.S., Ritter, R.E. "Symposium on Octane in the 1980s," ACS Div. Petro. Chem., Sept. 0-15, (1978)
5a. Breck, D.W., "Zeolite Molecular Sieves", Robert E. Krieger Pub. Co., 1984, p94
5b. S.D. Griffith, Private Communication, 1/30/87.
6.   John, J.R., DeCanio, S.J., Fritz, P.O., Lunsford, J.H., J.P. Chem, 1986, 90, 4847-4851.
7.   Rabo, J.A., Pellet, R.J., Magee, J.S., Mitchell, B.R., Moore, J.W., Magnusson, J.E., Upson, L.L., NPRA AM 86-30, 3/23/86.
8.   Bremer, H., Wendlandt, K.P., Vogt, F., Becker, K., Weber, M., Acta Phys. Chem. 1985, 31, 376.
9.   Beyerlein, R.A. McVicker, G.G., Yacullo, L.M., Ziemiak, J.J., 1986, Symposium on Fund. Chem. Promoters and Poisons in Hetero. Cat., 190-197.

RECEIVED March 30, 1988

Chapter 7

Strategies for Catalytic Octane Enhancement in a Fluid Catalytic Cracking Unit

G. C. Edwards, K. Rajagopalan, A. W. Peters, G. W. Young, and J. E. Creighton

Davison Chemical Division, W. R. Grace & Company, 7379 Route 32, Columbia, MD 21044

Commercial catalysts can achieve octane improvements by using ultra stable faujasite of low cell size, by using an active amorphous matrix, by using small amounts of an additive containing ZSM-5, or by a combination of two or three of these techniques. An analysis of gasolines from these three types of catalysts shows markedly different compositions. Ultra stable faujasite produces an increase in olefins at the expense of paraffins over conventional rare earth stabilized catalysts of high cell size. An active amorphous silica alumina catalyst produces a large increase in olefins, but less aromatics. The effect of an additive containing ZSM-5 is discussed in other papers in this symposium. Among USY catalysts, USY hydrothermally dealuminated to a cell size of about 2.426 nm has the best selectivity for octane and coke. In practice, USY catalysts hydrothermally dealuminate during use to about the same activity and selectivity regardless of the procedure used in the initial preparation. Previous studies have shown that a low sodium content is required for high octane. New results show that it is not the presence of the sodium but the presence of sodium during the dealumination process that affects octane. Octane increases if sodium is removed from the zeolite before dealumination. Octane, however, is insensitive to the sodium content of the dealuminated zeolite.

  To the extent that motor octane is dependent on aromatic and isoparaffin content, motor octane increases in an FCC unit will be difficult to achieve. Thermodynamics does not allow the production of highly branched isoparaffins in an FCC unit, and blending studies show that motor octane is relatively insensitive to the aromatic content of an FCC gasoline in the range of 35-50% aromatics. However, a more aromatic gasoline may have better blending characteristics in that less aromatics from other sources will be required to achieve the same motor octane number increase.

0097–6156/88/0375–0101$06.00/0
© 1988 American Chemical Society

Gasoline quality is largely determined by motor and research octane numbers. There is a strong correlation between octane and the structure of the C_5 to C_{12} hydrocarbons typically present in gasoline, Table I. For paraffins, octane decreases as molecular weight increases and increases with degree of branching. The same is true of olefins.

Table I.   Octanes of Selected Organic Compounds
                  Typically Found in Gasoline

Paraffins	RON[a]	MON[b]
Pentane	62	62
Hexane	25	26
3-Methylpentane	75	74
2,2-Dimethylbutane	92	93
Olefins		
1-Pentene	91	77
1-Hexene	76	63
trans-2-Hexene	93	81
2-Methyl-2-pentene	98	83
Aromatics		
Toluene	>100	>100
Xylenes	>100	>100

[a] Research Octane Number

[b] Motor Octane Number

Catalytic strategies for making high octane gasolines include:

● Decrease the amount of higher molecular weight, less branched paraffins.
● Isomerize paraffins to a more highly branched product.
● Produce more olefins or aromatics.

A number of catalytic processes in current use make use of these strategies including reforming, isomerization, dimerization, alkylation and fluid catalytic cracking (FCC). The object of this paper is to discuss the catalytic strategies available to produce octane in the FCC unit.

Experimental

Gasoline analyses were performed by gas chromatography using a 50 m dimethyl silicon capillary column temperature programmed to 280°C.
      Hydrothermally dealuminated Y zeolite was prepared by heating NH_4^+ exchanged Y faujasite, 2.5 Si/Al ratio and 0.7% Na_2O, at 650°C for 3 hrs. in 100% steam giving a Si/Al framework ratio ~5 at 2.447 nm unit cell.
      Chemically dealuminated Y zeolite was prepared starting from NH_4^+ exchanged Y (2.5 Si/Al ratio) using the procedure of Skeels

and Breck (1). The product had 0.7% Na₂O and Si/Al ~5 at 2.447 nm unit cell.

Sodium impregnation experiments were performed using sodium carbonate.

Except for the results reported in Table III, all catalytic activity and selectivity results were obtained using a micro-activity test (MAT), ASTM D-3907-80.

Catalysts were prepared using a spray dried slurry of the appropriate zeolite, clay and a proprietary inert binder.

Catalyst deactivation was carried out under the following conditions unless otherwise specified: 830°C, 12 hrs., 0.30 atm. steam.

All catalysts were tested only after deactivation.

The ^{27}Al magic angle spinning nuclear magnetic resonance (MASNMR) spectra were acquired using a 30° pulse at 0.1 sec. intervals. About 5000 to 7000 scans were acquired on a Bruker AM-400. The chemical shift is relative to aluminum nitrate in water solution which contains $Al(H_2O)_6^{3+}$.

The properties of the West Texas Gas Oil feedstock used are given in Table II.

Table II. Properties of West Texas Gas Oil (WTGO) Feedstock

API at 15.5°C			27.4
Specific gravity 15.5°C			0.8905
Aniline Point °C		:	93
Sulfur	Wt.%	:	0.38
Total Nitrogen	Wt.%	:	0.07
Basic Nitrogen	Wt.%	:	0.019
Conradson carbon	Wt.%	:	0.07
Metals, ppm			
Ni			<1
V			≤2
Fe			≤1
Cu			≤1
Distillation Vol.%, °C @ atm			
IBP			354
10			386
30			404
50			422
80			458
95			488
K-Factor			12.08

Octane Catalysts

Catalytic cracking occurs at about 800°K (527°C, 980°F) and at these temperatures the formation of olefins and aromatics is favored while isomerization of paraffins to branched products is

not. An effective octane enhancement catalyst will make more
olefins and aromatics compared to a conventional catalyst.

There are three different kinds of octane catalysts in current
use. Some are based in part on an active non-zeolite matrix
composed of a porous silica/alumina component. Others are based on
low cell size (2.425-2.428 nm) ultra stable faujasite (USY), a
catalyst composition developed in 1975 (2) for the purpose of
octane enhancement. A third catalyst system makes use of a small
amount (1-2%) of ZSM-5 as an additive. While the net effect in all
cases is an increase in the measured octane number, each of the
three catalytic systems have different characteristic effects on
the composition and yield of the gasoline. The effects of the
ZSM-5 component on cracking is described in other papers of this
symposium and will not be discussed here.

Table III compares the gasoline composition from three steam
deactivated catalyst systems. The first contains 10% rare earth
exchanged faujasite (RE FAU) in an inert silica/clay matrix at a
cell size of 2.446 nm; the second contains 20% of an ultra stable
faujasite (Z-14 USY) at a unit cell size of 2.426 nm in inert
matrix. The third contains 50% amorphous high surface area
silica-alumina (70% Al_2O_3; 30% SiO_2) and 50% clay; the nitrogen
BET surface area of this catalyst after steam deactivation is
140 m^2/g. All three catalysts were deactivated for 4 hrs. at 100%
steam and at 816°C.

The results show that the low cell size USY catalyst reduces
paraffins and increases olefin content dramatically with a slight
loss of aromatics. The stoichiometry of these changes is consistent with inhibition of a disproportionation or hydrogen
transfer reaction involving the reaction of 4 olefins to form 3
paraffins plus 1 aromatic. USY catalysts have a similar gasoline
yield but improved coke selectivity compared to conventional rare
earth catalysts. At higher conversions the coke selectivity
advantage of USY can result in increased gasoline aromatic
content. The use of an active amorphous silica alumina system
produces still more olefins and fewer aromatic and paraffin
components. However, there is little net effect on the gasoline
octane and especially on the MON. This is true in part because the
increased olefins come at the expense of lower molecular weight
higher octane paraffins as well as aromatics. The amorphous active
material typically produces less gasoline and more coke.

Dealuminated Faujasite Catalysts

The increase in octane observed using dealuminated faujasite
compared to high cell size rare earth exchanged faujasite has been
correlated with the Si/Al ratio of the sieve and with the sodium
content (3). While the relationship between Si/Al ratio as
measured by unit cell is confirmed by pilot unit studies in our
laboratory, Figure 1, the relationship with sodium content is more
complicated, Figure 2. Sodium added to the catalyst after
hydrothermal dealumination reduces activity but does not affect
octane, while sodium present before hydrothermal dealumination
increases activity but does reduce octane. This result implies
that selectivity for octane is related to structures formed during

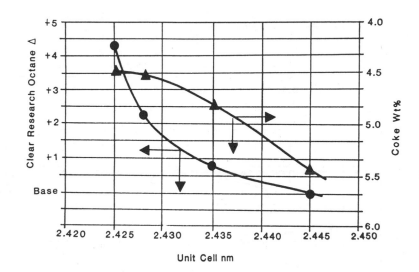

Figure 1.   Selectivity for coke and gasoline octane as a function of unit cell. Gasoline octane curve (●) obtained in a fixed fluid bed reactor at 65% conversion, 4 C/O, 30 WHSV, 510°C.

Coke selectivities as Wt.% of feed (▲) were measured on a MAT unit, 3 C/O, 16 WHSV, 510°C, WTGO feed.

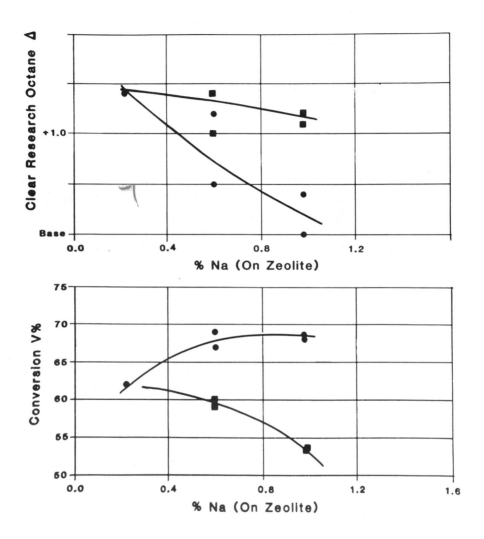

Figure 2.   Conversion and octane measured in a fixed fluidized bed reactor, 40 C/O, 30 WHSV, 510 $^{\circ}$C using USY catalyst, 0.2% Na on zeolite.

● % Na on zeolite; Na added as Na_2CO_3 before steam deactivation.

■ % Na on zeolite; Na added as Na_2CO_3 after steam deactivation.

Table III.　　　　　Gasoline Compositions and Yields
　　　　　　　　　　　(Fixed Fluidized Bed Reactor Tests)

	10% RE FAU 90% Inert Matrix	20% Z-14 USY 80% Inert Matrix	50% SiO_2/Al_2O_3 50% Clay
Catalyst/Oil	6	4	6
WHSV*	20	30	20
T,°C	510	510	510
Wt.% Conv.	52.0	53.0	55.0
$C_5 - C_6$			
Normal Paraffins	1.4	1.1	0.8
Isoparaffins	12.5	8.9	6.5
Olefins	13.3	19.9	21.4
$C_7 - C_8$			
Normal Paraffins	1.6	1.4	1.2
Isoparaffins	10.7	8.0	6.0
Olefins	8.7	14.3	18.2
Aromatics	8.2	6.9	6.3
C_9^+			
Paraffins	11.4	10.0	9.5
Aromatics	14.1	13.3	12.8
Total			
Paraffins	37.5	29.3	23.9
Olefins	21.9	34.2	39.6
Naphthenes	12.6	12.1	12.0
Aromatics	22.4	20.2	19.0
RON (clear)	88.6	92.6	93.1
MON (clear)	77.4	80.0	80.0
Gasoline Selectivity (Wt.%/Wt.% conversion)	0.74	0.79	0.69

* Weight hourly space velocity

the dealumination process perhaps involving nonframework alumina.
Since sodium has a stabilizing effect, an effective catalyst should
have 0.6% to 0.8% Na2O present on zeolite for activity retention.
    The other advantage of dealumination is improved coke selec-
tivity. While coke selectivity correlates with unit cell size, the
correlation is different than the one for octane, and there is no
correlation between coke selectivity and sodium content (4, 5).
The differences in the way octane and coke selectivity relate to
the unit cell are illustrated in Figure 1.

Comparison of Hydrothermally and Chemically Dealuminated Faujasite

If nonframework alumina contributes to the selectivity or activity
of USY based catalysts, then catalysts containing zeolites prepared
by the two methods would be expected to give different results
after steam deactivation. Zeolite Y chemically dealuminated, using
(NH4)2SiF6, to a unit cell of 2.450 nm containing 35 Al/unit
cell (1, 6) will contain half as much nonframework alumina as the
hydrothermally prepared material where the starting NaY has a Si/Al
ratio of 2.5 and 55 Al/unit cell. After steam deactivation a Si/Al
ratio of ~20-28 or 7-10 Al/unit cell at a unit cell of 2.426 nm
is achieved in both cases. However, the results in Table IV show
identical selectivities for gasoline volume and composition. The
results in Table V show that the relative isomerization selectivities are also identical. Compared to the thermodynamically
expected product distribution (7), both zeolites are ineffective in
isomerizing paraffins, but do isomerize C5 olefins. The paraffin
distribution reflects the type of structures observed in petroleum
(high degree of monomethyl branching) rather than the distribution
expected from thermodynamics.

Table IV.   Cracking Selectivities of Dealuminated Y Zeolites
                    Hydrothermally Deactivated
         MAT Conditions: 16 WHSV; 3 C/O; 500°C, WTGO Feed
                  40% Zeolite/60% Inert Matrix

	$SiF_6^=$	Hydrothermal
Wt. % Conversion	74.7	76.2
Paraffins	42.7	40.2
Olefins	13.1	13.8
Naphthenes	13.5	13.9
Aromatics	30.6	32.0
Wt. % Gasoline/Conv.	0.74	0.75

The fact that catalysts prepared from hydrothermally and chemically
dealuminated zeolites are similar may be related to the catalyst

preparation process. Typical catalysts binders are prepared from
acid silica/alumina sols in the pH range of 3-4 at which alumina
has some solubility. The zeolite, clay and any other materials
required are mixed in a slurry with the binder at a typically low
pH and spray dried. The preparation of a catalyst slurry in this
pH range is equivalent to a mild chemical treatment or acid wash
that would be expected to dissolve some of the nonframework alumina
created during hydrothermal dealumination. During commercial
catalyst preparation, the zeolite is exchanged and slurried at a
low pH of 2.5 to 4.0 for periods of time typical of process
residence times. Figure 3 shows ^{27}Al MASNMR spectra of a hydrothermally dealuminated zeolite before and after a simulated
commercial processing at pH ~3.0. The processing steps remove
nonframework alumina. Since defects due to aluminum removal are
also easily annealed (8), after the processing required for
catalyst manufacture, hydrothermally and chemically dealuminated
zeolites at the same cell size are expected to be similar in
structure and catalytic selectivity, especially after further steam
deactivation.

Table V. Isomerization Selectivities of Dealuminated Y Zeolites

| | 40% Dealuminated Y / 60% Inert Matrix | | |
	$(NH_4)_2SiF_6$	Hydrothermal	Thermodynamic Distribution (800°K)
C5 Paraffins			
Pentane	.09	.09	.40
2-Methylbutane	.91	.91	.54
2,2-Dimethylpropane	--	--	.06
C6 Paraffins			
Hexane	.09	.08	.26
2-Methylpentane	.52	.52	.32
3-Methylpentane	.32	.31	.25
2,3-Dimethylbutane	.07	.08	.07
2,2-Dimethylbutane	--	--	.10
C5 Olefins			
1-Pentene	.08	.08	.05
trans-2-Pentene	.23	.22	.12
cis-2-Pentene	.13	.12	.12
2-Methyl-1-butene	.19	.19	.24
2-Methyl-2-butene	.37	.38	.43
3-Methyl-1-butene	.01	.01	.05

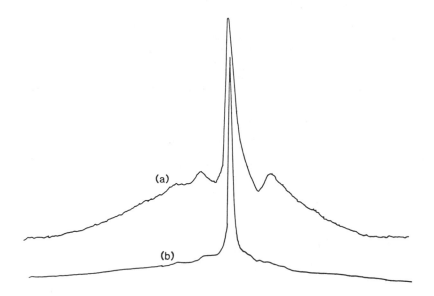

Figure 3. ^{27}Al MASNMR spectra of hydrothermally
             dealuminated faujasite.

a)   After dealumination, 2.454 nm unit cell,
     3.6% Na$_2$O, 75.1% SiO$_2$, 21.0% Al$_2$O$_3$,
     bulk Si/Al atom ratio = 3.

b)   After dealumination and simulated catalyst
     processing at pH 3.0 – 5.0, 2.454 nm unit cell,
     0.2% Na$_2$O, 82.6% SiO$_2$, 17.1% Al$_2$O$_3$,
     bulk Si/Al atom ratio = 4.1.

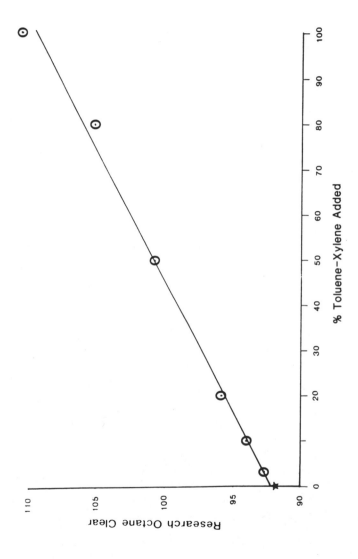

Figure 4.   Effect of added weight % aromatics
(50% Toluene / 50% Xylene mixture) on research
octane (clear) of an FCC gasoline from
a USY type of octane catalyst.

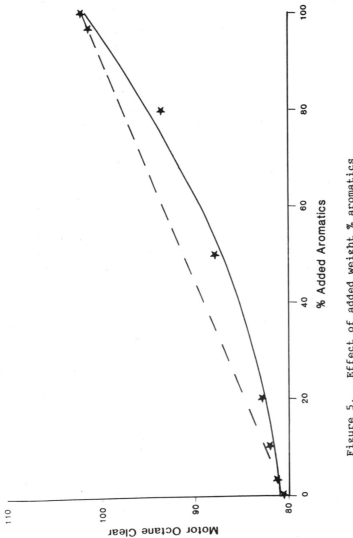

Figure 5.   Effect of added weight % aromatics
(50% Toluene / 50% Xylene mixture) on motor
octane (clear) of an FCC gasoline from a USY type of
octane catalyst.

Octane Enhancement Potential

Isomerization of paraffins using current octane catalysts under
current conditions is favorably away from equilibrium. Additional
isomerization activity would make more normal paraffins and a lower
octane at FCC temperatures. A much more olefinic gasoline is a
possibility. However, additional olefins above the current olefin
levels of 10-30% would have decreased effectiveness, especially on
the motor octane number.

A more desirable strategy is to prepare catalysts that will
aromatize the gasoline without yield loss. Aromatization is
thermodynamically favorable under FCC conditions of temperature
($\sim$500°C) and pressure ($\sim$2 atm). Blending studies show that
the increase in research octane is about proportional to the amount
of added aromatics, Figure 4. However, motor octane does not
respond to initial increases in aromatic content in the blend but
rises more sharply as aromatic content continues to increase,
Figure 5.

The results show that higher motor octane in an FCC gasoline
will be difficult to achieve. A catalyst that increased aromatics
by as much as 20% could yield a gain of $\sim$1-2 MON. However, the
next 20% increase in aromatic content of the gasoline would produce
an increment of $\sim$4 MON. As a result of the non-linear blending
characteristics of gasoline, a more aromatic FCC gasoline may have
greatest value as a blend component with an aromatic reformate.

Acknowledgments

We would like to thank M. Wallace, S. Roush and J. Mangano for
preparing samples, C. Petr, A. Wadsworth and G. Lundquist for help
with the gasoline analysis, and M. Shatlock for the MASNMR spectra.

Literature Cited

1.   Skeels, G. W.; Breck, D. W. In Proc. Sixth International
     Zeolite Conf.; Olsen, D.; Bisio, A., Eds.; Butterworths: UK,
     1984, pp 87-96.
2.   Lussier, R. J.; Albers, E. W.; and Magee, Jr., J. S. US Patent
     3 994 800, 1976, assigned to W. R. Grace & Co.
3.   Pine, C. A.; Maher, P-J; Wachter, W. A. J. Catal. 1984, 85,
     466.
4.   Rajagopalan, K.; Peters, A. W. Preprints ACS Div. Petr. Chem.
     1985, 30 (3), p. 538.
5.   Rajagopalan, K. and Peters, A. W. J. Catal. 1987, 106, 410.
6.   Elliott, C. H., US Patent 3 933 983, 1976, assigned to
     W. R. Grace & Co.
7.   Alberty, R. A. J. Phys. Chem. 1983, 87, 4999; 1985, 89, 880;
     I&EC Fundamentals 1983, 22, 318.
8.   Grobet, P. J.; Jacobs, P. A.; Beyer, H. K. Zeolites 1986, 6,
     47.

RECEIVED March 17, 1988

Chapter 8

Catalytic Control of SO$_x$ Emissions from Fluid Catalytic Cracking Units

E. H. Hirschberg and R. J. Bertolacini

Amoco Research Center, Amoco Oil Company, Naperville, IL 60566

This paper identifies alumina, rare earths, platinum, and magnesia as important SOx capture materials. Alumina is either incorporated directly into the matrix of a cracking catalyst or added as a separate particle. Cerium is shown to promote the capture of SO$_2$ on high alumina cracking catalyst, alumina, and magnesia. Other rare earths are ranked by their effectiveness. The promotional effect of platinum is shown between 1200 and 1400°F for SO$_2$ capture on alumina. Silica, from free silica or silica-alumina in the matrix of cracking catalyst, acts as a poison by migrating to the additive. Silica from zeolite migrates less readily. In the magnesia-alumina system, spinel, as identified by X-ray diffraction, is inactive for SO$_2$ removal. The effect of temperature on steam stability, oxidative adsorption and reductive desorption of SO$_2$ are described. Five commercial catalyst types are ranked for SOx removal.

It has been ten years since Amoco announced the UltraCat process (1) for SOx control in FCC units. In those ten years, as well as in the years previous to the announcement, much work was done to develop catalysts that would control SOx emissions. The evidence is the 80 or more U.S. patents that have issued in that time to Amoco and others. One of the first patents issued was to Amoco in 1974 (2) for the addition of magnesia and other group IIA oxides to cracking catalyst. This paper reviews the SOx catalyst developments and emphasizes the work done at Amoco to identify the active materials, explain the deactivation mechanism and, finally, to make a side-by-side comparison of various catalytic systems that are being pursued commercially today.

0097–6156/88/0375–0114$09.00/0
© 1988 American Chemical Society

Historical

Early History. Some of the earliest work on the catalytic control
of SOx was started at Amoco by Healy and Hertwig (3) who, in 1949,
reported that, with a silica-magnesia cracking catalyst, sulfur
could be shifted from coke to dry-gas with a corresponding decrease
in sulfur emissions in the flue gas. As Vasalos (1) later
indicated, other catalyst changes caused a steady decrease in flue
gas emissions through improvements in coke selectivity. CO burning
technology (4) also lowered SOx emissions by lowering coke on
regenerated catalyst. During this early period, a new mechanism
for catalytic control of SOx emerged, which was related to the
ability of the catalyst to capture SOx, and this led to the
development of an entirely new approach for emission control from
FCU's (1).

The UltraCat Process. The UltraCat process for SOx control entails
oxidative capture by a metal oxide, MO, of SO$_2$ from the burning of
sulfur in coke on the regenerator side of the FCU,

$$S \text{ (coke)} + O_2 \longrightarrow SO_2 \qquad (1)$$

$$SO_2 + \tfrac{1}{2}O_2 + MO \longrightarrow MSO_4 \qquad (2)$$

and release of the SO$_2$ on the reactor side by reduction with
hydrogen or hydrocarbon:

$$4H_2 + MSO_4 \longrightarrow MO + H_2S + 3H_2O \qquad (3)$$

The oxidative adsorption of SO$_2$, as shown in Equation 2, can
be enhanced by using an oxidation promotor. If metal sulfide, MS,
instead of metal oxide forms from the reduction of the sulfate, the
sulfide must hydrolyze to MO by the action of steam in the stripper
section of the FCC unit:

$$MS + H_2O \longrightarrow MO + H_2S \qquad (4)$$

If the sulfide does not hydrolyze, sulfur will be carried to
the regenerator and reappear as SO$_2$ after oxidation in the flue gas
with no net change in sulfur emissions. The FCU regenerator
operates at temperatures from about 1250-1350°F, while the reactor
and stripper operate at about 900-1000°F.

Selection of Oxides. At Amoco, previous studies in the literature
on SO$_2$ removal from flue gas have been used to guide the selection
of oxides for the UltraCat process but they have been of limited
direct usefulness. This was true because of the peculiar
requirements of the UltraCat process of high adsorption
temperature, low regeneration temperature, and non-interference
with the cracking reactions. The previous literature studies
generally assumed that SO$_2$ would be adsorbed at temperatures close
to a stack gas temperature of 600°F, and desorb at either the same
temperature or higher. The conditions of these studies was set,

not by conformance to an existing process, like catalytic cracking, but by economic considerations.

The early work of Bienstock (5) at 625°F showed manganese, copper and cobalt oxides to be active. But these materials have not been used for the UltraCat Process probably because of the adverse effect on the cracking reactions.

Similar work, again at lower temperatures of about 600°F, was done by two groups who investigated the adsorption of SO_2 on metal oxides supported on high area alumina. At Gulf, Vogel et al. (6) found copper and strontium oxides to be exceptional but also recommended group IA and IIA oxides. Koballa and Dudukovic (7) ranked Ni and Mn as best followed by Co, Fe, and Zn oxides. Of these materials only magnesia proved to be successful in the UltraCat process.

In a theoretical study, Lowell et al. (8) selected oxides from thermodynamic considerations for a process in which SO_2 was adsorbed at temperatures greater than 100°C and desorbed by decomposition of the sulfate or sulfite formed, at temperatures below 750°C. Under these constraints, all of 47 oxides considered had potential for adsorption but only 16 had low enough decomposition temperatures to make a process economical. Intuitively, sulfate decomposition temperature should correlate loosely with reducibility of sulfates, so it is interesting that many of the 16 oxides chosen by Lowell, which included cerium and aluminum, have been shown to be useful in the UltraCat process.

DeBerry and Sladek (9) followed up on the work of Lowell by measuring the rates of SO_2 adsorption on the oxides selected by Lowell. Cerium oxide was found to have one of the highest rates.

More recently, workers at Unocal (10) have used thermodynamics to select oxides for SOx removal from FCU's and have identified the oxides of 20 elements as likely candidates. This list was narrowed further (11) to several candidates, Ce, Al, Co, Ni and Fe, by matching the decomposition and reduction temperatures of their sulfates to the conditions of the process.

Selection of Promotors. Lowell et al. (8) ranked metal oxides by their ability to oxidize SO_2 and, therefore, to promote the oxidative adsorption of SO_2 according to Equation 2. The ranking was referenced to platinum which has high activity; V_2O_5 and Fe_2O_3 were ranked high followed by the moderately active oxides, CuO and TiO_2; CeO_2, MnO_2 and SnO_2 were considered to have only slight activity; Bi_2O_3, PbO_2 and UO_2 were listed as having no oxidation activity.

In the ensuing years several announcements of SOx capture catalysts were made by catalyst and petroleum companies (10,12-18) as shown here:

```
1977 Amoco -- UltraCat Process
1978 Arco/Engelhard -- Soxcat
1981 Unocal -- Unisox
1981 Chevron -- Transox
1983 Arco -- HRD 276
1984 Engelhard -- Ultrasox
1985 Arco -- HRD 277
1985 Davison -- Additive R
1986 Chevron -- Transcat
```

In addition, many patents were issued, which have been summarized up to 1982 by Habib (19). Since 1982, an additional 30 or so patents have appeared but, the important elements and compounds that have surfaced from the patent literature still are alumina, rare earths, platinum and magnesia.

Experimental

Apparatus and Procedure. A simple glass and Teflon fixed-bed apparatus, shown in Figure 1, was used to test for SO$_2$ removal from a mixture of 1000 ppm SO$_2$, 2.7% O$_2$ and about 2% water in helium flowing at 10 cc/min. The charge to the apparatus was 1.00 g of material which, in most cases, included a cracking catalyst with low capacity for SO$_2$, as diluent. SO$_2$ was measured continuously using a DuPont 400 UV analyzer and reported as $\mu\ell$ at 70°F and 1 atm. Catalysts are compared either from plots of time vs. %SO$_2$ removed or by integral amounts of SO$_2$ removed after an arbitrary time, usually 92 minutes. The dead space in the apparatus preceding, as well as following, the catalyst was kept to a minimum but about 10 minutes elapse before SO$_2$ reaches the detector. In addition, the SO$_2$ flowing through the apparatus forms a diffuse front. Both these factors, the diffuse front of SO$_2$ and the dead space, lead to a unit factor or an amount of SO$_2$ that seems to be removed even with an inert material or an empty tube. This unit factor is accounted for by simply subtracting it from the total amount of SO$_2$ removed. Adsorption temperatures ranged from 1250 to 1500°F. Catalyst regenerations were made with 10 cc/min. hydrogen for 15 minutes. Steam deactivation of catalysts was done at various temperatures in 100% steam and for various times as indicated in the text.

Catalysts. A variety of commercial and in-house catalysts was used in this work. The preparations of the in-house catalysts are described in the text.

Analytical. Silicon analyses of deactivated catalysts were made on cross-sectioned samples with SEM-EDAX.

Results and Discussion

Cracking Catalyst Composition. Several workers (20-21) have reported differences among cracking catalysts to remove SOx which correlated qualitatively with alumina content. Our work confirmed these reports as shown on Figure 2. Plotted are %SO$_2$ removal

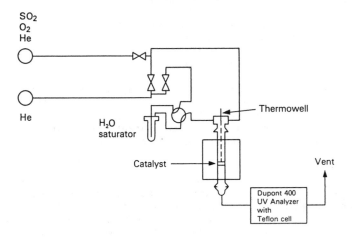

Figure 1.   Schematic of Apparatus.

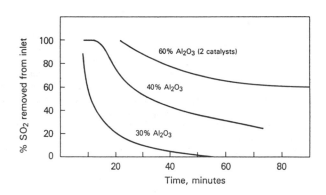

Figure 2.   Effect of Cracking Catalyst Composition.

curves for four catalysts with alumina contents from 30 to 60%.
The curve shown for 60% Al_2O_3 actually represents two catalysts:
one with and one without rare earth exchange. At first, the
similarity of these two catalysts underestimated the importance of
rare earth content.

To show the alumina effect quantitatively, a series of
catalysts was made in which the amount of alumina in the matrix was
varied from 25 to 100% by adding alumina sol to a 25% alumina,
silica-alumina slurry. These catalysts were formulated with REY
molecular sieve. The results for SO_2 removal are shown in Figure 3
where SO_2 removal (corrected for unit factor) increases with
increasing alumina. Our conclusion that alumina was important for
SO_2 adsorption also confirmed the results of Blanton and Flanders
at Chevron (22). The non-linearity of the relationship implies an
antagonistic effect between silica and alumina. The silica-alumina
antagonism will be discussed relative to deactivation subsequently.

The SO_2 removal capability of cracking catalysts with high
alumina matrix can be enhanced. For instance, we found that
zeolite type could be important. Figure 4 shows that for catalysts
formulated with a matrix containing 60% alumina, a well-exchanged
rare earth Y zeolite, as measured by a sodium content of 0.1%, gave
better SO_2 removal than either a moderately exchanged rare earth Y
zeolite, 2% sodium, or an ultrastable Y zeolite (23). These
cracking catalysts were formulated by adding alumina sol and
zeolite to a low alumina silica-alumina gel. Both REY catalysts
contained 15% zeolite; the USY catalyst 25%. The improvement in
SO_2 removal was observed only if the catalyst was formulated with a
high alumina matrix. The unusual enhancing effect of the
well-exchanged REY remains unexplained, but the results led to more
experiments with both rare earths and alumina.

Rare Earths and Alumina. A much easier and cheaper way of getting
the SO_2 removal enhancement from rare earths that was observed with
the well-exchanged rare earth Y zeolite was to add rare earths,
especially cerium, by direct impregnation to high alumina cracking
catalyst (24).

The effect of cerium was shown by measuring the sulfate/cerium
molar ratio observed when cerium was added at 5, 10 and 20 ppm by
impregnation to a high alumina, commercial cracking catalyst which
contained no rare earth. After SO_2 adsorption at 1250°F for 140
minutes the catalysts were analyzed for sulfate. The results are
shown in Figure 5 where the mole ratio is plotted vs. cerium on
catalyst. The mole ratios, which were calculated to exclude the
sulfate adsorbed by the cracking catalyst without cerium, are much
greater than the stoichiometric ratio of 1.5 or 2.0 for cerous or
ceric sulfate, demonstrating a large catalytic effect. The
sulfate/cerium mole ratio declines with cerium content in this
experiment because the amount of sulfate accumulated was relatively
insensitive to the amount of cerium added to the catalyst. A large
effect was observed with the first incremental amount added with
proportionately smaller effects with subsequent amounts. This
observation supports the conclusion that cerium is catalytic.

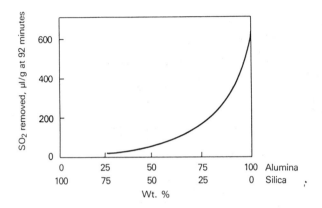

Figure 3.   Effect of Matrix Composition.

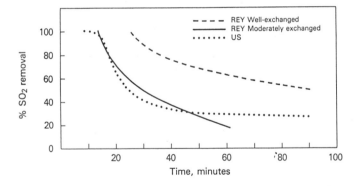

Figure 4.   Effect of Zeolite Type.

Independence from cracking catalyst composition has been shown by adding cerium and alumina to cracking catalyst (25). The data on Table I demonstrate this.

Table I. Effect of Cerium and Alumina Added to Cracking Catalyst

Catalyst Description	Net SO$_2$ Removed at 1250°F, μl after 92 minutes
FC Catalyst	0
FCC + 25 ppm Ce (on FCC)	44
FCC + Al$_2$O$_3$ (5%)	54
FCC + 25 ppm Ce (on FCC) + Al$_2$O$_3$ (5%)	127
FCC + 25 ppm Ce (on Al$_2$O$_3$) + Al$_2$O$_3$ (5%)	130

Results are shown as net gain over the cracking catalyst which showed poor SO$_2$ removal ability. The cracking catalyst was a low alumina–REY type. Addition of 25 ppm cerium to the cracking catalyst increased SO$_2$ adsorption even though the catalyst already contained rare earths including cerium. Cerium was added by impregnation from an aqueous solution of ceric ammonium nitrate. Addition of alumina, as a separate particulate, also had a positive effect even though the catalyst contained alumina. Adding both cerium and alumina, whether the cerium is on the cracking catalyst or on the alumina, however, increased SO$_2$ adsorption disproportionately. Again, from these results we concluded that cerium was a catalyst for the oxidative adsorption of SO$_2$.

The promotional effect of cerium is not confined to alumina as shown by the data for magnesia (26) in Table II.

Table II.   Effect of Cerium and Magnesia Added to Cracking Catalyst

Catalyst Description	Net SO$_2$ Removed at 1250°F, μl after 92 minutes
FCC + 500 ppm MgO	113
FCC + 500 ppm MgO + 25 ppm Ce (on MgO)	235

Results, again, show net gain over the same cracking catalyst used previously for cerium/alumina case. Cerium, moreover, seems to act as a promotor for other rare earths as could be implied from the synergistic effect observed between cerium and lanthanum (27). Our conclusions about the catalytic effect of cerium have been confirmed recently by others (28).

Other rare earths, including yttrium (29) and lanthanum (30) are active for SO$_2$ removal as shown on Table III.

Table III. Effect of Other Rare Earths

Rare Earth	Relative SO_2 Removal
Ce	1.0
Y	1.0
Mixed (Ce Rich)	0.9
La	0.8
Pr	0.6
Dy	0.6
Gd	0.4
Nd	0.4
Sm	0.4

These materials were made to contain 10 wt% oxides on gamma
alumina. The percentage of SO_2 removed after 50 minutes was
measured, at 1250°F, for these additives at the 1 wt% level mixed
with cracking catalysts. They were then ranked by the ratio of the
% removed to that removed by cerium on alumina.

Platinum. Other materials are effective promotors for the
oxidative adsorption of SO_2. Figure 6, for instance, demonstrates
the effect of platinum which is the best promotor and the earliest
one used for the UltraCat process (31). The figure, which compares
SO_2 removal curves for alumina alone and with 2 and 100 ppm Pt at
1200, 1300 and 1400°F, indicates that alumina promoted with
platinum at both levels is more efficient for removing SO_2 than
pure alumina. The catalytic effect of platinum, not unexpectedly,
becomes less pronounced as the temperature is increased as can be
seen by inspecting the curves and also by comparing the percentage
of SO_2 removed after 100 minutes as shown on Table IV.

Table IV. Catalytic Effect of Platinum

Temperature, °F	% SO_2 Removed at 100 Minutes Platinum Concentration, ppm		
	0	2	100
1200	36	85	98
1300	43	78	90
1400	50	68	86

Without platinum, alumina becomes more effective for removing
SO_2 as the temperature is increased. In this unpromoted case, the
rate of oxidative adsorption of SO_2 controls the amount of SO_2
removed. Increasing the temperature increases that rate.
    In contrast, with platinum, SO_2 removal, while always greater
than the unpromoted case, tends to decrease with increasing
temperature. The presence of platinum increases the rate of
oxidative adsorption of SO_2 to the point that the capacity of
alumina becomes the limiting factor rather than the rate. The
capacity, limited by thermodynamics, decreases with increasing
temperature because of the stability of surface sulfate species

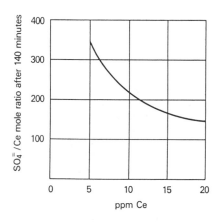

Figure 5.   Catalytic Effect of Cerium.

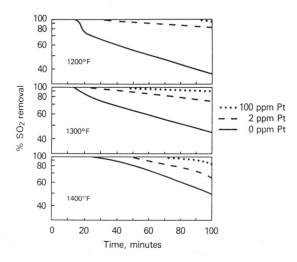

Figure 6.   Catalytic Effect of Platinum.

being formed. Presumably, at a high enough temperature platinum
would have no catalytic effect and the capacity of alumina would be
lowered more. These results extend those found previously by
Summers (32).

Platinum, as well as other promotors, can cause problems such
as NOx formation or other unfavorable side effects. The rare
earths do not have these drawbacks so a good deal of attention has
been given to their development for SOx removal.

Deactivation

Pilot Plant Testing. Pilot plant testing of 10% cerium on alumina
mixed with cracking catalyst showed a discrepancy in the extent of
observed and predicted deactivation. During the test, which was
made at 1350°F, a common FCU regeneration temperature, the catalyst
was sampled and tested in several ways. We used our bench test to
measure SO_2 removal ability on the samples before and also after
reduction with hydrogen at 1350°F, to remove sulfate. Then, the
additive portion of the samples was separated by float-sink using
tetrabromoethane. Estimates of the efficiency of the separation
were made by microscopic inspection and found to be greater than
about 95% in all cases. The differences in shape and appearance
made it easy to distinguish visually cerium/alumina additive from
cracking catalyst. Losses by attrition were calculated from the
weight of the recovered additive. Surface area losses were
measured by comparing the surface area of the fresh additive to the
surface area of the separated additive. Losses in SO_2 removal
ability were predicted from relationships between surface area,
weight percent of additive, and SO_2 removal. Reduction had no
effect indicating that sulfate accumulation was not important. The
large differences between predicted and observed losses shown on
Table V indicated that other factors were involved in the
deactivation.

Table V. Pilot Plant Deactivation of Cerium/Alumina Additive

| | % Loss in SO_2 Removal | | |
Time, Hrs.	Predicted	Observed	Δ
30	12	28	16
40	25	49	24
60	27	52	25
80	29	62	33

SEM–EDAX examination of cross-sectioned samples taken from the
pilot plant test at 30, 60 and 80 hours show the presence of
silicon. This is indicated in the photomicrographs in Figure 7.
The outlines are cerium/alumina particles; the bright white dots
represent silicon. Qualitatively, silicon contamination increases
with time.

The presence of silicon on the deactivated additive raised
several questions about the silicon source and how it gets to the
additive. The effect of steam was examined first.

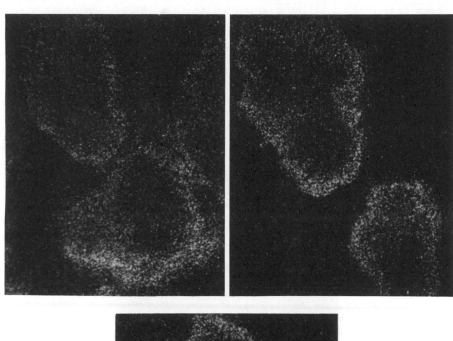

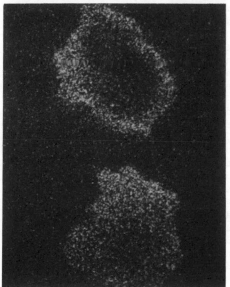

Figure 7. SEM—EDAX Analysis of Pilot Plant Samples: Silicon.
Top left, 30 hours; top right, 60 hours; and bottom, 80 hours.

Bench Scale Steaming Experiments. Steaming experiments showed that
steam deactivation of the cerium/alumina catalyst was more severe
when deactivated in the presence of cracking catalyst. Figure 8
shows how SO_2 removal decreases with steaming time at 1350°F. The
results are shown for three experiments in a fluidized bed
apparatus. In the first, cerium on alumina additive was steamed in
a Vycor tube without cracking catalyst. The additive was sampled
at various times during the steaming and tested for SO_2 removal
ability. In the second and third experiments, the cerium on
alumina additive was steamed in the presence of two commercial FC
catalysts of different compositions: high and low alumina. Again,
the catalyst-additive mixtures were sampled at various times. The
additive portion of the samples, which was separated by float-sink
method, was tested for SO_2 removal ability. As the data in
Figure 8 indicate, there was some deactivation in all cases, but a
strong interactive effect between additive and cracking catalyst is
evident in that the rates of deactivation are much greater for
steam deactivation in the presence of cracking catalyst. However,
the early deactivation, especially, is less pronounced for steam
deactivation in the presence of high alumina cracking catalyst
compared to a low alumina cracking catalyst. The presence of the
high alumina cracking catalyst seems to retard deactivation.
Similar experiments with dry nitrogen showed that steam was
necessary for the observed deactivation.

The steamed samples were again examined by SEM-EDAX. The
results in Figure 9 are for samples taken at 2 and 24 hours for
cerium on alumina additive steamed without and with high and low
alumina cracking catalyst. Again, the outlined shapes are the
cerium on alumina additive and the bright spots silicon. Some
silicon is present in all the samples inspected, even the sample
steamed in the absence of cracking catalyst, showing that the
additive has been contaminated with silicon from the Vycor steaming
tube. The level of silicon, however, is much greater for samples
steam-deactivated in the presence of a cracking catalyst, even for
those steamed for as little as two hours. Also, especially for the
two-hour samples, the amount of silicon on the additive deactivated
in the presence of high alumina (low silica) cracking catalyst
seems to be substantially less than either of those samples
deactivated in the presence of low alumina (high silica) catalysts.
Surface area losses for all the samples were about the same.

Silica Added Directly. Direct addition of silica to cerium on
alumina also deactivates the additive. To show this, the additive
was impregnated with aqueous solutions of "silicic acid" prepared
by ion exchange of sodium silicate with IR-120 acid ion exchange
resin, then dried and calcined at 1000°F for 5 hrs. SO_2 removal
ability was measured on the as-prepared samples and after steaming
at 1400 and 1550°F for 5 hrs. The results shown in Figure 10
indicate that the deactivating effect of silica is much worse after
the samples are steamed. The mere presence of silica is not
enough. An interaction between the cerium/alumina additive and
silica brought about by steam and/or heat is necessary for the full
deactivating effect of silica to be observed.

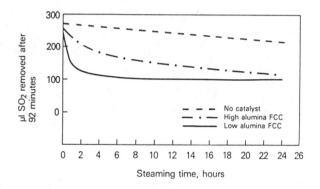

Figure 8.   Steam Deactivation of Cerium on Alumina.

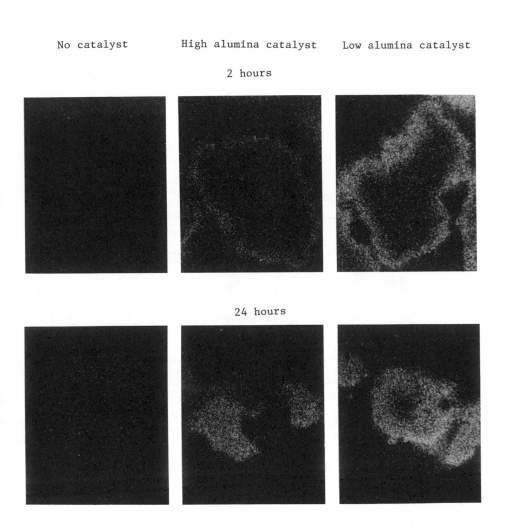

Figure 9.   SEM-EDAX Analysis of Steam-Deactivated Samples:
            Silicon.

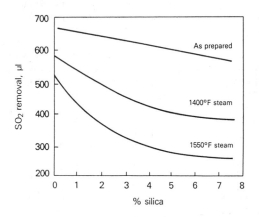

Figure 10. Effect of Silica and Steam.

Source of Silica. Silica can migrate either from free silica present in the cracking catalyst or from the silica alumina matrix but not as readily from the zeolite. Figure 11 shows SEM-EDAX silicon scans of cerium/alumina steamed in the presence of these three sources of silica. Again, the bright dots represent silicon. Qualitatively the sample steamed with pure silica contains more silicon than the sample steamed with silica-alumina. The sample steamed with zeolite shows silicon at the surface of the cross-sectioned particle but little in the interior. The surface silicon comes from dusting of the particle with very finely divided zeolite.

We are not alone in implicating silica in the deactivation mechanism of SOx additives. Our results support Blanton's concern about silica (33) and also agrees well with the work of several others (15,17,34).

The Mobility of Silica in Steam. The reactivity of silica and silica-containing materials to steam has been assumed in the literature to explain several phenomena, a few of which are: the sintering of silica (35), the aging of amorphous silica alumina cracking catalysts (36) and the formation of ultrastable molecular sieves (37). The basis of all these explanations is the interaction of siliceous materials with water to form mobile, low molecular weight silicon compounds by hydrolysis (38) such as:

$$-(SiO_2)_n- + 2H_2O \longrightarrow Si(OH)_4 + (SiO_2)_{n-1} \tag{5}$$

Silica is known to be volatile in steam (39-40). For instance, the equilibrium concentration of silica in steam at 1 atmosphere from 1200 to 1450°F has been found to range from 0.2 to 0.5 ppm (by weight) showing that the availability of silica in the vapor phase can be substantial under the conditions used in our work. Unfortunately, we cannot predict how much silica will be transferred in our experiments since the rates of either hydrolysis or adsorption on the cerium on alumina additive are unknown.

The rates of hydrolysis of siliceous materials will be affected by several factors. For instance, the rate will be directly related to surface area, explaining the low rates observed for silica deposition from the Vycor apparatus. Also, the composition of the siliceous material will influence the rate of hydrolysis, explaining the differing amounts of silica transferred from pure silica, silica alumina, zeolite, and the high alumina cracking catalyst.

Mechanism of Deactivation. The detailed mechanism for silica poisoning of cerium on alumina additive is unknown but we suggest that silica, as volatile silicic acid, adsorbs strongly, and, under the influence of steam and/or heat reacts to irreversibly remove sites that are required for the oxidative adsorption of SO₂. Silicic acid reacts in what can be considered a simple acid base type reaction and permanently lowers the capacity of the additive.

More work would have to be done to show whether silica interacts with cerium and/or alumina. Iler (41), however, has remarked that alumina and silica are considered to have a

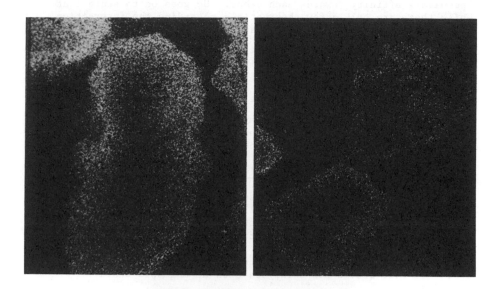

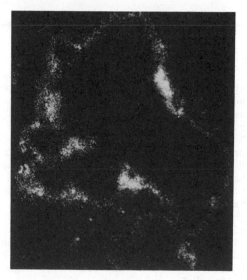

Figure 11.   SEM—EDAX Analysis of Cerium/Alumina: Silicon.
Top left, pure silica; top right, silica alumina; and
bottom, molecular sieve.

"peculiar" affinity towards each other. He goes on to state that
while there are only a few observations regarding the interaction
with silicic acid, it has been established from solution chemistry
that Si(OH)$_4$ strongly adsorbs onto the surface of hydroxy alumina
oxide and also reacts with gamma alumina. In some cases an
aluminosilicate with the haloysite composition forms:

$$Al_2Si_2O_5(OH)_4$$

On an anhydrous basis the above composition would contain 46%
alumina. From Figure 3 such a material would have lower SO_2
removal capacity compared to alumina.

How to Solve the Deactivation Problem. Solutions to the
deactivation problem are difficult. The patent literature (42) has
claims that either sodium, manganese or phosphorous added to
alumina prevents deactivation by silica. In addition, removal of
matrix silica from cracking catalyst formulations should prevent
further deactivation because zeolitic silica, as we have shown,
migrates more slowly. There is at least one patent relating to
very high alumina matrix cracking catalysts (43). Another solution
is to use more active SOx catalysts such as magnesia-based
materials.

Magnesia

The high capacity material described in the patent
literature (44-45) is a cerium promoted "over-based"
magnesia-alumina in which magnesia is added in excess of the
stoichiometric spinel composition, $MgAl_2O_4$. To better understand
this system, a series of catalysts was prepared with various
amounts of magnesia and alumina from alumina sol and magnesium
hydroxide slurry. After drying and calcining, these materials were
impregnated with ceric ammonium nitrate to 6% CeO_2. The data in
Figure 12 show how SO_2 removal changes with composition. The data
are expressed in terms of percent approach to the stoichiometric
amount of SO_2 that could have been adsorbed based on CeO_2, MgO, and
Al_2O_3 assuming complete sulfate formation. The tests were made at
1350°F for 92 minutes. In all cases, removal of SO_2 was measured
on the same weight of catalyst. Magnesia is at least an order of
magnitude more efficient for removing SO_2 than alumina. In
addition, there is an unfavorable interaction between magnesia and
alumina as indicated by the non-linear relationship between SO_2
removal and composition with the full effect of magnesia unobserved
until well above 50 mole%.
     There is no clear evidence to identify the active material for
SO_2 removal in a $MgAl_2O_4$ "stoichiometric" system. Figure 13 shows
results for a 50-50 mole% magnesia-alumina material prepared from
magnesium hydroxide and alumina sol and calcined at various
temperatures. An attempt was made to correlate SO_2 removal with
compound formation, as measured by X-ray diffraction, and surface
area. As indicated in the figure, SO_2 removal ability decreased
with increasing calcination temperature as did surface area. X-ray
diffraction analysis showed spinel formation increases as

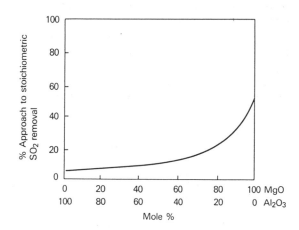

Figure 12.   Magnesia–Alumina System: 6% Ceria.

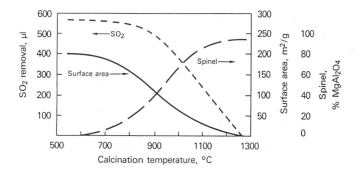

Figure 13.   Effect of Calcination Temperature: 50–50 Mole%
MgO–Al$_2$O$_3$.

calcination temperature increased. The only other materials found
by XRD were minor amounts of gamma alumina in some of the samples
calcined at low temperature and very minor amounts of free magnesia
in the samples calcined at high temperature.

Temperature Effects

An understanding of temperature effects is important to maximize
the benefit from SOx removal agents. There are three areas in
which temperature effects are particularly important:

            -- steam stability,
            -- oxidative adsorption of SO_2, and
            -- reductive desorption of SO_2

Steam Stability. Steam stability of SOx removal agents is strongly
affected by temperature. We have seen previously that at 1350°F
deactivation of cerium/alumina additive, caused by silica
poisoning, was influenced by how long the additive was steamed and
whether the additive was steamed in the presence or absence of
cracking catalyst. These results were extended to other
temperatures.
      Two sets of experiments were made to show the effect of
steaming temperature on stability. In the first set, steaming was
done non-interactively. Cerium/alumina additive was steamed (100%
steam, 1 atm) for 5 hours in a fixed bed from 1200 to 1450°F. SO_2
removal ability was then measured on these steamed samples diluted
with cracking catalyst. The data in Figure 14 show that, for
steamings done separate from cracking catalyst, losses of SO_2
removal ability are small but become more pronounced above 1350°F.
      Losses incurred in the non-interactive steamings, however,
were lower than those found in the second set of experiments where
the cerium/alumina additive was steamed together with a low alumina
cracking catalyst at various temperatures. The results from this
second set of experiments, shown in Figure 14, indicate that losses
are important at temperatures above 1200°F. It should be noted
that SO_2 removal ability was measured under the same conditions in
both sets of experiments. Also, these fixed bed steaming seem to
be harsher than fluidized bed steamings because the losses incurred
are greater.

Oxidative Adsorption of SO_2. Oxidative adsorption of SO_2 is also a
strong function of temperature as shown on Figure 15. Plotted is
the amount of SO_2 removed after 92 minutes from room temperature to
1500°F. The material used for these experiments was a rare earth
stabilized Rhone-Poulenc alumina which was tested without dilution
with cracking catalyst. A fresh charge of alumina was used at each
temperature.
      As the data in Figure 15 show, a plot of SO_2 adsorbed vs.
temperature yields a curve with the classical shape of an
adsorption isotherm divided, as indicated on the figure, into three
distinct regimes. From the literature (46), we can speculate about
the chemistry. Regime 1 is associated with the strong
chemisorption of SO_2 as sulfite and is controlled thermodynamically

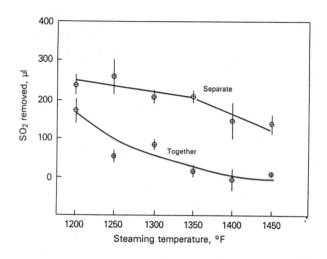

Figure 14.   Effect of Steaming Temperature.

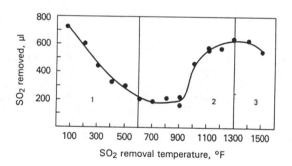

Figure 15.   Effect of Adsorption Temperature.

by the stability of the sulfite species. As the temperature is
increased the sulfite species becomes less stable but at a high
enough temperature, Regime 2, oxidation of sulfite to sulfate
becomes fast enough so formation of sulfate becomes the important
process. In Regime 2, adsorption of sulfate is limited by the
oxidation kinetics. The amount of SO_2 adsorbed increases with
temperature in Regime 2 until the stability of the surface sulfate
species becomes important. At that point, Regime 3, adsorption
begins to decrease with temperature and once again the process is
limited by thermodynamics.

The shape of the curve describing the temperature dependence
of SO_2 adsorption in the temperature range of FCC regenerators,
1200-1350°F, is critical as to how a given SO_2 adsorption material
will perform. As indicated in Figure 15, a maximum is observed for
the stabilized Rhone-Poulenc alumina in that range. Other
materials, as we have seen previously for platinum promoted
alumina, will have a somewhat different shape in that temperature
region. A curve very similar to the one shown in Figure 15 was
previously reported for high alumina cracking catalyst
(Hsieh, C. K., Amoco Oil Co., unpublished data, 1976).

Reductive Desorption of SO_2. The reductive desorption of
oxidatively adsorbed SO_2 is also a strong function of temperature
as shown graphically in Figure 16. Shown are the results for
cyclic use of a magnesia-based SOx additive. Each cycle, indicated
by a cycle marker, consists of adsorption of SO_2 at 1350°F for
100 minutes followed by a 15 minute reduction with hydrogen. In
all cases, the adsorption temperature was held constant at 1350°F
but the reduction temperature was changed from 1350° to 950°F. For
each cycle the amount of SO_2 adsorbed is then plotted on the
Y-axis. The data show a gradual decline in the amount of SO_2
removed in successive cycles of adsorption-reduction from a
reduction temperature of 1350 to 1150°F. This minor gradual
decline is caused by permanent deactivation of the catalyst rather
than incomplete reduction as indicated by the failure at the end of
the test to restore the adsorption capacity of the additive by a
high temperature reduction. There is a sharp drop in the amount of
SO_2 adsorbed in successive cycles when the reduction temperature is
lowered to 1050°F. The amount of SO_2 adsorbed in successive cycles
does not change significantly when the reduction temperature is
lowered further to 950°F.

The results from this "temperature programmed reduction"
indicate that there are two regimes as indicated in Figure 16. In
Regime 1, at temperatures above 1050°F there is virtually complete
removal of SO_2 under the conditions of our test. In Regime 2,
characterized by the step jump downward at 1050°F in the amount of
SO_2 adsorbed in successive cycles, there is only partial removal of
SO_2. This observation suggests two kinds of surface sulfate
species present on this material, one easily and another more
difficultly removed as indicated by Andersson (47).

Commercial Catalysts

Five types of commercial SOx catalysts were tested for comparative
ranking. Three of these commercial-type additives were well
defined materials: high surface area gamma alumina; 10% Ce, as
cerium oxide, on gamma alumina; and 100 ppm Pt on gamma alumina.
Two of the materials were furnished by catalyst companies and are
referred to as magnesia-based or magnesia and lanthanum-based or
lanthanum. These latter materials are both known to contain cerium
and alumina as well.

Figure 17 shows a comparison of the fresh SO_2 removal ability
for these five major types of commercially available SOx catalysts.
The materials were tested at 1350°F at various concentrations with
a very low capacity cracking catalyst. The magnesia-based catalyst
is much better than lanthanum-based catalyst followed by platinum
or cerium on alumina and finally alumina alone. The reverse order
in activity observed for the lanthanum-based and cerium additives,
compared to the relative results given previously for lanthanum and
cerium, was not investigated, but may be related to the presence of
cerium on the lanthanum-based additive (27).

Fresh activity, however, only partially determines the
efficacy of these catalysts. Among other important factors, as we
have seen, are how easily the catalyst releases SO_2 during the
cracking cycle and how resistant it is to deactivation by steam.

Commercial catalysts vary in the degree to which they are
regenerable at reactor temperatures as shown on Figure 18. The
initial SO_2 removal for all five materials was adjusted to an equal
basis by varying the amount of additive used: 0.8% magnesia-based,
3% lanthanum-based, 10% of both cerium/alumina and
platinum/alumina, and finally 30% of alumina in mixtures with a low
capacity cracking catalyst. SO_2 removal was measured at 1350°F for
the fresh additives and after regeneration with hydrogen at 930°F.
Six such adsorption-regeneration cycles were made after which
release was 76 and 70% for platinum and cerium on alumina
respectively and 38% for magnesia and lanthanum, and 42% for
alumina. Raising the regeneration temperature above 1100°F
restores the additives to near fresh capacity after the several
cycles of this test. The commercial effect of incomplete release
of SO_2 would be to require more additive to achieve a given SO_2
removal.

In our test, steaming five commercial SOx additives in the
presence of cracking catalyst, shown in Table VI, indicated that
deactivation by silica poisoning is important.

Table VI. Steam Deactivation of Commercial Additives

Additive Type	% Loss of SO_2 Removal
Magnesia-Based	52
Platinum/Alumina	52
Lanthanum-Based	55
Cerium/Alumina	57
Alumina	79

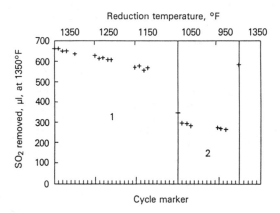

Figure 16.   Effect of Reduction Temperature.

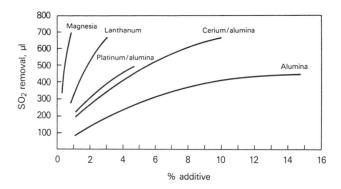

Figure 17.   Fresh Activities of Commercial Catalysts.

These data were obtained by mixing the SOx additive with a low alumina cracking catalyst and steaming at 1400°F in 100% steam in a fixed bed for 5 hours. The concentration of additive was adjusted so that the initial activity was approximately the same for all materials. (The amounts were the same as those used for the regenerability test.) The SO$_2$ removal ability was then measured before and after steaming and the % loss calculated. The average deviation was ±7%.

These tests show that composition of the additive has little effect on controlling deactivation from silica poisoning. On an equal initial activity basis, four of the five additives tested showed very similar deactivation. Alumina, however, had a much higher susceptibility.

A final ranking of the five SOx control catalysts can be made by assuming that the losses in SO$_2$ removal from incomplete regeneration (% L$_R$) and steaming (% L$_S$) can be compensated by addition of more catalyst assuming a linear response:

$$EAC = IA + \%L_R \cdot \frac{IA}{100} + \%L_S \cdot \frac{IA}{100} \qquad (6)$$

where: EAC = Effective Additive Concentration, Wt%, and
        IA = Equalized Initial Activity, Wt%

Using this assumption, the ranking for the five commercial materials is shown in Table VII.

Table VII. Ranking of Commercial Additive Types

Additive Type	EAC, Wt%
Magnesia-Based	2
lanthanum-Based	7
Pt/Alumina	18
Ce/Alumina	19
Alumina	71

Magnesia and lanthanum based materials are the most effective of the samples tested to date.

Thermodynamics

Free energy changes were calculated, using values from three sources (48-50), for reduction of sulfate with either hydrogen or methane and adsorption of SO$_2$ in the presence of oxygen to form sulfate. Calculations were made for magnesia, alumina, and other group IA and group IIA oxides. Unfortunately, thermodynamic values are not available for other elements of interest such as lanthanum.

The reduction of magnesium sulfate is thermodynamically feasible at reactor temperatures of 900°F and above, especially if H$_2$S is the product. Figure 19 shows the standard ΔG_{rx} for the reduction of magnesium sulfate with hydrogen or methane as a function of temperature to make either H$_2$S or SO$_2$ as the reduction product. (The calculations have all been made on the basis of 1 mole of SO$_2$.) Also shown are the values for the reduction of SO$_2$

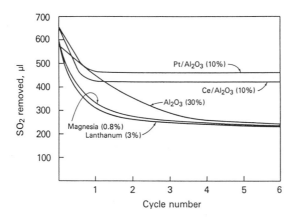

Figure 18.   Regeneration of Commercial Catalysts.

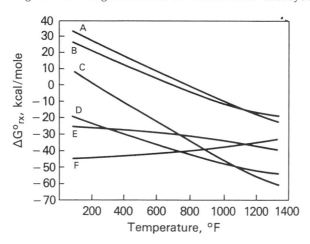

A. $MgSO_4 + 1/4CH_4 = MgO + SO_2 + 1/4CO_2 + 1/2H_2O$
B. $MgSO_4 + H_2 = MgO + SO_2 + H_2O$
C. $MgSO_4 + CH_4 = MgO + H_2S + CO_2 + H_2O$
D. $MgSO_4 + 4H_2 = MgO + H_2S + 3H_2O$
E. $SO_2 + 3/4CH_4 = H_2S + 3/4CO_2 + 1/2H_2O$
F. $SO_2 + 3H_2 = H_2S + 2H_2O$

Figure 19.   Thermodynamics of Reduction: MgSO4.

with hydrogen or methane to make H$_2$S. This is thermodynamically very favored and shows that the formation of H$_2$S as a product from the reduction of the sulfate is more favorable than the formation of SO$_2$. The reactions using methane, while less favorable than hydrogen, are nevertheless still feasible at reaction temperatures of 900 to 1000°F. The same calculations made for aluminum sulfate, using hydrogen as the reducing agent are even more favorable thermodynamically as indicated on Figure 20.

The thermodynamic data shown in Figure 21 indicate, post factum, how magnesia and alumina fit the requirements for the UltraCat process. The figure shows values for standard ΔG_{rx} for reduction of the sulfate with hydrogen at 980°F to make SO$_2$ for elements in groups IA, IIA, and aluminum. Values of standard ΔG_{rx} are also shown for the adsorption of SO$_2$:

$$MO + SO_2 + \tfrac{1}{2}O_2 = MSO_4 \tag{7}$$

All calculations were made on the basis of 1 mole of SO$_2$.

An appropriate material for the UltraCat process should have favorable thermodynamics for both SO$_2$ release and capture. The most favored elements are designated in the boxed area on Figure 21 and include alumina and magnesia. Berylium is also included, but the decomposition temperature of berylium sulfate, 1000-1100°F, indicates that it is probably not suitable, even if it were not hazardous.

If the free energy changes for the reduction of the sulfate to make H$_2$S rather than SO$_2$ had been considered in this analysis, the oxides of several more elements would have been included in the boxed-off area of appropriate materials. From past practice, however, it is known that oxides of calcium, strontium and lithium, for instance, are not as effective. An appropriate future area of research would be to investigate those materials more thoroughly.

Conclusions

Although industrial and patent literature contains a large amount of information about SOx catalysts, it is difficult to make comparisons or sort out the important factors. This paper has made an attempt to clarify some SOx issues but in almost all cases more questions were raised than answered.

For cracking catalyst composition, we showed that alumina content is important by showing how catalysts synthesized to contain various amounts of alumina removed SO$_2$. Although for years alumina content has been considered important by the industry, it was difficult to find a conclusive reference showing that fact.

Rare earths have also been included as desirable SOx catalyst components in early patents but the catalytic behavior of cerium, in particular, had not been clarified. This paper has presented evidence that cerium catalyzes the oxidative adsorption of SO$_2$ on high alumina cracking catalyst, alumina, and magnesia. We also have shown the catalytic character of platinum. The details of the catalysis especially by cerium, however, remain unexplained.

Patent and industrial literature has been concerned with the deactivating effect of silica for several years. Our work confirms

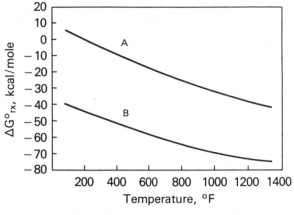

A. $1/3\ Al_2(SO_4)_3 + H_2 = 1/3\ Al_2O_3 + SO_2 + H_2O$
B. $1/3\ Al_2(SO_4)_3 + 4H_2 = 1/3\ Al_2O_3 + H_2S + 3H_2O$

Figure 20.   Thermodynamics of Reduction: $Al_2(SO_4)_3$.

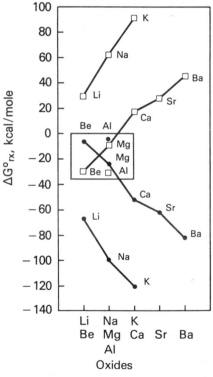

☐ $MSO_4 + H_2 = MO + SO_2 + H_2O$ 800°K (980°F)
● $MO + SO_2 + 1/2O_2 = MSO_4$ 1000°K (1340°F)

Figure 21.   Thermodynamic Selection of Oxides.

this concern and shows that the source of the silica is either free silica or silica-alumina in the matrix of the cracking catalyst but not the zeolite. We also have shown that cracking catalyst composition is important in retarding the deactivating effect of silica.

The detailed mechanism of poisoning by silica, however, is unknown. We have suggested that an interaction of silicic acid generated by hydrolysis of silica or silica-alumina reacts with the active sites on the additive lowering the overall capacity of the material to form sulfates. More work must be done to show the chemistry of this mechanism.

Recently, high capacity additives, based on magnesia and alumina, have been suggested as SOx additives. Patent literature identifies the active material in these systems as spinel. Our work has shown, however, that magnesia is the active material being at least an order of magnitude more active than alumina. The stoichiometric spinel, $MgAl_2O_4$, appears to be inactive for SO_2 adsorption. The role of the alumina and excess magnesia in this system should be clarified.

Finally, the side-by-side comparison of five major types of commercially available SOx additives show that these materials differ not only in initial activity but also in regenerability, or the ability of the material to release SO_2. We can rank these materials but have left unanswered the important questions as to why these catalysts differ especially in regenerability.

Literature Cited

1. Vasalos, I. A.; Strong, E. R.; Hsieh, C. K. R.; D'Souza, G. J. API Refining Dep. Proc. 1977, 56, 182-91.
2. Bertolacini, R. J.; Lehmann, G. M.; Wollaston, E. G. U.S. Patent 3 835 031, 1974.
3. Healy, J. W.; Hertwig, W. R. Prepr. Gen. Pap. - Am. Chem. Soc., Div. Pet. Chem. 1949, 65-76.
4. Horecky, Jr., C. J.; Fahrig, R. J.; Shields, Jr., R. J.; McKinney, C. O. U.S. Patent 3 909 392, 1975.
5. Bienstock, D.; Field, F.J. J. Air Pollution Control, 1960, 10, 121-125.
6. Vogel, R. F.; Mitchell, B. R.; Massoth, F. E. Environ. Sci. Tech. 1974, 8, 432-436.
7. Koballa, T. E.; Dudukovic, M. P. AIChE Symp. Ser., 1977, 165, 199-228.
8. Lowell, P. S.; Schwitzgebel, K.; Parsons, T. B.; Sladek, K. J. Ind. Eng. Chem. Process Des. Dev., 1971, 10, 384-390.
9. DeBerry, D. W.; Sladek, K. J. Can. J. Chem. Eng., 1971, 49, 781-785.
10. McArthur, D. P.; Simpson, H. D.; Baron, K. Oil and Gas Journal 1981, 78(8), 55.
11. Baron, K.; Wu, A. H.; Krenzke, L. D. Prepr.-Symposium on Advances in Catalytic Cracking - Am. Chem. Soc., Div. Pet. Chem. 1983, 934-943.
12. Chem. Eng. (N.Y.), 1978 85(3), 49.
13. Blanton, W. A. Oil and Gas Journal 1982, 80(21), 62.
14. Edison, R. Chem. Eng. (N.Y.) 1983, 90(9), 13.

15. Byrne, J. W.; Speronello, B. K.; Leuenberger, E. L. Oil and
     Gas Journal 1984, 82(42), 101.
16. Siefert, K. S.; Chuang, K. C.; Foster, R. L. 78th Air Pollut.
     Control Assoc. Annu. Meeting (Detroit (6/16-21/85), Pap.
     #85-57.2.
17. Ritter, R. E.; Peters, A. W.; Rheaume, L.; Wallace, D. N.;
     Wormsbecker, R. F. NPRA Annual Meeting, March 24-26, 1985,
     Paper No. AM85-47.
18. Pettersen, F. A.; Blanton, Jr., W. A. Nat. AICHE Meeting,
     8/26/86, Boston, Session No. 37.
19. Habib, E. T. Oil and Gas Journal, 1983, 81(32), 111.
20. Demmel, E. J.; Lim, J. C. 44th API Refining Dep. Mid-Year
     Meeting, 1979, Prepr. 4-79.
21. Upson, L.L., NPRA Annual Meeting Mar. 25-27, 1979, Paper
     No. AM 79-39.
22. Blanton, W. A.; Flanders, R. L. U.S. Patent 4 071 436, 1978;
     and others.
23. Bertolacini, R. J.; Hirschberg, E. H.; Modica, F. S.
     U.S. Patent 4 376 103, 1983.
24. Bertolacini, R. J.; Hirschberg, E. H.; Modica, F. S.
     U.S. Patent 4 423 019, 1983.
25. Bertolacini, R. J.; Hirschberg, E. H.; Modica, F. S.
     U.S. Patent 4 423 019, 1983.
26. Bertolacini, R. J.; Hirschberg, E. H.; Modica, F. S.
     U.S. Patent 4 381 991, 1983.
27. Green, G. J.; Yan, T. Y. U.S. Patent 4 589 978, 1986.
28. Bhattacharyya, A. A.; Woltermann, G. M., Yoo, J. S.,
     Karch, J. A.; Cormier, W. E. Prepr. Div. Fuel Chem., Am.
     Chem. Soc., 1987, 32(4), 411.
29. Bertolacini, R. J.; Hirschberg, E. H.;Modica, F. S.
     U.S. Patent 4 405 443, 1983.
30. Bertolacini, R. J.; Hirschberg, E. H.; Modica, F. S.
     U.S. Patent 4 369 108, 1983.
31. Vasalos, I. A.; Ford, W. D.; Hsieh, C. K. R. U.S.
     Patent 4 153 535, 1979.
32. Summers, J. C. Env. Sci. Tech., 1979, 13, 321.
33. Blanton, W. A.; Flanders, R. L. U.S. Patent 4 115 249, 1978;
     and others.
34. Mester, Z. C.; Aitken, E. J.; Ritz, P. G. Prepr. Div. Fuel
     Chem., Am. Chem. Soc., 1987, 32(4), 396.
35. McDaniel, C. V.; Maher, P. K. in Zeolite Chemistry and
     Catalysis; Rabo, J. A., Ed.; ACS Monograph 171, American
     Chemical Society: Washington, D.C., 1976, p. 303.
36. Iler, R. K. The Colloid Chemistry of Silica and Silicates,
     1955, Cornell Univ. Press: Ithica, N.Y., p. 270.
37. Breck, D. W. Zeolite Molecular Sieves, 1979, John Wiley and
     Sons: New York, N.Y., p. 507.
38. Iler, R.K. The Chemistry of Silica, 1979, John Wiley and
     Sons: New York, N.Y., p. 4.
39. Ibid, p. 12.
40. Hugett, L. G. ICI Symposium on Steam Reforming, 1964 as
     quoted by Schwarzenbek, E. F. U.S. Patent 4 098 678, 1978.
41. Iler, R.K. The Chemistry of Silica, 1979, John Wiley and
     Sons: New York, N.Y., p. 173.

42. Blanton, W. A. U.S. patent 4 252 635, 1981.
43. Blanton, W. A.; Flanders, R. L. U.S. Patent 4 259 176, 1981.
44. Yoo, J. S.; Jaecker, J. A. U.S. Patent 4 469 589, 1984.
45. Bertolacini, R. J.; Hirschberg, E. H.; Modica, F. S. U.S. Patent 4 497 902.
46. Chang, C. C. J. Catalysis, 1978, 53, 374-385.
47. Andersson, S.; Pompe, R.; Vannerberg, N. Applied Catalysis, 1985, 16, 49-58.
48. JANAF Thermochemical Tables, 1971, 2nd edition, National Bureau of Standards.
49. Barin, I. and Knacke, O. Thermochemical Properties of Inorganic Substances, Springer-Verlag, New York, 1973.
50. DeKock, C. W. Thermodynamic Properties of Selected Metal Sulfates and Their Hydrates, 1986, Bureau of Mines, Information Circular 9081.

RECEIVED March 29, 1988

Chapter 9

Use of Catalysts To Reduce SO_x Emissions from Fluid Catalytic Cracking Units

L. Rheaume and R. E. Ritter

Davison Chemical Division, W. R. Grace & Company, 7379 Route 32, Columbia, MD 21044

SOx emissions from fluid catalytic cracking units (FCCU's) can be reduced by the use of catalysts. These catalysts, called SOx transfer catalysts, capture SOx (SO_2+SO_3) in the FCCU regenerator and release it, as H_2S, in the FCCU reactor and steam stripper. The H_2S leaves the FCCU with the cracked products. The H_2S is removed from the cracked products by conventional techniques. The different types of SOx catalysts are described. The mechanism by which these catalysts operate is discussed and supporting data presented. Laboratory results are given on the factors which affect the efficiency of SOx catalysts, namely regenerator temperature, oxidation activity, oxygen concentration and contaminant metals. Also data are given on the aging and deactivation of these catalysts by loss of surface area and adsorption of silica.

Source of SOx Emissions

Hydrocarbon feedstocks for fluid catalytic cracking units (FCCU's) contain organo-sulfur compounds. The sulfur content of these feedstocks is about 0.3% to 3.0%, expressed as elemental sulfur.

When a virgin feedstock is cracked in the FCCU reactor, about 50 ± 10% of the feed sulfur is converted to H_2S, about 43 ± 5% of the feed sulfur remains in the liquid products, and about 7 ± 3% of the feed sulfur ends up in the coke. During the coke-burning step in the FCCU regenerator, the sulfur in the coke is converted to SO_2 (>90%) and SO_3 (<10%), i.e., SOx. After the SOx is produced in the regenerator, it becomes part of the flue gas and is discharged to the atmosphere. It is this discharge of SOx to the atmosphere which we seek to control by use of catalysts.

The amount of SOx produced in the regenerator is determined by the amount of coke produced in the reactor and the sulfur content of that coke (1). These two factors, in turn, depend on the type of feedstock, the amount of sulfur in the feedstock, the coke-making

0097–6156/88/0375–0146$06.00/0

properties of the cracking catalyst, the conversion level, and the severity of steam-stripping.

The amount of SOx produced in the regenerator can be consider-able. For example, consider a 50,000-barrels-per-day unit, with a catalyst inventory of 500 tons and a catalyst circulation rate of 50,000 tons a day. The unit operates at a catalyst to oil ratio of 6. The feedstock contains 2.0% sulfur, and 7% of the sulfur in the feedstock goes to coke. For this unit, the daily SOx emissions would be 23.3 tons, expressed as SO$_2$, or 11.7 tons, expressed as elemental sulfur.

Environmental Control Laws

Increasingly strict environmental control laws have resulted in a need to reduce the SOx emissions from most stationary sources, including FCCU's. The United States Environmental Protection Agency has proposed that limits be placed on the amount of SOx emissions from new, modified and rebuilt FCCU's (2). Several local agencies have already placed limits on SOx emissions. For example, the California South Coast Air Quality Management District, in which 10 refineries are located, has an SOx emissions limit of 60 kg (132 lbs) of SOx (expressed as SO$_2$) per 1,000 barrels of oil fed to the FCCU.

In order to meet the California South Coast Air Quality Manage-ment District SOx emissions limit, the 50,000-barrels-per-day unit, referred to above, would have to reduce its SOx emissions from 23.3 tons a day to 3.3 tons a day, a reduction of 86%.

SOx Transfer Catalysts

Catalysts which reduce SOx emissions from FCCU's are called SOx transfer catalysts, or more simply, SOx catalysts.

The feasibility of using catalysts to reduce SOx emissions from FCCU's was first described by Bertolacini, Lehman and Wollaston in 1974 (3). A review of the catalyst technology was published by Habib in 1983 (4). Use of catalysts is the least expensive method of reducing SOx emissions from FCCU's. Alternatives, such as flue gas scrubbing and hydrotreating of feedstocks, are about 5 to 10 times more expensive (5,6).

There are two types of SOx catalysts. In one, the SOx catalyst agent is incorporated within the cracking catalyst particle. In the other, the SOx catalyst agent is a separate particle, mixed with the cracking catalyst. This second type is also called an SOx additive, since it can be added to the FCCU independently of the cracking catalyst. The physical properties (particle size, density, attrition resistance) of an SOx additive are similar to those of a cracking catalyst. An example of an SOx additive is Additive R, a proprietary product of the Davison Chemical Division of W. R. Grace & Co.

Of the two types of SOx catalysts, the SOx additive has proven to be the more popular. Its main advantage is that it can be added to the unit at any time, and it need be added only in amounts required to give the desired degree of SOx reduction. This is especially important for units using feedstocks which vary in sulfur content. Also, use of an SOx additive does not interfere with the type of cracking catalyst used or the addition rate of the cracking catalyst.

This paper will describe the chemistry and other factors which affect SOx catalysts in general, and Davison's Additive R in particular.

Mechanism for Catalytic Reduction of SOx Emissions

Catalytic SOx reduction involves the capture of SOx in the FCCU regenerator and its release, as H_2S, in the FCCU reactor and FCCU stripper (3). Reaction mechanisms by which this occurs have been discussed by others (3,4,6,7). A schematic of a generally accepted mechanism is shown in Figure 1.

In the regenerator, the coke on the spent cracking catalyst is burned to give a regenerated cracking catalyst. During the coke burning, the sulfur in the coke is converted to SO_2 (>90%) and SO_3 (<10%) (Equation 1 of Figure 1). The SO_2 is then oxidized to SO_3 (Equation 2). The SO_3 is adsorbed onto the SOx catalyst to form a surface metal sulfate (Equation 3). The SOx catalyst in Equation 3 is depicted as a metal oxide. Equation 3 represents the capture of SOx in the regenerator.

The regenerated cracking catalyst and the SOx catalyst then move to the FCCU reactor. In the reactor, the cracking catalyst cracks the hydrocarbon feedstock to lighter hydrocarbons, H_2, H_2S and sulfur-containing coke. At the same time, the metal sulfate on the surface of the SOx catalyst is reduced by H_2 to metal sulfide (Equation 4) or to metal oxide with release of H_2S in the reactor (Equation 5).

The spent, i.e. coked, cracking catalyst and the SOx catalyst then move to the FCCU stripper. In the stripper, they are treated with steam to flush out the volatile hydrocarbons. The steam also hydrolyzes the metal sulfide on the surface of the SOx catalyst to give metal oxide and release H_2S in the stripper (Equation 6).

The spent-and-stripped cracking catalyst and the rejuvenated SOx catalyst then move from the stripper to the FCCU regenerator for the start of another cycle.

The H_2S, released in the reactor and stripper, leaves the FCCU with the cracked products. This H_2S would increase the total amount of H_2S in the cracked products by only about 10-15%. The H_2S in the cracked-product stream is removed by conventional techniques.

In the application of this mechanism to Additive R, we found that 85% of the sulfur captured in the regenerator is released in the reactor (Equation 5), and 15% is released in the stripper (Equation 6). This result was for reactor and stripper temperatures of 980°F. This result was determined by a comparison of the SOx capability of Additive R when stripped with steam vs. nitrogen. The relative SOx capabilities were 1.0 for steam stripping and 0.85 for nitrogen stripping. Since nitrogen stripping is not expected to cause the release of sulfur in the stripper, this means that 85% of the sulfur was released in the reactor during the cracking reaction. The remaining 15% was released in the stripper during the steam stripping.

In SO_2 adsorption experiments, we found that 100% steam did not release any sulfur from Additive R at 980°F. Steam released sulfur from Additive R only after the Additive R had been reduced.

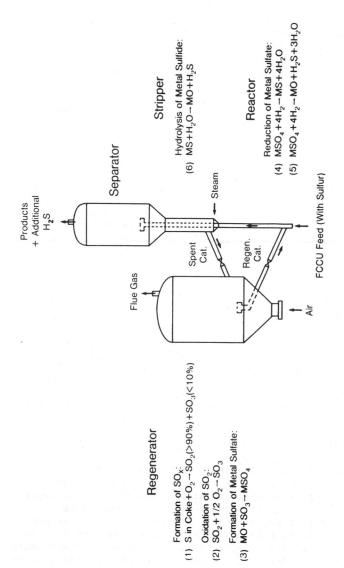

Figure 1.   Mechanism for catalytic reduction of SOx emissions.

The general reaction scheme, as applied to Additive R, is shown in Figure 2.

Capacity Required for a Viable SOx Additive

Let us consider the 50,000-barrels-a-day unit, referred to earlier. In order to meet the California South Coast Air Quality Management District regulation on SOx emissions, the unit requires a reduction in SOx emissions of 20 tons a day, expressed as SO_2 or 10 tons a day, expressed as elemental sulfur. The catalyst in that unit undergoes 100 cracking-stripping-regeneration cycles a day (catalyst circulation rate of 50,000 tons a day ÷ 500 tons per cycle = 100 cycles a day). In order to reduce emissions by 10 tons of sulfur a day, the SOx additive must, during each cycle, capture 0.1 ton of sulfur in the regenerator and release it in the reactor and stripper.

A preferred upper limit in the use of an SOx additive is about 10% SOx additive in the catalyst inventory. So for a case of 10% SOx additive (50 tons) in the catalyst inventory of the unit under consideration, the additive must capture and release 0.20% sulfur, based on the weight of the additive, during each cycle. For SOx additives with capacities greater than 0.20% sulfur per cycle, smaller amounts of the additives would be required in the inventory.

In commercial practice, for units with a variety of SOx reduction requirements, the amounts of SOx additive used have ranged from about 1% to about 10% of the catalyst inventory.

The Sulfur Captured Needs to be Released

Habib (4) has emphasized the importance of the sulfur-release step in the mechanism for SOx reduction. If a catalyst captures SOx but cannot release it, it soon becomes saturated and ineffective. For example, if CaO captured SOx until it was transformed to $CaSO_4$, it would capture 57% sulfur, based on the weight of the CaO. For the FCCU under consideration, 50 tons of CaO added to the 500-ton unit (10% additive) would capture 28.6 tons of sulfur. At a sulfur capture rate of 10 tons a day, the CaO would be effective for only 2.9 days. Since the average catalyst residence time in the unit is 100 days, use of such a material would not be practical.

Davison's Laboratory SOx Tests

Davison's primary test for the evaluation of catalysts for SOx reduction is the Davison SOx Index Test. In this test, the SOx catalyst or blend of cracking catalyst and SOx additive undergoes multiple gas oil cracking-stripping-regeneration cycles at conditions similar to those seen in commercial FCCU's. The SOx measurements made during this test are expressed as a Davison SOx Index at a given regenerator temperature. The greater the reduction in SOx emissions, the greater the Davison SOx Index of the catalyst at the given regenerator temperature.

Another test involves use of the Davison full-circulating riser pilot unit (8). This unit is utilized mainly for testing and evaluating the aging properties of the most promising catalyst formulations.

Prior to testing, the catalysts and additives are steam deactivated at 1350°F, 100% steam, 15 psig, for 8 hours. This is Davison's S-13.5 steam deactivation.

Oxidation catalysts are used in FCCU's to oxidize CO to CO$_2$ in the regenerator during the coke-burning step. These oxidation catalysts are called "combustion promoters". Usage in commercial units is about 0.5 pound to 8 pounds of combustion promoter per ton of cracking catalyst. The amount used depends on the degree of CO oxidation desired. Generally, 3 to 7 pounds of combustion promoter per ton of cracking catalyst will give essentially complete CO oxidation. Such units are said to be fully promoted with combustion promoter.

Our SOx test work was done with samples which were fully promoted with Davison CP-3 Combustion Promoter (7.4 pounds per ton of cracking catalyst, 0.37%). The only exception is the data in Table II which shows the effect of not using combustion promoter.

The Davison SOx Indices of S-13.5 steam-deactivated catalysts correlate fairly well with their performance in commercial units. This is seen in Figure 3. This correlation curve best applies to SOx emissions of about 800 ppm.

SOx Indices of Cracking Catalysts and Additive R
at a Regenerator Temperature of 1350°F

Davison's Super D cracking catalyst is assigned an SOx Index of zero. This cracking catalyst is used as a base case.

Another Davison cracking catalyst, called DA-250, has an SOx Index of 3 at a regenerator temperature of 1350°F. In a commercial unit, an SOx Index of 3 could mean a reduction in SOx emissions of about 10%, over a base-case catalyst with an SOx Index of zero.

The SOx Indices of blends of DA-250 and Additive R increase almost linearly with the amount of Additive R in the blend. The SOx Index, initially 3 without Additive R, increases to 86 for a blend containing 10% Additive R. This is seen in Table I along with the estimated SOx reductions for commercial units operating at a regenerator temperature of 1350°F.

Table I. Davison SOx Indices of Cracking Catalysts and Additive R at a Regenerator Temperature of 1350°F

Catalysts[a]	Davison SOx Index at Regen. Temp. of 1350°F	Possible % SOx Reduction from FCCU Regenerator Operating at 1350°F
Super D[b]	0	0
DA-250[b]	3	10±2
DA-250 + 2% R	18	40±5
DA-250 + 5% R	41	60±5
DA-250 + 10% R	86	85±10

a. Samples fully promoted with CP-3 (0.37%) and steam deactivated at 1350°F, 100% steam, 15 psig, 8 hrs.
b. A Davison fluid cracking catalyst.

Regenerator (1350°F)

$R + SO_x \rightarrow R\text{-}SO_x$

Reactor (980°F)   Sulfur Release

$R\text{-}SO_x + H_2 \rightarrow R + H_2S\uparrow + H_2O$ 85%

$R\text{-}SO_x + H_2 \rightarrow R\text{-}S + H_2O$

Steam Stripper (980°F)

$R\text{-}SO_x + H_2O \rightarrow$ No Sulfur Released

$R\text{-}S + H_2O \rightarrow R + H_2S\uparrow$ 15%

                                                   100%

Figure 2.   General reaction scheme for SOx reduction applied to
            Additive R.   Amount of sulfur released in reactor and
            steam stripper.

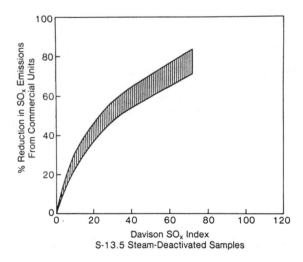

Figure 3.   Correlation of Davison SOx Index with commercial—unit
            results.

Effect of Regenerator Temperature

The Davison SOx Index of a catalyst decreases with increasing regenerator temperature. We have observed this for all the materials we have tested. These materials covered a variety of chemical compositions. This effect of temperature is believed to be due to the thermodynamic stability of the sulfate-type complex on the surface of the catalyst. Data are shown in Figure 4 for DA-250 + 10% Additive R.

Effect of Oxidation Activity

Davison CP-3 Combustion Promoter, by itself, has a very low SOx Index. At a 0.37% level in a catalyst blend, it contributes less than 0.3 of an SOx Index unit at regenerator temperatures of 1250°F to 1350°F. Its contribution to SOx reduction derives from its ability to catalyze the oxidation of SO$_2$ to SO$_3$ (Equation 2 in Figure 1).

Data on four SOx catalyst systems show that the presence of combustion promoter causes an increase in the SOx Index at a regenerator temperature of 1250°F (Table II). This implies that, without combustion promoter, the rate-controlling step in SOx reduction is the oxidation of SO$_2$ to SO$_3$ (Equation 2 in Figure 1). The use of combustion promoter increases the rate of oxidation of SO$_2$ to SO$_3$, thereby causing an increase in the SOx Index.

Table II.   Effect of Oxidation Activity on SOx Capability of
Catalysts at a Regenerator Temperature of 1250°F

| | Davison 1250°F SOx Index | |
	With Combustion Promoter[b]	Without Combustion Promoter
Catalyst[a]		
SOx Material A	138	98
SOx Material B	48	21
SOx Material C	28	13
SOx Material D	22	9

a. Samples steam deactivated at 1350°F, 100% steam, 15 psig, 8 hrs.
b. Samples contain 0.37% CP-3 Combustion Promoter.

It should be noted that the effectiveness of a combustion promoter decreases with increasing regenerator temperature. The reason is that the rate of oxidation of SO$_2$ to SO$_3$ increases with temperature, while the SOx adsorptive capacity of the SOx catalyst decreases. Therefore, at some temperature, the rate of oxidation of SO$_2$ to SO$_3$ is fast enough, without combustion promoter, to supply all the SO$_3$ which the SOx catalyst can accommodate. That temperature would vary for different SOx catalyst systems. For DA-250 + Additive R it is about 1425°F.

Effect of Oxygen Concentration

The oxygen concentration in a regenerator is generally referred to
in terms of "excess oxygen". "Excess oxygen" is the oxygen which is
not consumed in the regenerator, i.e., the oxygen in the regenerator
flue gas.

For an operation with essentially no excess oxygen (0.1% O_2),
the average oxygen concentration in the regenerator would be about
4% (estimated from the log mean of the inlet concentration of about
21% and the outlet concentration of 0.1%). Similarly, for an
operation with, say 3% excess oxygen, the average oxygen concentration in the regenerator would be about 10%.

Since the oxidation of SO_2 to SO_3 is a step in the operation of
SOx catalysts, an increase in oxygen concentration should favor the
reaction, and thereby increase the efficiency of SOx catalysts. The
evidence indicates that this occurs. Baron, Wu and Krenzke (9) have
shown that an increase in excess oxygen from 0.9% to 3.4% resulted
in a 20% reduction in SOx emissions. This was for a steam-
deactivated catalyst in a laboratory unit at 1345°F (no combustion
promoter).

Contaminant Metals

High-sulfur feedstocks can contain high levels of contaminant
metals, such as nickel and vanadium. SOx catalysts must be able to
perform in units which use such feedstocks.

We have found that Additive R has very good metals tolerance.
Laboratory metals-impregnation studies show that 5,000 ppm Ni + V
(33% Ni, 67% V) has no effect on the SOx reduction capability of
Additive R. At a higher metals level of 10,000 ppm Ni + V (33% Ni,
67% V), Additive R loses only 9% of its SOx reduction capability.
This is seen in Figure 5 for DA-250 + 10% Additive R + 0.37% CP-3.
In this study, the DA-250 and Additive R were impregnated with
metals; then CP-3 was added and the 3-component blend steam
deactivated at 1350°F, 100% steam, 15 psig, 8 hours.

Deactivation of Additive R

Deactivation of Additive R, during laboratory steaming of a blend of
cracking catalyst and Additive R, and during use in a commercial
unit, occurs by two mechanisms: loss of surface area and poisoning
by silica. These two mechanisms operate simultaneously. The silica
comes from the cracking catalyst. All cracking catalysts in use
today contain silica. In the presence of steam there is vapor phase
transport of silica from the cracking catalyst to Additive R. This
silica poisons the Additive R.

In the laboratory, the two deactivation mechanisms can be
separated by steaming the cracking catalyst and Additive R separately. In this case, there can be no transfer of silica from the
cracking catalyst to Additive R during the steaming. The Additive R
only loses surface area. The steamed components are then blended
together for SOx activity measurements.

The base cases for this study were samples steamed at 1350°F
(100% steam, 15 psig, 8 hours, fixed bed). They were compared with
samples steamed at 1500°F (100% steam, 0 psig, 5 hours, fluid bed).

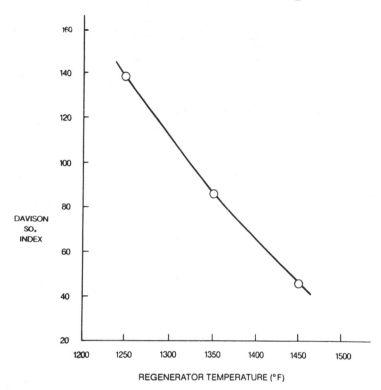

Figure 4.   Effect of regenerator temperature on the Davison SOx Index for a blend of DA-250 + 10% Additive R + 0.37% CP-3.   The blend was steam-deactivated at 1350°F, 100% steam, 15 psig, 8 hrs.

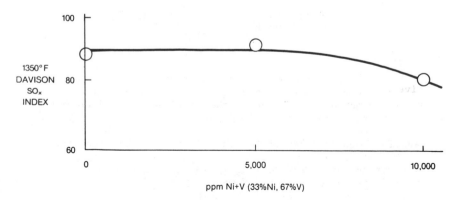

Figure 5.   Effect of contaminant metals on the SOx reduction capability of a blend of DA-250 + 10% Additive R + 0.37% CP-3.

The surface area of Additive R was 93 m^2/gm after the 1350°F
steaming and 83 m^2/gm after the 1500°F steaming. This 11% loss in
the surface area of Additive R caused a 23% loss in SOx activity
(blend components steamed separately, then blended).

　　The poisoning of Additive R by silica during the steam deactivation is seen by comparing the case of the blend components
steamed separately with the case of the blend components steamed
together. For the 1350°F steaming, silica poisoning caused a 45%
loss in SOx activity. For the 1500°F steaming, it caused an 18%
loss in SOx activity. The data are given in Table III.

Table III.　Deactivation of Additive R

Steaming Conditions	Surface Area of Additive R (m^2/gm)	Relative 1350°F SOx Index DA-250 + Additive R + CP-3		
		Blend Components Steamed Separately (Loss of Surface Area Only)	Blend Components Steamed Together (Loss of Surface Area and Poisoning by Silica)	
1350°F, 100% steam, 15 psig, 8 hrs, fixed bed	93	1.00	−45% ⟶	0.55
		↓ −23%		
1500°F, 100% steam, 0 psig, 5 hrs, fluid bed	83	0.77	−18% ⟶	0.63

　　The more severe poisoning by silica in the 1350°F steaming is
likely due to the higher steam pressure and fixed bed of the 1350°F
steaming versus the lower steam pressure and fluid bed of the 1500°F
steaming.

Evidence for the Transport of Silica from the
Cracking Catalyst to Additive R

Technique Used

The evidence was obtained by electron microprobe analysis of
Additive R. In this analysis a part of the Additive R particle is
sliced off, exposing the inside of the particle. The following
measurements are made on the sliced particle:

●　　An SEM photo is taken of the face of the sliced particle.

●　　The surface of this face is analyzed for silicon by obtaining
　　　what is called a silicon dot map. This technique analyzes the
　　　whole surface for silicon to a depth of one micron. The
　　　resulting photo shows the distribution of silicon on the face
　　　of the particle.

●　　The silicon concentration gradient across the face of the
　　　particle is also determined by doing what is called a

qualitative silicon line scan analysis. This technique
analyzes for silicon in a straight line (one micron wide and
one micron deep) across the face of the particle. The result
is expressed graphically.

Steam-Deactivated Samples

The blends of DA-250 + Additive R + CP-3 in Table III, steamed at
1350°F, were used for this study.

For the case in which the blend components were steamed separately, there was no evidence of silica on the Additive R.

For the case in which the blend components were steamed
together, the electron microprobe analyses showed the presence of
silica on Additive R. This means that silica was transported from
the cracking catalyst particles to the Additive R particles during
the steam deactivation. The amount of silica transported and the
distance the silica penetrated into the Additive R particles varied
from particle to particle. The silica penetration ranged from about
10 microns to complete penetration of an entire particle. The
amount of silica transported, expressed as the peak concentration
observed in the outer section of the particle, varied from about
0.5% to about 8% SiO$_2$ (estimates).

An example is shown in Figure 6. In this example, the silica
penetrated into the Additive R particle to a depth of about 16
microns. The peak silica concentration in this 16-micron layer is
estimated to vary from about 4% to 6% SiO$_2$.

Another example is shown in Figure 7 (silica line scan only).
In this example, some silica penetrated the entire particle. The
peak silica concentration in the outer layer is about 8% SiO$_2$. In
the middle of the particle, the silica concentration is about 1%
SiO$_2$.

Commercially-Aged Samples

Commercially-aged samples of Additive R, taken from two commercial
units, looked like the steamed sample. The silica penetration
varied from about 8 microns to complete penetration of the entire
particle. The amount of silica transported varied from about 1.5%
to about 14% SiO$_2$ (peak concentration in the particle).

An example is shown in Figure 8 (silica line scan only). For
this particle of Additive R, the silica penetrated to a depth of
about 10 microns. The peak silica concentration was about 6% SiO$_2$.

Another example is shown in Figure 9. In this case there was a
fairly uniform silica penetration through the entire particle. The
average silica concentration throughout the particle was about 8%
SiO$_2$.

These results on commercially-aged samples show that silica is
transported from the cracking catalyst particles to the Additive R
particles during commercial-unit aging, just as it is during a
laboratory steam deactivation. More importantly, the data show that
silica deactivates Additive R in a commercial unit (loss of SOx
capability) just as it does in a laboratory deactivation.

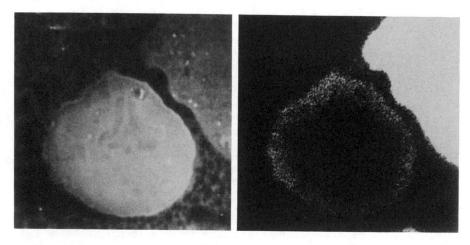

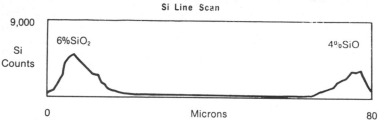

Figure 6.   Silica concentration and distribution in steam-
deactivated Additive R (Blend components steamed
together). Particle No. 1. Left, SEM photo and
right, Si map.

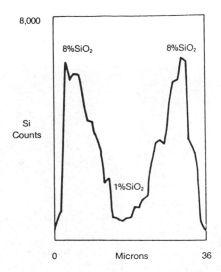

Figure 7.   Silica concentration and distribution in steam-
deactivated Additive R (Blend components steamed
together).   Particle No. 2.

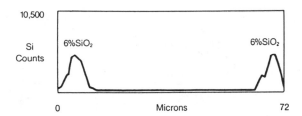

Figure 8.   Silica concentration and distribution in commercially-
aged Additive R.   Particle No. 1.

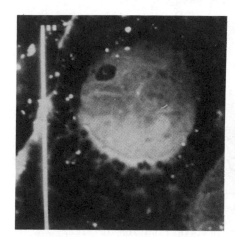 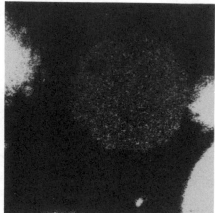

Si Line Scan

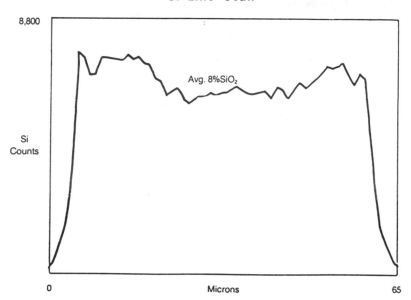

Figure 9.   Silica concentration and distribution in commercially
aged Additive R.   Particle No. 2.   Left, SEM photo
and right, Si map.

Other Evidence.

Our results on silica transfer from the cracking catalyst to
Additive R are similar to results reported by Byrne, Speronello and
Leuenberger (7) on an Engelhard SOx additive. They showed that
silica did transfer from the cracking catalyst to their SOx additive
during steaming and during use in a commercial unit, and that the
silica deactivated their SOx additive.

Conclusion

SOx emissions from FCCU's can be reduced by the use of SOx
catalysts, especially SOx additives which can be added to the FCCU
independently of the cracking catalyst. The effectiveness of these
catalysts is favored by lower regenerator temperatures, the presence
of combustion promoter, and higher oxygen concentrations.
Deactivation of these catalysts occurs by loss of surface area and
poisoning by silica. We believe that SOx additives will eventually
be used by most refiners to control SOx emissions from FCCU's,
either on a spot or continuous basis.

Literature Cited

1. Huling, G. P.; McKinney, J. D.; Readal, T. C.; Oil & Gas J.,
   May 19, 1975, p. 73.
2. Federal Register, Vol. 49, Nov. 11, Jan. 17, 1987, p. 2058.
3. Bertolacini, R.; Lehman, G.; Wollaston, E.; U.S. Patent
   3,835,031, Sept. 10, 1974.
4. Habib, E. T., Jr.; Oil & Gas J., Aug. 8, 1983, p. 111.
5. Vasalos, I. A.; Strong, E. R.; Hsieh, C. K. R.; D'Souza, G. J.;
   Oil & Gas J., June 27, 1988, p. 141.
6. McArthur, D. P.; Simpson, J. D.; Baron, K.; Oil & Gas J.,
   Feb. 23, 1981, p. 55.
7. Byrne, J. W.; Speronello, B. K.; Leuenberger, E. L.;
   Oil & Gas J., Oct. 15, 1984, p. 101.
8. Creighton, J. E.; Young, G. W.; Presented at 8th North American
   Meeting of the Catalysis Society, Philadelphia, PA, May 1983.
9. Baron, K.; Wu, A. H.; Krenzke, L. D.; In Preprints, American
   Chemical Society, Div. Pet. Chem. 1983, 28 (4), 934-43.

RECEIVED March 17, 1988

Chapter 10

Cracking Metal-Contaminated Oils with Catalysts Containing Metal Scavengers

Effects of Sepiolite Addition on Vanadium Passivation

Mario L. Occelli

Unocal Science & Technology Division, Unocal Corporation, P.O. Box 76, Brea, CA 92621

The addition of layered magnesium silicate particles such as sepiolite to a high activity commercial fluid cracking catalyst (FCC), generates dual-functional cracking catalyst (DFCC) mixtures that, even when metal contaminated with as much as 1.5 wt% vanadium, are capable of retaining useful cracking activity (70% conversion) when cracking a light gas oil (with an API gravity of 29.6) at microactivity test (MAT) conditions. Improved coke and hydrogen selectivity were also observed. Transport experiments have been used to show that the DFCC enhanced vanadium resistance can be attributed to the gas phase transport of this metal from the host catalyst to the diluent (sepiolite) where it is sorbed and passivated.

Recently, it has been reported in the patent literature that vanadium (and nickel) resistance in a FCC can be significantly enhanced by the addition of certain diluents capable of acting as metal scavengers (1-4). In fact, addition of alumina and alumina-containing materials with (1) or without (2) passivating agents (such as Sn or Sb) or addition of natural layered magnesium silicates (3) as well as addition of certain natural zeolites (4) can inhibit the deleterious effects that metal contaminants (like Ni and V) in gas oils have on the cracking activity and selectivity of commercial fluid cracking catalysts (FCC). The addition of metakaolin microspheres to improve a commercial catalyst resistance to metals poisoning has been proposed by Bartholic (5).

It is the purpose of this paper to report and explain the high resistance to metals deactivation of a dual-function cracking catalyst (DFCC) obtained by diluting a high activity cracking catalyst (Davison GRZ-1) with sepiolite granules 100 x 325 mesh in size. Sepiolite (and attapulgite) are fibrous clay minerals composed of tetrahedral chains of silica laying in planes joined together (through shared oxygens) by magnesium (and aluminum) atoms in octahedral coordination. Their structure has been described in details by Grim (6). These layered magnesium silicates could

0097–6156/88/0375–0162$06.00/0

passivate nickel contaminants by forming stable silicates (7) similar to garnierite. (Garnierite is a hydrous nickel-magnesium silicate similar to chrysotile with nickel in octahedral sites.) Vanadium passivation could result from the formation of heat stable vanadates (7).

Experimental

Materials and Gas Oil Cracking.   The reference catalyst used (Davison's GRZ-1) is a high-activity cracking catalyst containing about 35% calcined rare-earth exchanged zeolite Y (CREY). The 100 x 325 mesh granules of "Spanish Sepiolite" (from TOLSA, S.A.) used to study metals transport at hydrothermal conditions, have been found to contain a clay mineral characterized by a typical fibrous structure, high surface area (142 m^2/g), and pore volume (0.68 cc/g); its chemical composition is shown in Figure 1. This mineral was essentially free from phase impurities and gave an x-ray pattern in excellent agreement with JCPDS (Joint Committee on Powder Diffraction Standards) pattern No. 13-595, see Figure 1. After steaming (760°C/5h) this clay retained 70% of its original BET surface area and its pore volume remained essentially unchanged at ∿0.68 cc/g.

Catalytic evaluation was performed using a microactivity test (MAT) similar to the one described by Ciapetta and Anderson (8). The weight hourly space velocity (WHSV) was 14-15; the reactor temperature was 510°C. A catalyst-to-oil ratio of 3.5-3.8 was used. The chargestock's slurry oil (S.O., b.p. >354°C), light cycle gas oil (LCGO, 232°C < b.p. <354°C) and gasoline content was 62.7 vol%, 33.1 vol% and 4.2 vol% respectively; additional feed properties are given in Table I. Vanadium naphthenates (in benzene) were used to metal load the fresh catalysts according to an established procedure (9). Decomposition of the naphthenates was performed by heating for 10 hours at 540°C in air. All catalysts were steam-aged for 5 hours with ∿100% steam at 760°C.

Metals Transport Experiments. Metals transport was investigated by studying compositional changes in two DFCC mixtures: one containing 40 wt% Spanish sepiolite with 2 wt% vanadium and 60 wt% fresh FCC; the other was prepared by first placing the metal on the FCC surface and then by mixing the catalyst with 40 wt% fresh Spanish sepiolite granules. Schematics of the experiments are shown in Figures 2A-2B. Details of the reactor used are given in Figure 2C; the steamer was immersed into a 3-zone Lindberg furnace. After placing the DFCC mixture in the reactor, the catalyst was fluidized with nitrogen and the temperature raised to 760°C. Steam (10 cc H_2O/h) was then introduced and the nitrogen flow was gradually reduced until a ∿100% steam flow was obtained. Steam aging of the fluidized catalysts was then continued for 5 h.

Electron Microprobe Measurements.   Compositional   information regarding transport of nickel and vanadium in the catalysts uppermost 10,000A surface layers was obtained from electron microprobe analysis of the samples. Scanning electron micrographs and x-ray spectra were obtained with a JEOL 733 scanning electron

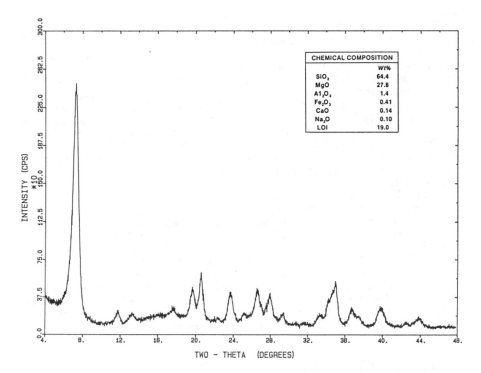

Figure 1.   X-ray diffractogram and chemical composition of the Spanish sepiolite (from TOLSA S.A.) used in this work.

TABLE I. CHARGESTOCK INSPECTIONS

Gravity, API	29.6
Sulfur, wt%	0.20
Nitrogen, wt%	0.017
Hydrogen, wt%	13.7
Conradson C, wt%	0.20
Aniline point, °C	88.8
Iron, ppm	0.9
Nickel, ppm	0.2
Copper, ppm	<0.1
Vanadium, ppm	<0.1
Saturates, wt%	70.0
Monoaromatics, wt%	13.5
Diaromatics, wt%	7.7
Triaromatics, wt%	1.9

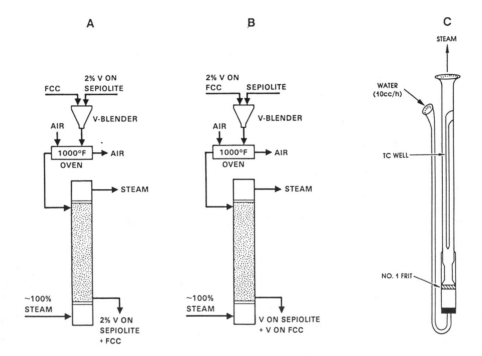

Figure 2. Schematics of the experiment used to investigate the transport of metals from: (A) the diluent to the host catalyst and (B) from the host catalyst to the diluent. The microreactor used to investigate metals transport under hydrothermal conditions is shown in (C).

microprobe with four wavelength spectrometers. In a previous paper (10), intraparticles transport of Ni and V was investigated using energy dispersive x-ray (EDAX) spectra measured with a Tracor-Northern TN-2000 system attached to the probe column. In this paper, spectra from the crystal spectrometer were instead obtained to improve energy resolution (approximately by a factor of 100), thus facilitating V detection in the presence of Ti. Micrographs were obtained at magnifications of 6000 X. Samples were prepared by sprinkling the catalyst onto a double-backed tape previously attached on one side to a standard SEM stub. Samples were then carbon-coated (in a vacuum evaporator) to provide sufficient electrical conductivity for performing analysis of the insulated samples. Typically, 5-10 particles were analyzed at random from the sample to ensure that representative spectra were measured. Cracking catalyst microspheres can be easily distinguished from sepiolite granules on the basis of particle morphology differences. In the spectra given, L is the detection position (that is, the distance between the x-ray generation source and the analyzing crystal) and is related to E (KeV), the x-ray photon energy, by the identity $E = 862.3/L$.

Results and Discussion

Metals Transport. Investigation of nickel and vanadium mobility under hydrothermal conditions was conducted by analyzing surfaces of the steamed materials by electron microprobe. This task was greatly facilitated by the different morphologies of the host catalyst and the metal scavenger (sepiolite). Scanning electron micrographs show that the cracking catalyst is composed of microspheroidal particles fairly uniform in size while the metal scavenger (sepiolite) consists mainly of granules irregular in size and shape. Probe analysis of two DFCC containing 2% vanadium alternatively on the host catalyst and on the diluent (sepiolite) indicate that heating in air at 540°C does not induce any significant migration of vanadium from particle to particle. However, when heating was performed in a fluidized bed in the presence of ~100% steam, vanadium migrates from the FCC to the sepiolite granules surface but not vice versa, see Figures 3A-3D. In fact, figures 3A and 3B show that after steaming (760°C/5h) a DFCC mixture composed of (2%) vanadium-loaded FCC microspheres and (metals-free) sepiolite granules, a substantial amount of vanadium migrates from the V-loaded FCC microspheres to the sepiolite surface. In contrast, when V is loaded only on the sepiolite, intraparticle transport of vanadium from the diluent to the host catalyst is negligible and only trace amounts of V can be observed on the FCC surface, see Figures 3C and 3D. In Figure 3A, diffraction lines for Ce, La and Pr result from the calcined rare-earth exchanged Y zeolite (CREY) contained in the FCC under study. In preparing CREY crystals, NH_4Y is repeatedly exchanged with solutions of rare earth chloride mixtures until the desired lanthanide level (15-20% Re_2O_3) is obtained. Diffraction lines for Ti are attributed to titanium dioxide, an impurity usually present (1.5-2.5% TiO_2) in kaolinite, another common component of commercial cracking catalysts.

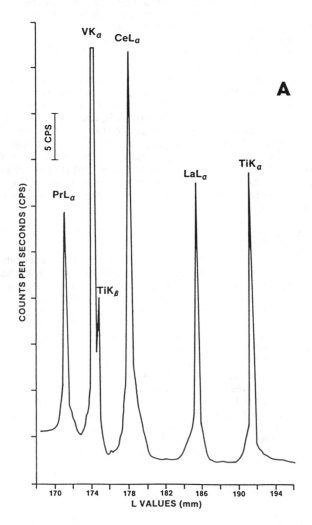

Figure 3A. Microprobe analysis of a DFCC system containing 2% V on the host catalyst. Continued.

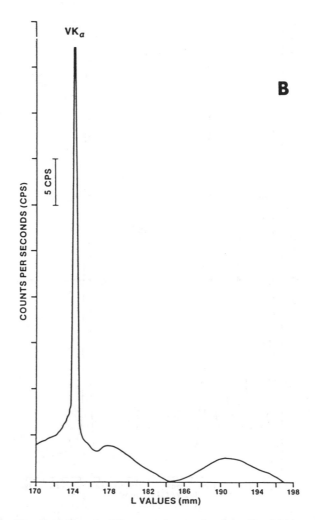

Figure 3B. Continued. Microprobe analysis of a DFCC system containing 2% V on the host catalyst. Steaming induced V migration to the sepiolite surface. Continued.

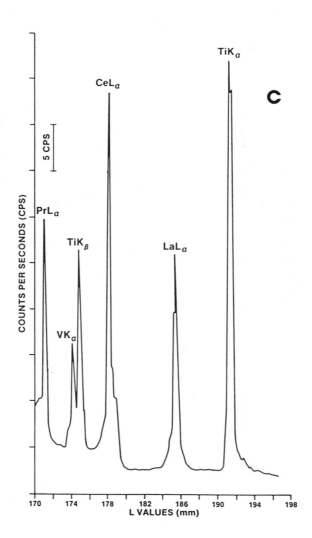

Figure 3C. Continued. When 2% V is placed on the sepiolite granules, intraparticle transfer of the metal to the FCC is minimal. Continued.

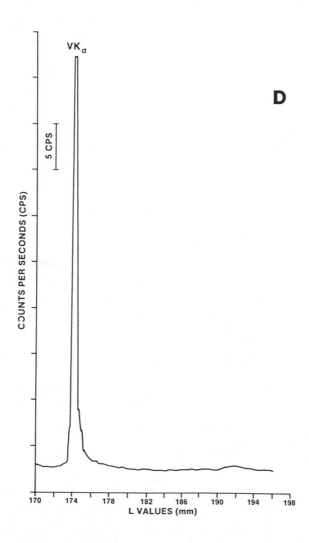

Figure 3D. Continued. Vanadium remains mostly on the sepiolite because of strong metal-surface interactions and vanadate formation.

Intraparticles V-transfer was also observed in DFCC mixtures containing 60% GRZ-1 and 40% metakaolin microspheres. Unlike sepiolite (or attapulgite) metakaolin cannot retain V, thus allowing the migration of this metal to the host catalyst during steaming. This, in part, explains the low cracking activity of V-contaminated DFCC systems containing Kaolin as metal scavenger (2,3).

Analysis of two nickel-containing DFCC revealed that neither heating in air or in steam induced intraparticle transfer of nickel at the thermal and hydrothermal conditions used to age the fresh catalysts (11) prior to microactivity testing.

Gas Oil Cracking. Dilution of commercially available FCC with low cost metals scavengers lowers catalyst costs while enhancing resistance to deactivation from metals contaminants (1,4). However, DFCC systems become advantageous only when a certain critical metal contaminants level is present in the feed. Figure 4 shows, qualitatively, the FCC decrease in cracking activity with increasing metals concentration levels on the catalyst surface. Metals scavenger addition to the cracking catalyst generates a DFCC mixture that initially (because of a dilution effect) is less active. However, the metal scavenger (in principle) selectively sorbs metals contaminants and, therefore, as the feed metal level increases, deactivation of the DFCC will occur at a much lesser rate than in the FCC. As a result, "cross-over point" is reached after which the diluted catalyst becomes more active than the host catalyst. Cross-over points will have to be determined experimentally; they represent DFCC properties which allow cracking of metals-contaminated feedstocks to occur in a cost effective manner. Gas oil composition, host catalyst initial activity and metals scavenger properties will determine cross-over points in a given FCCU operation.

At the MAT conditions used, this cross-over point occurs when the metal level on the catalyst is in the 0.25-0.50 wt% vanadium range, see Figure 5. Initially, after diluting the host FCC with 40% sepiolite, conversion and gasoline make decrease to 88% and 58% from 93% and 67% respectively. However, this DFCC mixture retains most of its useful cracking properties (70% conversion and 51% gasoline) even when loaded with as much as 1.5 wt% V. In contrast, GRZ-1 (that is, the undiluted host FCC) becomes essentially inactive in the presence of ∿1.0% V and almost twice as much vanadium is required to collapse the DFCC surface and catalytic properties, see Figure 5. The GRZ-1 deactivation rate shown in Figure 5 is somewhat greater than that reported in the literature (12) for this commercial catalyst probably because of the higher (760 vs 730°C) steam aging temperature (and other different MAT conditions) used in this study.

Feed composition effects on cross-over points were investigated by cracking a heavy gas oil (with API gravity of 23.7) containing 71% slurry oil. The high (34%) aromatics content of this feed is believed responsible for the greater coke make and increased deactivation rate of the host catalyst. As a result, a cross-over point below 0.25 wt% vanadium is obtained, see Figure 6. A loss of carbon selectivity is observed also in the DFCC mixture. In fact,

with 1% V, the coke/conversion ratio is 0.112, a value almost twice
as great as that observed when cracking the lighter oil in Table I
with the same V-loaded DFCC.

In general, the DFCC retention of cracking activity correlates
well with its retention of surface area (and pore volume) after
metal loading, calcination in air at 540°C/10h and steam aging (at
760°C for 5h), see Figure 7. The host catalyst's surface properties
are controlled by its high ($\sim$35%) zeolite content. Since vanadium
readily destroys a zeolite in an hydrothermal environment (760°C,
100% steam), it is not surprising that the commercial FCC stability
strongly depends on vanadium loadings (12). With 2% V, the surface
area of the steam-aged sepiolite decreased only to 71 m^2/g from 99.4
m^2/g in the metal-free aged clay. Thus, the addition of a metal
scavenger like sepiolite gives a DFCC mixture whose surface (and
catalytic) properties are less affected by vanadium levels, Figure
7. In fact, with 1.5% vanadium, GRZ-1, after steaming at 760°C/5h,
lost its surface area and cracking activity. In contrast, the DFCC
mixture retained 60% of its BET surface area and gas oil conversion
decreased only to $\sim$70% from 88.4%, Figure 5. The stable microporous
structure of the diluent is believed capable of interacting with
metals like vanadium, giving unreactive metal oxide compounds that
prevent (or limit) vanadium from migrating to the host catalyst (7).

Liquid product yields as a function of V-loading are shown in
Figures 8 and 9. The rapid decrease in gasoline make for vanadium
levels greater than 1.5% exhibited by GRZ-1 represent losses in
catalyst activity due to zeolite degradation. Sepiolite addition
prevents V from migrating to the host catalyst, thus preserving
cracking activity and gasoline yields; even after loading the DFCC
mixture with 1.5% V, a 51% gasoline make was obtained, Figure 8.
Selectivity plots in Figures 9 and 10 indicate that as
the catalysts activity increases (following reduction in V-levels),
the heavy fractions (SO and LCGO) are cracked to produce more
gasoline and light gases. Liquid products distribution (and light
gas make) change in a manner controlled by catalyst activity and not
by selectivity effects due to the presence of sepiolite granules.
However, the metal scavenger seems to affect the DFCC carbon and
hydrogen make.

In cracking catalysts (with or without V), plots of the
coke/conversion ratio vs conversion gives curves that monotonically
increase with cracking activity (13, 14), see Figure 11A. In
contrast, as the DFCC cracking activity monotonically decreases with
increasing V-levels, the carbon and hydrogen generation increased to
5.0 wt% and 430 SCF/BBL from 4.3 wt% and 87 SCF/BBL, respectively.
Thus, this V-loaded DFCC gives selectivity plots in which the
hydrogen make and the coke/conversion ratio decrease with
(increasing) conversion levels, Figures 10 and 11. In metals
resistant DFCC systems, carbon and hydrogen generation in the
V-range (0.0 to 2.0 wt%) investigated is controlled mainly by
V-levels and not by the catalyst activity. The steam-aged,
metal-free Spanish sepiolite shows little cracking activity (30%
conversion at 510°C). As the V-level is gradually increased to 2%,
conversion remains unchanged at 30% while the carbon and hydrogen
make of this metal scavenger increased to 4.6% and to 404 SCF/Bbl
from 1.4% and 138 SCF/Bbl, respectively. These results indicate

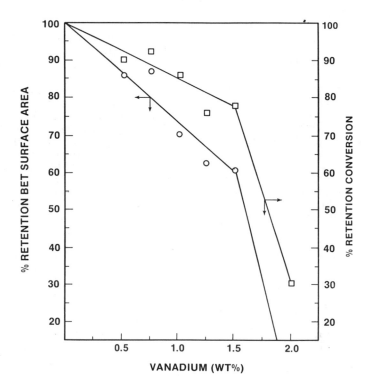

Figure 7.   Retention of surface area and conversion with
V-loadings.

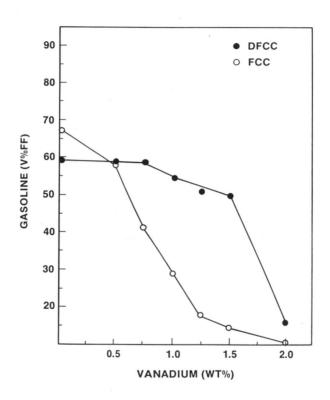

Figure 8.   Vanadium effects on gasoline make.

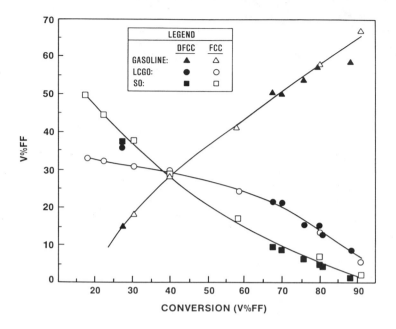

Figure 9. Liquid products selectivities.

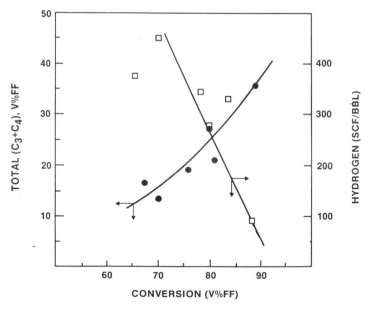

Figure 10. Total C_3 + C_4 and hydrogen generation as a function of
conversion in V-loaded DFCC mixtures containing sepiolite.

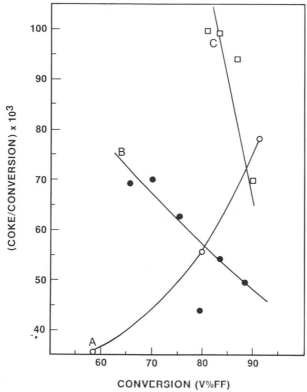

Figure 11. Carbon make in V-loaded FCC (A) before and after addition of a metal scavenger like (B) Spanish sepiolite and (C) alumina granules (11).

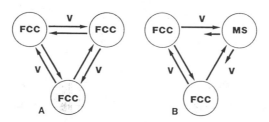

Figure 12. At the hydrothermal conditions used for catalyst regeneration, vanadium [probably as $H_4V_2O_7$ (7)] moves from FCC particle-to particle (A). In the presence of a metal scavenger (MS) like sepiolite, V is sorbed as a stable vanadate [like β-$Mg_2V_2O_7$ (7)] and prevented from migrating to the FCC surface thus preserving the catalyst cracking activity (B).

that V-loaded sepiolite may form strong dehydrogenation centers, thus converting into coke and hydrogen, components that could be upgraded to gasoline range hydrocarbons.

Similar results have been obtained with DFCC mixtures containing alumina-granules as metal scavengers (11). The higher carbon make observed when using alumina (see Figure 11) is attributed to this diluent strong Lewis acidity which favor the sorption of aromatics which are then retained as coke.

Summary and Conclusions

The high metals tolerance of a DFCC containing sepiolite as a metal scavenger can be explained in terms of retention of surface properties and by the ability of the clay to render metal contaminants inert by stable compound formation (7). Microprobe analysis has shown that at the hydrothermal conditions at which cracking catalysts are tested, vanadium can migrate from a DFCC's host particle and when it reaches the metal scavenger, it is trapped on the sepiolite surface, Figure 12, probably as a stable vanadate (7). Nickel, in contrast, does not migrate and remains on the catalyst surface where it can either form an inert nickel-silicate-like phase or, if free, act as a dehydrogenation center (13).

DFCC systems appear to have the necessary metals tolerance to process residual oils and the abundant, cheaper, but heavily vanadium-contaminated, Venezuelan and Mexican crudes (1-4). Therefore, the dual function fluid cracking catalyst (DFCC) concept could lead to the generation of important catalysts for U.S. refineries should Middle East politics cause another sudden escalation in crude oil prices and availability. The concept is practical and easily implementable and it may offer a cost advantage over conventional commercial cracking catalysts.

Acknowledgments

Special thanks are due to Dr. E. Goldish and Mr. M. Bell (Unocal) for providing x-ray data and electron microprobe measurements. Finally, we thank TOLSA S.A. for providing the sepiolite sample used in this study.

Literature Cited

1.   Occelli, M. L. and Swift, H. E., U.S. Patent No, 4,466,884 (1984).
2.   Occelli, M. L. and Kennedy, J. V., U.S. Patent No. 4,650,564 (1987).
3.   Occelli, M. L. and Kennedy, J. V., U.S. Patent No. 4,465,588 (1984).
4.   Occelli, M. L., U.S. Patent No. 4,615,996 (1986).
5.   Bartholic, D. B., U.S. Patent No. 4,289,605 (1981).
6.   Grim, R. E., "Clay Mineralogy," McGraw-Hill, New York, NY (1968).

7. Occelli, M. L. and Stencel, J. M. in Preprints "Advances in FCC" Symposium, National ACS Meeting, New Orleans, LA, 1987, submitted.
8. Ciapetta, F. G. and Anderson, D., Oil and Gas J., 65, 88 (1967).
9. Mitchell, B. R., Ind. Eng. Chem. Prod. Res. Dev. 19, 209 (1980).
10. Occelli, M. L. in Preprints "Advances in FCC" Symposium, National ACS Meeting, New Orleans, LA 1987, submitted.
11. Occelli, M. L. and Stencel, J. M., "Cracking Metals-Contaminated Oils with Catalysts Containing Metal Scavengers. Part II. The Effect of Aluminuma Particles Addition on Vanadium Passivation." (In preparation)
12. Occelli, M. L., Psaras, D. and Suib, S. L., J. Catal., 96, 363 (1985).
13. Cimbalo, R. N., Foster, R. L., and Wachtel, S. J., "Symposium on New Developments in FCC;" 37th Meething of the API's Division of Refining; Preprint No. 87-72, New York, NY (1972).
14. Occelli, M. L., Kowalczyk, D. C., and Kibby, C. L., Appl. Catal. 16,227 (1985).
15. Occelli, M. L. and Stencel, J. M., "Surface-metals Interactions in Fluid Cracking Catalysts During the Upgrading of Nickel Contaminated Gas Oils," 9th Int. Congr. Catalysis, Calgary, Canada (1988), accepted.

RECEIVED February 25, 1988

Chapter 11

Effects of Ni and V in Catalysts on Contaminant Coke and Hydrogen Yields

Paul F. Schubert[1] and Carol A. Altomare

Engelhard Corporation, Edison, NJ 08818

During cracking, low levels (<5000 ppm) of nickel on cracking catalysts have generally been found to make two to five times as much contaminant coke as vanadium, with the relative effect of nickel decreasing with higher loadings. However, the catalyst properties that affect contaminant coke and hydrogen have not been well established. The dehydrogenation and dehydrocyclization activity of nickel and vanadium are highly dependent on catalyst characteristics. For certain types of impregnated non-zeolitic particles, in microactivity tests (MAT), nickel is much less active than on particles containing zeolite, and surprisingly, vanadium produces more coke and hydrogen than nickel. On particles containing zeolite, the results of this study were consistent with earlier work showing nickel to be more active than vanadium. The relative contributions of each of these metals were greatly reduced by changing the chemical composition of the non-zeolitic catalyst constituent.

The effects of nickel and vanadium on cracking catalysts have long been known. These metals act as dehydrogenation/ dehydrocyclization catalysts, leading to the generation of hydrogen and coke (1). Nickel has generally been reported to be more active than vanadium for dehydrogenation and dehydrocyclization, producing from two to five times more coke and hydrogen than vanadium (2). Furthermore, the relative effect of nickel decreases as the level of the contaminant metals increases. In addition to producing coke and hydrogen like nickel, vanadium has also been reported to destructively react with a zeolite, accelerating catalyst deactivation (3).

[1]Current address: Phillips Research Center, Bartlesville, OK 74003

This work has taken advantage of the recent development of extremely high activity cracking components (4) (high zeolite level) to examine contaminant metals effects on both zeolitic and non-zeolitic particles at reasonable cat-to-oil and conversion levels. Specifically, it has focused on understanding the activity and selectivity of the metals present on different catalyst structures with varying chemical compositions in both multicomponent systems (containing both zeolitic and non-zeolitic particles) and integrated zeolite-matrix particles. Work in dual component systems to study the effects of nickel and vanadium has been previously undertaken (5,6). However, with the use of very high activity cracking components, catalyst systems composed almost exclusively of inactive, non-zeolitic particles could be studied. In general, our results indicate that zeolite enhances the dehydrogenation and dehydrocyclization activity of nickel on active catalyst particles. Furthermore, on non-zeolitic particles of relatively low silica content, vanadium is more active than nickel toward these secondary cracking reactions. Therefore, it should be advantageous to concentrate the metals on non-zeolitic particles not only to minimize the activity loss resulting from vanadium attack on the zeolite, but also to minimize the selectivity effects of the contaminant metals. Thus, catalysts which consist of a mixture of high activity particles (i.e., high zeolite content) with vanadium immobilizing particles having no zeolite would be desirable (5,6).

Experimental

Catalyst Preparation. For most of the experiments conducted in this study, nickel or vanadium impregnated non-zeolitic particles were blended with metals-free high activity cracking component. This allowed us to examine the effects of the metals on the non-zeolitic component. The high activity zeolitic particles were prepared by in-situ zeolite synthesis on kaolin-based microspheres (4,7).

Non-zeolitic silica-alumina particles of >10 m^2/g surface area were prepared by steaming commercial FCC catalysts until no zeolite was detected by X-ray diffraction (100% steam, 1600°F, typically 4 hours).

Non-zeolitic, low matrix surface area (<10 m^2/g) silica-alumina particles were prepared to test the effects of catalyst composition at constant surface area and silica to alumina ratio ($SiO_2/Al_2O_3 = 1.15$). Unpromoted silica-alumina particles were prepared by spray drying kaolin followed by calcination for 1 hour at 1800°F. Rare earths were added to these unpromoted particles by incipient wetness impregnation with mixed rare earth nitrates to obtain approximately 4.3% rare earth oxides on the final particles. Following impregnation the particles were dried at 250°F for 16 hours, and then calcined for one hour at 1100°F. Microspheres containing magnesium (19.5% MgO) were prepared by adding magnesium compounds to the kaolin slurry prior to spray drying. These were then processed in the same manner as the unpromoted microspheres. To eliminate the influence of the steam treatment used to destroy the zeolite in the higher surface area non-zeolitic particles, all low surface area microspheres were also given a final steam treatment for 4 hours at 1600°F prior to further testing.

Catalysts were contaminated with nickel and vanadium according to the method of Mitchell (8), using metal naphthenates. Prior to blending, all contaminated materials were steamed (1450°F, 4 hrs, 90% steam, 10% air) to age the metals. The selectivity effects of the metals on the non-zeolitic component were determined by blending impregnated non-zeolitic components with 20% of the steamed, uncontaminated high activity zeolitic component such that the overall blend yielded 70% conversion.

To show the effect of having zeolite present in the contaminated particles, a REY commercial cracking catalyst with a matrix surface area of ca. 85 m^2/g was also contaminated with nickel and vanadium, and steamed (1450°F, 4 hrs, 90% steam, 10% air) to age the metals. Its selectivities were compared to the non-zeolitic additive having the same surface area and chemical composition blended with sufficient metals-free active cracking component to give the same conversion.

Catalytic evaluations were conducted using microactivity tests (MAT) (4) at 910°F initial temperature, 15 WHSV, 6.0 g catalyst, and a 5.0 cat-to-oil ratio. The feedstock was a metals-free mid-continent gas oil. Each data point shown is the average of two MAT runs. Only MAT runs with acceptable mass balance were used (96 to 101%). Additionally, MAT data was normalized to 100% mass balance. Extensive error analysis of conversion, coke, and hydrogen yields indicates the following respective standard deviations: 1.62, 0.29, 0.025. The effects of nickel and vanadium on the hydrogen and coke make were calculated by obtaining the difference between the yields obtained with uncontaminated catalysts and that of the contaminated catalyst at the same conversion.

Temperature Programmed Reduction. To determine whether impregnated nickel reduces more readily on zeolitic particles than on non-zeolitic particles, Temperature Programmed Reduction (TPR) experiments of nickel on zeolitic and non-zeolitic particles were carried out. In order to emphasize any differences in the nickel reducibility due to the presence of zeolite, a high zeolite containing material and a low matrix surface area, non-zeolitic material were compared. Prior to running the TPR, the samples were impregnated with nickel naphthenates as previously described, and then steamed (1450°F, 4 hours, 90% steam, 10% air). The final nickel concentrations on the zeolitic and non-zeolitic samples were 10,860 and 10,100 ppm respectively. Attempts at obtaining TPR results at nickel levels of 1000 to 4000 ppm as used in the catalytic portions of this study were unsuccessful. Samples tested were pretreated by calcining at 500°C for 30 minutes. In running the TPR, a 10% hydrogen in argon gas mixture was passed through the samples at a rate of 20 ml/min. The heating rate was 10°C/minute. Hydrogen consumption was measured.

Hydrocarbon Adsorption. Hydrocarbon adsorption experiments were carried out to determine the effect of the zeolite's acid sites on the activity of nickel. Hexane and 1-hexene adsorption on uncontaminated and nickel contaminated zeolitic and non-zeolitic components were studied at nickel levels from 1000 to 10,000 ppm. Henry's Law coefficients and initial heats of adsorption were determined by a gas chromatographic technique employing the test samples as the effective packing in four inch gas chromatographic columns. Samples were activated in the column at 425°C and studied over the range of 150 to 425°C. The Henry's Law constant was taken as an indication of the adsorptivity of test molecules towards the nickel contaminated catalyst particles when compared to the same quantities for their metals-free equivalents.

Results

Our initial experiments on contaminant selectivities were designed to compare the effects of nickel and vanadium. Comparison at equal metals levels (e.g. 2000 ppm) would allow determination of the effects of catalyst parameters on the individual metals. However, in catalytic cracking of heavy crudes, equal levels of metals are not deposited, and the concentration of vanadium on catalyst particles is typically 1.5 to 2 times that of nickel (9). Thus, determination of the relative contributions of these metals to the selectivity of actual catalysts requires comparing them at realistic, but unequal metals levels (e.g. 2000 ppm Ni vs 4000 ppm V or 1000 ppm Ni vs 2000 ppm V). It has generally been quite difficult to make these comparisons due to the propensity of vanadium to migrate from one particle to another, while nickel generally remains on the particle it is deposited on (6). Furthermore, zeolite destruction due to vanadium makes comparisons at both equal activity and equal metals level quite difficult. By blending presteamed components to constant activity (70% conversion), and varying which components were metals impregnated, we were able to overcome some of these difficulties.

Our current work on non-zeolitic particles shows that the contaminant coke and hydrogen yields due to both nickel and vanadium increase with increasing matrix surface area at constant conversion (70%) as shown in Figure 1. It is interesting to note that above 25 m^2/g, there is little, if any, effect of surface area on contaminant yields due to nickel. Surprisingly, on the non-zeolitic, relatively low-silica content particles in this study, Ni was consistently less active than vanadium at equal metals levels over the entire range of surface area tested (5 to 140 m^2/g). However, the matrix composition may significantly alter both the magnitude of the coke and hydrogen yields due to nickel and vanadium, and the contribution of nickel relative to vanadium.

At very low surface areas (about 5 m^2/g) and constant conversion (70%), the contaminant selectivities are dominated by the matrix composition (Table I). Rare earth and magnesium-containing microspheres were prepared to examine the effects of these metal oxides on catalyst selectivities in the presence of nickel and vanadium. These oxides were chosen because the literature (3,5,10-15) has shown them to be effective at reducing the deleterious effects of vanadium in cracking catalysts.

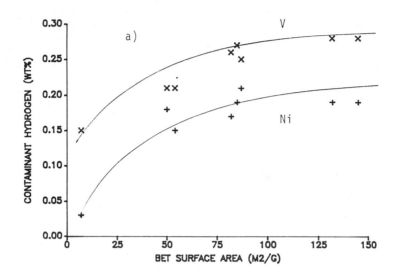

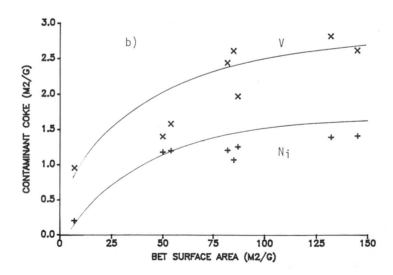

Figure 1. Contaminant hydrogen (a) and contaminant coke (b)
yields as weight percent of feed from non-zeolitic particles:
2000 ppm Ni (+); 2000 ppm V (x), at constant conversion (70%).

Although non-equivalent metal oxide levels were tested, approximately 5% rare earth oxide and 20% magnesium oxide give essentially equivalent levels of vanadium migration off non-zeolitic particles of this composition (Schubert, P. F.; Altomare, C. A.; Koermer, G. S., Engelhard Corporation; Willis, W. S.; Suib, S. L., University of Connecticut, manuscript in preparation). Additional work has shown that increasing the rare earth level does not substantially improve the contaminant vanadium effects (Martins, E., Engelhard Corporation, unpublished data). Furthermore, neither of these metal oxides significantly affect the nickel selectivity. At these low surface areas, nickel contributes very little to the contaminant coke and hydrogen yields, while vanadium shows significant variability in its contribution depending on the matrix. At 2000 ppm nickel, the contaminant coke and hydrogen yields were equal to or less than 0.4% and 0.06% respectively for all of the matrices studied. On the unpromoted matrix at 2000 ppm vanadium, contaminant hydrogen yields were significantly higher than the nickel yields, and contaminant coke was nearly five times as high. In contrast, on the magnesium promoted matrix, 2000 ppm vanadium made essentially no contaminant hydrogen, and less contaminant coke than the same level of nickel.

Table I.   Effect of Matrix Composition on the
Contaminant Selectivity Yields of
Low Surface Area Non-Zeolitic Materials

	SiO_2-Al_2O_3	5% REO on SiO_2-Al_2O_3	20% MgO in SiO_2-Al_2O_3
SiO_2 (wt%)	52.3	50.1	40.6
Al_2O_3 (wt%)	45.1	43.2	36.1
Rare Earth Oxides (wt%)	0.0	4.3	0.0
MgO (wt%)	0.0	0.0	19.5
Surface Area	5	6	8
Contaminant Hydrogen Yields (wt% of feed)			
1000 ppm Ni	0.04	--	0.01
2000 ppm Ni	0.06	0.04	0.04
2000 ppm V	0.15	0.07	0.00
4000 ppm V	0.24	0.17	0.02
Contaminant Coke Yields (wt% of feed)			
1000 ppm Ni	0.04	--	0.01
2000 ppm Ni	0.20	0.40	0.39
2000 ppm V	0.96	0.35	0.15
4000 ppm V	1.25	1.44	0.60

Contaminant selectivity yields measured at 70% conversion
SiO_2/Al_2O_3 equals 1.15

The data shown in Table II show interactions between matrix surface area and chemical composition at constant conversion. As expected, the increased matrix surface area of Matrix C caused increased coke and hydrogen yields compared to the lower surface area Matrix B, at constant silica content. However, the very low surface area of Matrix A does not compensate for the poorer selectivity due to its lower silica content relative to Matrices B and C.

Table II. Effect of Matrix Composition and Surface Area
on Contaminant Selectivity Yields of
Non-Zeolitic Silica-Aluminas

	Matrix Comp SiO_2/Al_2O_3	Surface Area (m^2/g)	V Effects		Ni Effects	
			Cont Coke[1] (wt%)	Cont H_2[1] (wt%)	Cont Coke[1] (wt%)	Cont H_2[1] (wt%)
A	Mod $SiO_2=52\%$	5	0.5	0.08	0.2	0.05
B	High $SiO_2=60\%$	10	0.3	0.04	0.1	0.04
C	High $SiO_2=60\%$	25	0.3	0.07	0.4	0.07
D	Low $SiO_2=42\%$	85	1.1	0.15	0.6	0.10

[1] Contaminant selectivity effect per 1000 ppm metal
Contaminant selectivity yields measured at 70% conversion

The effect of the presence of zeolites on the relative contaminant selectivity yields due to nickel and vanadium was studied using a low silica content (42% SiO_2) silica-alumina with about 85 m^2/g surface area (see Table III). Since the contaminated non-zeolitic particles constituted only 80% of the catalyst blend, the contaminant selectivity yields for these materials were divided by 0.8 to estimate coke and hydrogen yields. While this methodology may not give completely accurate results, we believe that the relative comparisons will be reasonable and useful. The data clearly show that at constant conversion (70%), both contaminant coke and contaminant hydrogen due to nickel are greater on zeolitic than non-zeolitic particles of relatively low silica content. However, at 4000 ppm vanadium, the presence or absence of zeolite does not affect the contaminant selectivity yields. Thus, the activity of nickel, but not vanadium, for dehydrogenation and dehydrocyclization is enhanced due to the presence of zeolites in the same particle.

Table III. Effect of the Presence of Zeolite on
Contaminant Selectivity Yields

	Particle Type	
	Zeolitic	Non-Zeolitic
Nickel Effect (2000 ppm)		
Contaminant Coke (wt% of feed)	2.3	1.2
Contaminant H_2 (wt % of feed)	0.34	0.19
Vanadium Effect (4000 ppm V)		
Contaminant Coke (wt% of feed)	3.6	3.8
Contaminant H_2 (wt % of feed)	0.52	0.52

Contaminant selectivity yields at 70% conversion

The TPR comparison (Figure 2) shows that nickel on non-zeolitic particles reduces at a lower temperature than nickel on zeolitic particles. The peak at 591.3°C in the TPR for the zeolitic sample is believed to be due to the reduction of cerium.
Hydrocarbon adsorption experiments show significant differences between the nickel contaminated zeolitic and non-zeolitic particles at metals levels comparable to those of the catalytic experiments. Neither hexane nor 1-hexene showed any interaction with nickel on the low surface area, non-zeolitic particles (the unpromoted material of Table I) at temperatures up to 425°C. Additionally, no interaction between hexene and the nickel on the zeolitic particles was observed over the temperature range studied. However, the nickel on the zeolitic component did cause significant retention of hexane at temperatures as low as 200°C with generation of what appeared to be higher molecular weight products. No cracking products were observed. With the uncontaminated zeolitic particles, hexane retention only occurred at temperatures above 300°C. Thus, the lower temperature retention for the contaminated particles appears to be due to the presence of nickel.

Discussion

We have found that the activity of nickel towards dehydrogenation and dehydrocyclization is increased on particles which contain zeolites relative to non-zeolitic particles of the same matrix composition and surface area. However, the coke and hydrogen making capability of vanadium does not depend on the presence or absence of zeolite. The increase in hydrogen and coke production by nickel when the zeolite is present in the matrix suggests that the zeolite increases the metal activity in catalyzing secondary

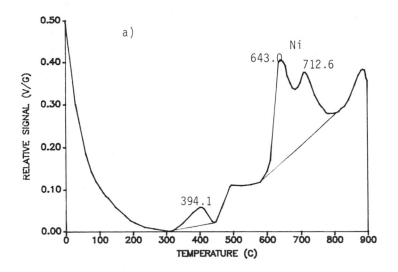

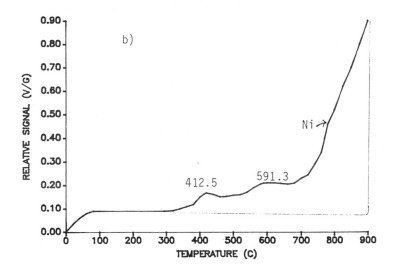

Figure 2. Temperature Programmed Reduction of Ni contaminated
catalyst components: a) non-zeolitic particles with 10,100 ppm
Ni; b) zeolitic particles with 10,860 ppm Ni. These materials
were impregnated using nickel naphthenate and then steamed
(1450°F, 4 hrs, 90% steam, 10% air) prior to running the TPR.
The Ni on the non-zeolitic particles reduced at a lower
temperature than that on the zeolitic particles.

cracking reactions. Several possible explanations for the source
of this activity enhancement for nickel are apparent. First, the
zeolite could represent a physical barrier to nickel migration,
thus enhancing the metal dispersion. Alternatively, the zeolite
could possibly facilitate reduction of nickel oxides to the more
active nickel metal. This could greatly increase contaminant coke
and hydrogen yields due to the increased contact time between the
hydrocarbons in the feed and the reduced nickel. A third
possibility is that the activity enhancement involves the
proximity of the metal sites to the zeolite's acid sites (16).
This might alter the electric field of the metal or that
experienced by the incoming hydrocarbon, leading to enhanced
dehydrogenation on the metal site, and cyclization on the nearby
acid sites. Neither of the first two routes would be expected to
increase the activity associated with vanadium, since vanadium is
much more mobile than nickel, and appears to remain as V^{5+} in
these systems (Schubert, P. F.; Altomare, C. A.; Koermer, G. S.,
Engelhard Corporation; Willis, W. S.; Suib, S. L., University of
Connecticut, manuscript in preparation). While vanadium might be
expected to be affected by proximity to the zeolite, this effect
could be masked by the destruction of the zeolite.

The second of these hypotheses (more facile reduction of
nickel on zeolitic particles) is contradicted by the results of
our TPR experiments. In fact, the TPR results on both nickel
contaminated zeolitic and non-zeolitic particles suggest that none
of the nickel on these materials is reduced under normal MAT
testing conditions, since the onset temperature of nickel
reduction (1100-1150°F) is considerably higher than the operating
temperature of the MAT (910°F).

Our third hypothesis, i.e., that the activity enhancement
involves the proximity of the zeolite's acid sites, appears to be
consistent with the hydrocarbon adsorption experiments, but may
also be due to differences in the nickel dispersion arising from
surface area differences between the two types of particles.
Clearly, the adsorption of hexane at lower temperature on the
nickel contaminated zeolitic particles suggests a significantly
altered environment from both the uncontaminated and the non-
zeolitic materials.

On the relatively low silica non-zeolitic particles studied
at length, vanadium had higher coke and hydrogen producing
tendencies than nickel at 70% conversion. The higher
dehydrogenation/dehydrocyclization activity for vanadium relative
to nickel on non-zeolitic particles for both coke and hydrogen
formation was surprising, given the higher activity of nickel
reportedly found when present on early amorphous silica-alumina
cracking catalysts (17,18). It was expected that the
dehydrogenation and dehydrocyclization activity of both nickel and
vanadium would increase with increasing surface area, evidenced by
an increase in coke and hydrogen production. While at very low
surface areas poor dispersion of nickel could account for its low
activity, we expected that, as the surface area was increased and
the dispersion of nickel improved, dehydrogenation and
dehydrocyclization activity would surpass that of vanadium.

However, even at higher surface areas the nickel showed no increase in relative activity compared to vanadium.

At essentially constant surface area and conversion, the chemical composition of the non-zeolitic particles determines the coke and hydrogen making capability of the two metals. By introducing materials into the matrix which interact with the contaminant metals, the nickel and vanadium contributions can be significantly altered. Both rare earth (19) and magnesium compounds (5) are known to reduce zeolite destruction by immobilizing vanadium. Other work (Schubert, P. F.; Altomare, C. A.; Koermer, G. S., Engelhard Corporation; Willis, W. S.; Suib, S. L., University of Connecticut, manuscript in preparation) has shown that at about 4.5% rare earth and 20% magnesium oxide, essentially equal levels of vanadium immobilization are achieved. However, in spite of this equivalent effect on mobility, there is considerable difference in their effect on selectivity. Thus, the mechanisms affecting vanadium's migration and dehydrogenation and dehydrocyclization activity are not necessarily the same. Rare earth at 4.3% causes a 30–50% reduction in the contaminant hydrogen yield, while magnesium oxide addition at 19.5% results in nearly complete quenching of vanadium induced dehydrogenation, and a substantial reduction in coke production. Further addition of rare earth does not significantly alter the level of vanadium migration, nor the selectivity at constant metals levels (Martins, E., Engelhard Corporation, unpublished data).

These immobilizers were present in low surface area matrices. Matrix composition can also overcome surface area effects. High silica content silica-aluminas generally produce less contaminant coke and hydrogen than lower silica content silica-alumina matrices of the same surface area, since silica-rich surfaces favor nickel sintering while alumina-rich surfaces favor nickel dispersion (16). Our results indicate that a high silica content silica-alumina had as good or better contaminant coke and hydrogen selectivities than a lower silica content silica-alumina having one-fifth of its matrix surface area. However, these matrices which reduce the detrimental activity of these metals toward coke and hydrogen production may not be as resistant to vanadium attack of the zeolite as those that contain more alumina (14). It is, therefore, not necessarily desirable to use high silica content matrix catalysts when cracking gas oils that contain both nickel and vanadium.

Conclusions

The results of this work suggest that the greatest contaminant metals effects are due not only to the most recently deposited metals, but to those recently deposited metals which are present on the most recently added zeolitic particles (i.e., those containing the most zeolite). At constant metals aging then, the contaminant selectivities due to nickel and vanadium are in a large part determined by: 1) the presence or absence of zeolite in the particle; 2) the non-zeolitic surface area of the particle; and 3) the chemical composition of the particle.

On non-zeolitic particles in the absence of a vanadium passivator, vanadium (when present at the 0.4 wt% level) makes a greater contribution to contaminant coke and hydrogen yields than nickel at constant surface area and metals loading. Incorporation of a vanadium passivator into the catalyst matrix can greatly alter the selectivity effects of vanadium, and can essentially negate its effect on non-zeolitic particles as in the case of magnesium.

Matrix composition can also overcome surface area effects. A high silica matrix of moderate surface area was found to have essentially the same contaminant selectivities as a moderate silica matrix having only very low surface area.

The presence of zeolite in the particle greatly enhances the activity of nickel towards dehydrogenation and dehydrocyclization, and causes it to become more active than vanadium. Therefore, it is advantageous to concentrate the metals on non-zeolitic particles not only to minimize the activity loss resulting from vanadium attack on the zeolite, but also to minimize the selectivity effects of the contaminant metals. Thus, catalysts consisting of high activity particles (i.e., high zeolite) mixed with particles having no zeolite should help in limiting the deleterious effects of the metals.

Acknowledgements

The authors wish to acknowledge the invaluable assistance of S. M. Kuznicki who conducted the hydrocarbon adsorption experiments, D. R. Anderson who ran and assisted in the interpretation of the TPR, and H. Furbeck who prepared the many samples tested.

Literature Cited

1. Parks, G. D., et al.; "Surface Studies of the Interaction of Nickel...," Symposium of the Petrol. Div. of the ACS, Houston March, 1980, p. 334.
2. Cimbalo, R. N., et al. Oil and Gas J. 1972, 70, (2), 112.
3. Jaras, S. Appl. Catal. 1982, 2, 207.
4. Brown, S. M.; Durante, V. A.; Reagan, W. J.; Speronello, B. K. U.S. Patent 4 493 902, 1985.
5. Occelli, M. L.; Kennedy, J. V. U.S. Patent 4 465 588, 1984.
6. Occelli, M. L.; Swift, H. E. U.S. Patent 4 466 884, 1984.
7. Haden, W. L.; Dzierzanowski, F. J. U.S. Patent 3 657 154, 1972.
8. Mitchell, B. R. Ind. Eng. Chem, Prod. Res. Dev. 1980, 19, 209–213.
9. Speronello, B. K., Reagan, W. J. Oil Gas J. 1984, 139.
10. Ritter, R. E.; Rheume, L.; Welsh, W. A.; Magee, J. S. Oil Gas J. 1981, 103.
11. Wormsbecher, R. F.; Peters, A. W.; Maselli, J. M. J. Catal. 1986, 100, 130–137.
12. Pompe, R.; Jaras, S.; Vannerberg, N. Appl. Catal. 1984, 13, 171–179.
13. Occelli, et al. U.S. Patent 4 466 886, 1984.
14. Occelli, et al. U.S. Patent 4 650 564, 1987.

15. Occelli, et al. U.S. Patent 4 615 996, 1986.
16. Occelli, M. L.; et al. J. Catal. 1985, 96, 363.
17. Rothrock, J. J.; Birkhimer, E. R.; Leum, L. N. I&EC 1957, 49 (2), 272-6.
18. Grane, H. R.; Proc. Am. Petrol. Inst, Sec. III, 1961, 41, 241-6.
19. Horvath, E. B.; Martins, E.; Tiethof, J. A.; Durante, V. A.; and Speronello, B. K. Eur. Pat. Appl. EP 189267 A2, 1986.

RECEIVED June 22, 1988

Chapter 12

Characterization of Dual-Function Cracking Catalyst Mixtures

Effects of Sepiolite Addition on Metal Passivation

Mario L. Occelli[1] and J. M. Stencel[2]

[1]Unocal Science & Technology Division, Unocal Corporation, P.O. Box 76, Brea, CA 92621
[2]Kentucky Center for Energy Research, P.O. Box 13015, Lexington, KY 40512

X-ray photoelectron spectroscopy (XPS) has been used to characterize sepiolite-containing DFCC mixtures in an effort to explain the high metals tolerance of this type of catalyst. High resolution electron spectra show vanadium to be present mostly as V(V). Hydrogen reduction experiments indicate that in a DFCC strong metal-sepiolite interactions exist and that passivation is probably the results of inert compounds formation. Raman spectroscopy indicates that vanadates, such as MgV_2O_6 and $Mg_2V_2O_7$, are formed; phase impurities in the sepiolite used may alter the nature of the vanadate generated upon steam aging.

Sepiolite passivates most of the nickel via formation of non interactive silicate-like materials. Heating at high temperatures induces migration of nickel to the interior and of vanadium to the exterior of the catalyst surface. Metal-surface interactions are observed also in Ni-loaded kaolin microspheres; however, V on kaolin behaves like bulk V_2O_5 with respect to reduction, thus explaining this clay's inability to passivate V-contaminants.

The deleterious effects that metals contaminants have on fluid cracking catalysts (FCC) activity and product selectivities can be drastically reduced by adding to the FCC heat stable materials with metals scavenging properties (1-3). Metals transport experiments and microprobe analysis have indicated that the dual function cracking catalysts (DFCC) high V-tolerance can be explained by the gas phase transport of this metal from the cracking component to the diluent where it is irreversibly sorbed and passivated (4). In a typical cracking unit, steam-stripping of occluded hydrocarbons from the catalyst surface is performed at temperatures in the 480-550°C range. The severe hydrothermal treatment, such as that at which vanadium has been observed to migrate, is necessary to reduce the structural and catalytic properties of certain fresh commercial catalysts to equilibrium values (aging) in a short (less than 10 h) period of time. Higher temperatures (650 to 750°C) are seen by the

0097–6156/88/0375–0195$06.00/0

catalyst in the regenerator where steam rarely exceeds the 20%
limit.   However, during the oxidative decomposition and removal of
carbonaceous deposits, temperatures on the catalyst surface can be
significantly higher than measured values.

In this paper, XPS and Raman spectroscopy have been used to
study the chemical state and location of Ni and V contaminants. The
effects of thermal and hydrothermal treatments on catalyst surface
properties, and the role of sepiolite in promoting metals tolerance
has been observed and reported.

Experimental

Samples Preparation. A Ca-vanadate sample was prepared by pressing
a $CaCO_3$-V_2O_5 mixture at 10,000 lbs/1 min and then heating the
resulting wafer in air at 800°C/1h (5). A melt was obtained that
gave an x-ray diffractogram consistent with JCPDS pattern No. 23-137
for CaV_2O_6, see figure 1A. Several Mg-vanadates were prepared by
high temperature calcination of MgO-V_2O_5 mixtures with different
MgO/V_2O_5 ratios. Heating in air at 1000°C/1h a wafer with MgO/V_2O_5
= 3 (prepared as described above) gave a compound with a melting
point in the 1100-1200°C range having an x-ray diffractogram consistent with JCPDS pattern No. 19-779 for $Mg_3V_2O_8$, see Figure 1E.
Trace amounts of V_2O_5 and/or MgV_2O_6 could be present in this
sample.   Heating at 650°C a mixture with MgO/V_2O_5 ~1.0 gave compounds with x-ray diffractograms consistent with JCPDS pattern No
34-14 for MgV_2O_6 (6), see Figure 1B. Similarly, heating at 650°C or
850°C a mixture with MgO/V_2O_5 = 2.0 gave α-MgV_2O_7 and β-$Mg_2V_2O_7$,
respectively; see JCPDS patterns No 31-816, No 29-877 and Figures
1C-1D. A Mg-vanadate sample from Atomergic was found to be a MgV_2O_6-
$Mg_2V_2O_7$ mixture containing trace amounts of V_2O_5 and of a phase which
could not be identified, see Figure 1F.

Differential thermal analysis (DTA) data was obtained using a
DuPont 1090 thermal analyzer using 0.04 SCF/h of air as purging gas
and heating rates of 10°C/min. All powder diffraction measurements
were obtained with a Siemens D-500 diffractometer at a scan rate of
1°/min using monochromatic Cu-K$_\alpha$ radiation. The preparation of DFCC
mixtures containing sepiolite has been described elsewhere (4).

X-Ray Photoelectron Spectroscopy. Materials in powdered form, were
pressed into thin, 13-mm diameter wafers and then mounted on a
4-sided sample probe attached to a Leybold-Hereaus LHS-10
XPS/Auger/ISS instrument. The base pressure in this instrument is
$2x10^{-10}$ bar whereas samples were generally analyzed at a pressure of
$2x10^{-8}$ bar. After spectral acquisition while using Mg K x-ray
excitation, the samples were Ar$^+$ bombarded for 10 minutes to expose
fresh sub-surface regions. The sputter profile removal rate for the
catalysts was estimated from separate sputtering experiments on
specially prepared 1.4 nm/min for Ni and 2.0 nm/min for Si.   Ar$^+$
sputtering was also used as an indicator of the reducibility of the
Ni species.

The catalysts were also exposed to 50 ml/min flowing H_2 at a
pressure of 1.5 bar and a temperature of 420°C for periods of 15 to
75 minutes. These exposures were facilitated by use of the high
pressure-high temperature reactor attached to the side of the LHS-10

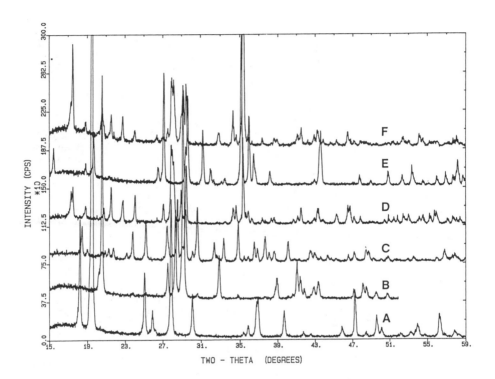

Figure 1.   X-ray diffractograms of (A) CaV_2O_6, (B) MgV_2O_6, (C) $\alpha\text{-}Mg_2V_2O_7$, (D) $\beta\text{-}Mg_2V_2O_7$, (E) $Mg_3V_2O_8$, and (F) $MgV_2O_6\text{-}Mg_2V_2O_7$ mixture.

analysis chamber. After H_2 exposure, the reaction chamber was evacuated to 10^{-2} bar after which the sample was moved into a preparatory chamber and finally to the analysis chamber. A typical time to cool, evacuate and move the sample to the analysis position is 10 minutes. All binding energies reported have been corrected for charging by assuming that the ubiquitous C 1s band is located at 284.6 eV.

Raman Spectroscopy. Raman spectra were recorded on a Spex Ramalog 1403 spectrometer equipped with a cooled RCA GaAs photomultiplier tube (CA 31034-02). The 4880 angstrom line of an argon-ion laser (Spectra Physics model 165) was used to generate Raman scattered light. The laser power impinging on the sample was limited to 50 mW. All spectra were recorded with a spectral resolution of 5 cm^{-1}. Signal pulses from the photomultiplier were passed through an amplifier/discriminator (Princeton Applied Research model 1182) and counted by a Nicolet data system. Typically, 50 scans per sample were averaged in order to obtain spectra with good signal-to-noise ratios. Samples were prepared for Raman measurements by pressing the V-loaded sepiolite into one cm-diameter wafers with a pressure of approximately 1000 psi. Each wafer was mounted in a sample holder and placed in the sample chamber of the spectrometer. The sample holder rotated at a rate of approximately 500 rpm in order to avoid temperature-induced chemical modification of the sample by the incident laser beam.

Results and Discussion

X-Ray Results. After an endotherm with peak minimum at about 125°C, the DTA profile for sepiolite is essentially featureless until 680°C where a second endotherm with peak minimum at 830°C begins. Between 830°C and 900°C, there is a sharp exotherm with peak maximum at 848°C. Similar results have been reported by Grim (8). X-ray analysis of the calcined samples indicate that at 680°C crystal water begins to be lost and at 800°C, $Mg_8Si_{12}O_{30}(OH)_4$ is observed; some quartz (α-SiO$_2$) is also present, see Figure 2A. The phase transition at 848°C represents recrystallization of the material into orthorombic MgSiO$_3$ (enstatite); some monoclinic MgSiO$_3$ (Clinoenstatite) may also have formed. After calcination at 540°C/10 h, sepiolite containing 5% V gives an x-ray diffractogram in agreement with that for $Mg_8Si_{12}O_{30}(OH)_4$, Figure 2B. Calcination of the same sample at 800°C/1h forms enstatite together with some quartz, Figure 2C; vanadates formation could not be observed. The steam aged sample is essentially enstatite with additional peaks at $2\theta = 21.77°$ and $29.39°$, see arrows in Figure 2D. The peak at $2\theta = 21.77°$ could be due to the presence of high temperature quartz. The peak at $2\theta = 29.39°$ is consistent with the presence of MgV_2O_6. However, since other strong diffraction lines typical of this compound are not present, these results cannot be interpreted as indicative of the presence of MgV_2O_6.

Raman Results. Raman spectra of two types of steam-aged (732°C/10h, ~100% steam) sepiolite granules containing 5% V and of several (unsupported) reference vanadates are shown in Figures 3 and 4.

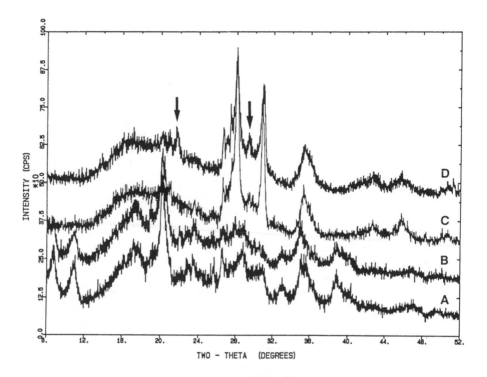

Figure 2. X-ray diffractogram of Spanish sepiolite after:
(A) calcination in air at 800°C/1h; (B) loading with 5% V
and calcination in air at 540°C/10h; (C) sample B calcined
at 800°C/1h and (D) sample D steam-aged.

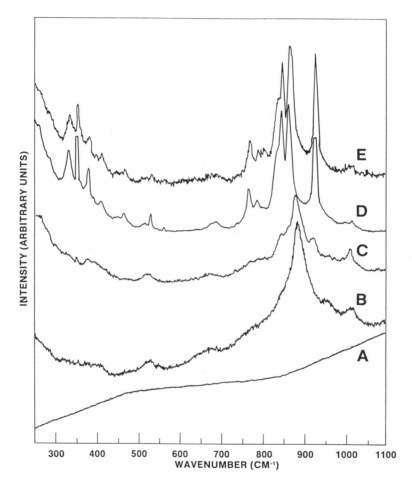

Figure 3. Raman spectra of: (A) Spanish sepiolite calcined at 800°C; (B) Spanish sepiolite containing 5% V, calcined at 800°C/1h, (C) Sample B steamed, (D) IMV-sepiolite containing 5% V, calcined at 800°C/1h, and (E) Sample D steamed.

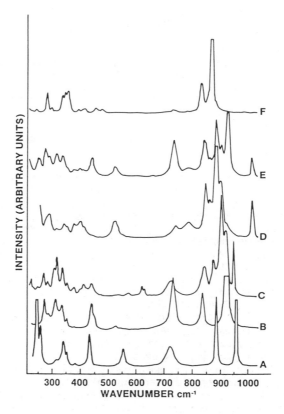

Figure 4. Raman spectra of unsupported: (A) CaV_2O_6, (B) MgV_2O_6, (C) α-$Mg_2V_2O_7$, (D) β-$Mg_2V_2O_7$, (E) MgV_2O_6-$Mg_2V_2O_7$ mixture and (F) $Mg_3V_2O_8$.

Band positions and intensities, together with vanadates data from the literature (9) are given in Table I. The parent sepiolite does not contain $V_2O_5^-$ nor tetrahedral VO_4 species, Figure 3A. However, after impregnation with 5% V and calcination in air, broad peaks appear and further broadening of these bands occur upon steaming, Figures 3B and 3C. Such broadening could be caused by H-bonding or, more likely, by the presence of a highly dispersed vanadate phase. In contrast, spectra of all the reference (unsupported) vanadates contain narrow and well defined Raman bands, Figure 4.

Bands at about 885, 845 and 525 cm^{-1} present in spectra of (V_2O_7)-containing samples (such as CdV_2O_7 (9) and the $MgV_2O_6-Mg_2V_2O_7$ mixture) are in general agreement with bands in the spectra of the V-containing Spanish sepiolites, see Table I. Furthermore, two bands, one at 959 cm^{-1} and the other at 885 cm^{-1}, in the spectrum of CaV_2O_6 and MgV_2O_6 are also in close proximity with bands observed in the V-containing Spanish sepiolite. Evidence of $Mg_3V_2O_8$ and $\alpha-Mg_2V_2O_7$ formation could not be observed in this sepiolite sample, see Figure 3.

Vanadium-surface interactions are easily affected by the presence of phase impurities in the sepiolite sample. Different vanadates are formed on a sepiolite rich in calcite and dolomite (obtained from Industrial Minerals Venture (IMV), Amargosa Valley, Nevada). This grade of sepiolite was used to generate cracking data with V-contaminated DFCC described in the patent literature (1). On the relatively pure Spanish sepiolite, Vanadium forms mainly $\overline{M}gV_2O_6-$ $\beta Mg_2V_2O_7$ mixtures whereas on the IMV-sepiolite, a third phase $(Mg_3V_2O_8)$ is also obtained, see Figures 3D and 3E. In fact, bands at 868 cm^{-1} and 929 cm^{-1} are well in agreement with the strong band at 863 cm^{-1} in $Mg_3V_2O_8$ and with the strong band at 921 cm^{-1} in MgV_2O_6. Similarly, bands at 882, 860, 845 and 788 cm^{-1} in the spectrum of $\beta-Mg_2V_2O_7$ are also observed in steam-aged (V-loaded) IMV-sepiolite granules, see Table I. Variations in Raman bands intensity are attributed to changes in the relative amounts of $[V_2O_6]$, $[V_2O_7]$ and $[V_2O_8]$ units present.

It is believed that, at the hydrothermal conditions at which cracking catalysts are tested, vanadium migrates from a DFCC's host particle and when it reaches the metal scavenger (sepiolite), it is trapped on the metal scavenger surface as a stable vanadate. When using Spanish sepiolite, V passivation is attributed to the formation of $MgV_2O_6-Mg_2V_2O_7$-like mixtures. When sepiolite admixed with calcite and dolomite (IMV-sepiolite) is used as a V-scavenger, a third phase, probably $Mg_3V_2O_8$, is also formed.

Griffith and Lesniak (9) have reported that isolated $[V_2O_7]^{4-}$ ions are present in $Cd_2V_2O_7$ and in aqueous $[V_2O_7]^{4-}$ solutions. Such isolated ions could be expected to form in the steam-aged sepiolite matrix where they would produce an intense band at ca 885 cm^{-1} with weaker bands at ca 850 cm^{-1} and 525 cm^{-1}, see Table I. However, the band at about 1014 cm^{-1} in the V-loaded sepiolites (observed in the $MgV_2O_6-Mg_2V_2O_7$ mixture) could result from combination and/or overtone modes but it is of sufficient strength to suggest that protonated species (such as $[HV_2O_7]^{3-}$ or $[HV_{10}O_{28}]^{5-}$) have formed within the sepiolite. Protonation of a terminal $V=O$ group will tend to both increase the bond order and vibrational frequency of the remaining $V=O$ groups and cause broadening of the vibrational bands.

TABLE I. RAMAN SPECTRA OF V-LOADED (5%) SEPIOLITES AND REFERENCE
COMPOUNDS (APPROXIMATE RELATIVE INTENSITIES GIVEN IN PARENTHESIS)[9]

SAMPLE	WAVENUMBER cm^{-1} (INTENSITY)
V_2O_5	997 (10), 846 (6), 788 (4.5), 729 (7.5), 670 (6), 605 (8)
$[(VO_4)^{3-}]$	827 (10), 780 (2)
$[Pb_5(VO_4)_3Cl]$	829 (10), 799 (2)
MgV_2O_6	921 (10), 836 (3), 730 (4), 523 (0.5)
CaV_2O_6	959 (10), 885 (5.5), 723 (1.5), 555 (1.5)
$[Cd_2V_2O_7]$	877 (10), 848 (3), 820 (2), 789 (0.5)
$[(V_2O_7)_{aq}^{4-}]$	877 (10), 850 (2), 810 (2), 503 (2)
α-$Mg_2V_2O_7$	948 (5.5), 919 (6.5), 902 (10), 873 (3.5), 842 (3), 723 (1.5), 631 (1), 621 (1), 570 (0.5)
β-$Mg_2V_2O_7$	1014 (3), 920 (1), 898 (5), 882 (10), 860 (3), 845 (4.5), 788 (1.5), 740 (1), 523 (1.5)
MgV_2O_6-$Mg_2V_2O_7$	1014 (2), 923 (10), 882 (6.5), 845 (4), 840 (4) 732 (4), 522 (1)
$Mg_3V_2O_8$	863 (10), 827 (2)
5% V/Sp-Sep, Steam	1014 (1.5), 952 (2.5), 885 (10), 850 (sh), 525 (1)
5% V/Sp-Sep, CA	1014 (2.5), 925 (4.5), 898 (sh), 885 (10), 850 (5), 525 (1)
5% V/IMV-Sep, Steam	1013 (1), 929 (9.5), 868 (10), 848 (9), 835 (5), 773 (3)
5% V/IMV-Sep, CA	1015 (0.5), 929 (10), 867 (9), 849 (8.5), 836 (5.5), 788 (2), 770 (3), 690 (0.5), 530 (1)

sh = shoulder

Alternately, considerable anion distortion of $[VO_3]$ groups in $[V_2O_7]$-units has been suggested to cause V-O stretching modes near $1000 cm^{-1}$ (11). Such distortion would be expected to be more important in the pure Spanish sepiolite than in the impurity-laden IMV clay. As a result, the relative intensity of the $1014 cm^{-1}$ band is greater in the Spanish sepiolite than in the IMV sepiolite sample. Wormsbecher and coworkers (12) have proposed that at the conditions (700°C, 20% steam) used to regenerate cracking catalysts, a volatile H_3VO_4 species is formed causing the destruction of the zeolite. Griffith and coworkers (9,10) in studying the Raman and infrared spectra of aqueous vanadates were able to demonstrate the presence of $[VO_3]_n^{n-}$ (pH <9.5), $[HV_2O_7]^{3-}$ (pH 9.5-11.9), $[V_2O_7]^{4-}$ and $(HVO_4)_2^{2-}$ (pH 11.9-14) ions. At pH > 14 (using 10M KOH solutions), the VO_4^{-3} ion was observed; its spectrum was characterized by a sharp and intense Raman line at $827 cm^{-1}$ and a weak line at $340 cm^{-1}$. Evidence of vanadic acid formation could not be observed in any of the steam aged V-loaded sepiolites examined. It is doubtful that the strong alkaline conditions required to form the VO_4^{-3} ions can be achieved on a FCC surface. The mineral Hummerite $(K_2Mg_2[V_{10}O_{28}]\cdot16H_2O)$ has its strongest Raman lines at $1000 cm^{-1}$ and $963 (9)$, which are in close proximity to the lines at $1014 cm^{-1}$ and $952 cm^{-1}$ in the steamed Spanish sepiolite. Hence, it is more likely that a protonated species like $[HV_2O_7]^{3-}$ or $[HV_{10}O_{28}]^{5-}$ are formed when steam aging V-loaded catalysts.

Figure 5 shows the excellent agreement between the Raman spectrum of natural garnierite (on hydrous magnesium-nickel silicate obtained from WARD's) and the spectra of calcined or steam aged Spanish sepiolite loaded with 5% Ni. Only the $600-800 cm^{-1}$ region is shown in these spectra since distinguishable Raman bands were not observed in the rest of the $0-1000 cm^{-1}$ region. The band at $685 cm^{-1}$ is probably the result of a symmetric SiO_n bending mode which is typically the most intense band in $(SiO_n)^{2-}$ containing samples. Steaming causes the $685 cm^{-1}$ band to increase in width while decreasing in intensity. Similar changes have been obserbed also when steaming V-containing sepiolite samples. Since the sepiolite does not contain Raman bands, the spectra in Figure 5 confirm the presence of $NiSiO_3$-like structures resulting from Ni-sepiolite interactions induced by the various heat treatments used to age the catalyst.

XPS Results. The XPS analyses of sepiolite granules and Kaolin microspheres loaded with 2% Ni or 2% V were performed to identify differences in elemental peak positions, reducibility and atomic concentrations. The V, O, Si and Mg peak positions in these materials, together with those of reference compounds like MgV_2O_6, $Mg_3V_2O_8$, $MgV_2O_6-Mg_2V_2O_7$ mixtures, $Ca\ Mg_2O_6$ and V_2O_5 are shown in Table II. Bands near 517 eV, 516 eV and 515 eV for $V2p_{3/2}$ imply the presence of V(V), V(IV) and V(III) species, respectively. In general, the V-containing clays (calcined in the 540-1000°C temperature range) show only a singlet V-peak near 517 eV; however, after steam-aging, an additional (weak) peak near 515 eV appears. Sputtering (as well as reduction under H_2 at 400°C) partially reduces the vanadium on the sepiolite surface to a mixture of V(V) and

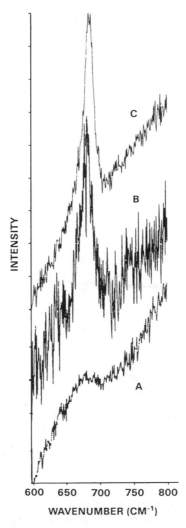

Figure 5.   Raman spectra of (A) 5% Ni on sepiolite after steaming, (B) 5% Ni on sepiolite after calcination, and (C) garnierite.

V(IV). Formation of V(III) species was observed only after sputtering V-loaded kaolin or V_2O_5 powders. The observed peak positions for 0, Si and Mg do not depend on the thermal pretreatment used.

Thermal treatment effects on Mg/Si, Mg/V and V/Si atomic ratios observed in the two V-loaded clays and reference compounds are shown in Table III. The Mg/Si ratio is fairly constant (0.70-0.75) in steam-aged samples, but it increases in samples calcined at 1000°C after sputtering (Table III). This change suggests that surface atoms, which otherwise would shield Mg from XPS detection, have been removed by the Ar^+-beam. Steaming at 732°C or calcination at 850°C give materials with V/Si atomic ratios (in the 0.005-0.007 range), which are relatively insensitive to Ar- sputtering. In contrast, The samples calcined at 1000°C exhibit a near ten-fold increase in the V/Si ratio and after sputtering this ratio decreases to 0.036 from 0.066 (Table III). The observed Mg/V atomic ratio greatly deviates from the stoichiometry typical of Mg-vanadates (Table III). However, calcination at 1000°C causes migration of V to the sepiolite surface thereby producing high V/Si atomic ratios and Mg/V ratios approaching those in Mg-vanadates (Table III). When placed on kaolin, vanadium seems to coat the microspheres surface and high V/Si atomic ratio similar to those measured on V-loaded sepiolite (calcined at 1000°C) are observed, see Table III.

Data in Table IV show the distribution of V(V), V(IV) and V(III) in clays and reference compounds after reduction in hydrogen at 400°C. Less V(IV) is formed from the MgV_2O_6-$Mg_2V_2O_7$ mixture than from the CaV_2O_6 sample. Furthermore, the amount of V(IV) in V-loaded sepiolites decreases in the order: $V(IV)[V_2O_5]$ > $V(IV)[1000°C,CA]$ > $V(IV)[850°C,CA]$ > $V(IV)[732°C, steamed]$. As seen in the sputtered samples, V(III) species could not be observed (after H_2-reduction experiments) in any of the sepiolite samples studied. In contrast, when placed on kaolin, vanadium reduces to V(IV) and V(III) species and the V(III)/V(IV) ratio seems independent of the thermal pretreatment used to age this clay. Similarly, V_2O_5 can be reduced to a combination of V(IV) and V(III) species.

These results together with those in Tables II and III show that V interacts with the sepiolite surface. Steaming at temperatures typically encountered in the regenerator of an FCC unit would not destroy this interaction. Upon calcination at 850°C the V becomes more reducible than in 732°C steamed clay, but substantially higher temperatures (1000°C) than those usually seen in FCCU operations are required before these V-sepiolite interactions are broken and vanadium migrates to the clay surface. Such migration produce compounds that are not as easily H_2-reduced as V_2O_5.

Meisenheimer (13) has reported that freshly vanadium-contaminated aluminosilicate catalysts required in excess of four hours at 750°C for full reduction of V(V) to V(III); four hours at 500°C resulted in 70% -30% V(III)-V(IV) mixtures. At the short contact times (4-8 seconds) and temperatures (480-520°C) existing in the cracking zone (the riser) of a FCC unit, V(V) reduction to V(IV) will probably be incomplete, $(V_2O_5 + H_2 = V_2O_4 + H_2O, \Delta G = -33.5$ Kcal/m) (14). Reduction of V_2O_4 to V_2O_3 is not as favorable $(V_2O_4 + H_2 = V_2O_3 + H_2O, \Delta G = -17.4$ Kcal/m). In the present case, H_2-treatment of V_2O_5 at 400°C for one hour resulted in 30% V(III)

TABLE II. THE XPS BINDING ENERGIES (eV) OF ELEMENTS IN 2% V LOADED KAOLIN,
2% V LOADED SEPIOLITE CATALYSTS AND IN REFERENCE COMPOUNDS

Sample		$V2p_{3/2}$		O1s		Si2p	Mg2p
2%V/Sep, 850°C, CA		517.1	-----	531.7		102.6	50.2
2%V/Sep, 850°C, H_2		517.0	515.3	532.0		102.9	50.6
2%V/Sep, 1000°C, CA		517.0	-----	531.8		102.7	50.4
2%V/Sep, 1000°C, SP		517.3	515.8	532.0		102.7	50.7
2%V/Sep, 1000°C, H_2		517.0	515.3	530.0		103.0	50.7
2%V/Sep, Steam		517.3	515.4	532.1		102.9	50.6
2%V/Sep, Steam SP		517.0	514.6	532.1		102.9	50.8
2%V/Sep, Steam H_2		516.9	515.6	531.7		102.6	50.2
2%V/Kaolin, 540°C, CA		516.6	-----	530.8		102.2	----
2%V/Kaolin, 540°C, H_2		516.2, 514.6		531.4		102.5	----
2%V/Kaolin, Steam		517.1, 516.2		531.7		103.3	----
2%V/Kaolin, Steam H_2		516.3, 515.0		532.0		103.4	----
MgV_2O_6	AR	517.2	-----	532.0	530.0	----	50.0
$Mg_2V_2O_7$	SP	517.2	514.7	532.0	529.9	----	50.0
Mixture	H_2	517.4	515.6	-----	530.4	----	50.4
CaV_2O_6,	AR	517.4	-----	532.2	530.2	----	----
CaV_2O_6,	SP	516.6	514.2	531.7	529.5	----	----
CaV_2O_6,	H_2	516.9	515.3	-----	529.3	----	----
V_2O_5, AR		517.2	-----	-----	530.2	----	
V_2O_5, H_2		516.0	514.7	-----	529.8	----	

CA: Calcined; H_2: H_2-treated, 400°C, 1 hr., 1.5 ATM; SP: Ar-Sputtered;
Steam: Steamed, 732°C/10 hr; AR: As-received.

TABLE III.   ATOMIC RATIO IN TWO METALS-LOADED CLAYS AND
REFERENCE COMPOUNDS

	Mg/Si	V/Si(x10^2) ·	Mg/V
2% V/Sep, 850°C, CA	0.52	0.53	98.0
2% V/Sep, 850°C, H$_2$	0.54	0.68	79.0
2% V/Sep, 850°C, SP	-	-	-
2% V/Sep, 1000°C, CA	0.53	6.6	8.0
2% V/Sep, 1000°C, SP	0.75	3.6	2.1
2% V/Sep, 1000°C, H$_2$	0.95	8.8	11.0
2% V/Sep, Steam, AR	0.75	0.63	119.0
2% V/Sep, Steam, SP	0.72	0.61	118.0
2% V/Sep, Steam, H$_2$	0.70	0.87	80.0
2% V/Sep, Bulk*	0.64	3.8	17.1
2%V/Kaolin, 1000°, CA	-	5.1	-
2%V/Kaolin, 1000°, H$_2$	-	7.2	-
2%V/Kaolin, Steam	-	6.2	-
2%V/Kaolin, Steam, H$_2$	-	6.3	-
MgV$_2$O$_6$ AR	-	-	1.6
Mg$_2$V$_2$O$_7$ SP	-	-	1.2
Mixture H$_2$	-	-	3.0

---

*From chemical analysis.

TABLE IV. DISTRIBUTION OF V-SPECIES IN 2% V-LOADED CLAYS
AND REFERENCE COMPOUNDS

	V(V)	V(IV)	V(III)
2% V/Sep, 850°C, CA	100	-	-
2% V/Sep, 850°C, H_2	77	23	-
2% V/Sep, 1000°C, CA	100	-	-
2% V/Sep, 1000°C, H_2	54	46	-
2% V/Sep, Steam	80	20	-
2% V/Sep, Steam, H_2	88	12	-
2%V/Kaolin, 1000°, CA	100	-	-
2%V/Kaolin, 1000°, H_2	0	57	43
2%V/Kaolin, Steam	65	35	-
2%V/Kaolin, Steam, H_2	0	52	48
MgV_2O_6 - AR	100	-	-
$Mg_2V_2O_7$ Mix., H_2	82	18	-
CaV_2O_6, AR	100	-	-
CaV_2O_6, H_2	70	30	-
V_2O_5, AR	100	-	-
V_2O_5, H_2	-	70	30

formation (Table IV). However, none of the V-loaded sepiolite granules could be reduced to V(III) probably because of strong V-sepiolite interactions.

The relative ease with which V_2O_5 can be reduced to V(III) in aluminosilicates indicate the existence of weak metal-surface interactions and the inability of the surface to effectively passivate vanadium. Similarly, V on Kaolin (and metakaolin) exist mostly as the "free" oxide and can (in part) be reduced to V(III) species. Therefore, DFCC systems containing metakaolin microspheres (or amorphous aluminosilicates (15)) should not be as effective as sepiolite in passivating metals like Ni and V. In fact, DCC mixtures loaded with 5000 ppm Ni-equivalents (that is 0.6% V + 0.38% Ni) are not metals resistant when metakaolin is used as a metals scavenger (1):

| | | GRZ-1 Diluted with 40% of: | |
	GRZ-1	Metakaolin	Sepiolite
Conversion (V% FF)	60.0	49.4	66.8
Gasoline (V% FF)	37.6	33.8	44.6
Carbon (Wt% FF)	5.2	3.1	4.2
Hydrogen (Wt% FF)	0.58	0.34	0.33

DFCC mixtures containing 40% sepiolite and 60% GRZ-1 are equally effective in passivating high (10,000 wtppm) levels of vanadium impurities (1). In both cases, metakaolin microspheres do not interact with vanadium or vanadium in the presence of nickel thus acting as inert diluents decreasing both cracking activity and gasoline selectivity (1):

| | | GRZ-1 Diluted with 40 wt% of: | |
	GRZ-1	Metakaolin	Sepiolite
Conversion (V% FF)	57.0	51.0	66.2
Gasoline (V% FF)	40.0	37.5	45.7
Carbon (Wt% FF)	2.5	2.3	3.6
Hydrogen (Wt% FF)	0.20	0.16	0.15

Vanadium pentoxide (V_2O_5) melts at 658°C, forming an oxygen-deficient semiconductor containing V(IV) ions as defects capable of reacting with Group II A metals, alkyl metals and aluminum (16). The resistance to V-deactivation of DFCC containing sepiolite granules (or sepiolite in a calcite-dolomite matrix) described in the patent literature (1), could be attributed to stable vanadates formation. At the conditions encountered during steam stripping, reactions of the type: $V_2O_5 + xMg(OH)_2 = Mg_xV_2O_{(5+x)} + xH_2O$ could occur; $1 < x < 3$. Similarly, during the oxidative decomposition of carbonaceous deposits in the regenerator: $V_2O_5 + xMgO = Mg_xV_2O_{(5+x)}$. Calcium compounds are believed to have a secondary role in passivating V-impurities since the data in Table III shows that calcium vanadate is more easily reduced (at test conditions) than magnesium vanadates. Depending on the host FCC composition, the metal resistance of the DFCC mixture could be enhanced by the presence of free La_2O_3 which could form $LaVO_4$ (17).

TABLE V. ATOMIC RATIOS IN 2% NI-LOADED CLAYS
AND REFERENCE COMPOUNDS

Sample	Ni/Si ($\times 10^2$)	Mg/Si	Mg/Ni
2% Ni/Sep, 850°C, CA	0.73	0.64	88
2% Ni/Sep, 850°C, SP	0.74	0.88	119
2% Ni/Sep, 850°C, H_2	0.88	0.64	73
2% Ni/Sep, 1000°C, CA	0.48	0.59	123
2% Ni/Sep, 1000°C, SP	1.1	0.91	83
2% Ni/Sep, 1000°C, H_2	-	-	-
2% Ni/Sep, Steam,	1.9	0.54	29
2% Ni/Sep, Steam, H_2	1.7	0.47	28
2% Ni/Sep, Steam, SP	-	-	-
2% Ni/Sep, Bulk	3.3	0.65	20
2%Ni/Kaolin, 540°C, CA	7.4	-	-
2%Ni/Kaolin, 540°C, H_2	4.9	-	-
2%Ni/Kaolin, Steam	4.5	-	-
2%Ni/Kaolin, Steam, H_2	5.0	-	-
Ni-Chrysotile, AR	50	0.12	0.24
Ni-Chrysotile, SP	33	0.12	0.36
Ni-Chrysotile, H_2	34	-	-

CA = Calcined; H_2 = H_2-treated 400°C, 1 hr., 1.5 ATM; SP = Ar-sputtered;
Steam = Steamed, 732°C, 10 hr; AR = As-received.

Acknowledgments

The many useful discussions and support received from the Unocal Analytical Department staff are gratefully acknowledged. Special thanks are due to Dr. E. Goldish, Mr. M. Bell, and Dr. P. Ritz for x-ray, electron microprobe and Raman measurements. Finally, we would like to thank TOLSA S.A. for providing the sample of sepiolite used in this study.

LITERATURE CITED

1. Occelli, M.L. and Kennedy, J.V., in U.S. Patent No. 4,465,588 (1984).
2. Occelli, M.L. and Swift, H.E., in U.S. Patent No. 4,466,884 (1984).
3. Occelli, M. L. in U. S. Patent No. 4,615,996 (1986).
4. Occelli, M. L. in "Advances in Catalytic Cracking" Symposium preprints. New Orleans, LA, 1987, Vol. 32, p. 658-662.
5. Perez, G., Frit, B., Bouloux, J. C. and Galy, J., C. R. Aud. Sc. Paris, t.270, 952 (1970).
6. Ng, H. N. and Calvo, C., Canadian J. Chem. 50, 3619 (1972).
7. Clark, G. M. and Morley, R., J. Solid State Chem. 14,429 (1976).
8. Grim, R. E., "Clay Minerology," 2nd Ed. McGraw-Hill (1968), p. 290.
9. Griffith, W. P., Lesniak, P. J. B., Chem. Soc. (A) 1066 (1969).
10. Griffith, W. P. and Wickins, T. D., J. Chem. Soc. (A), 1087 (1966).
11. Hanuza, J., Hermanowicz, K., Oganowski, W. and Trzebiatowska, Bull. Pol. Acad. Sci. 31, 139 (1984).
12. Worsbecher, R. F., Peters, A. W., and Maselli, J. M., J. Catal. 100, 130 (1986).
13. Meisenheimer, R. G., J. Catal., 1, 356 (1962).
14. Reed, J. B., "Free Energy of Formation of Binary Compounds," MIT Press, Cambridge, MA (1971).
15. Occelli, M.L. and Kennedy, J.V. in G.B. Patent No. 2,116,062A (1983).
16. Clark, R.J., The Chemistry of Vanadium and Titanium. Elsevier (1968).
17. W. Rudorff and H. Becker, Z. Naturfossel, 96, 613 (1954).

RECEIVED February 25, 1988

Chapter 13

X-ray Absorption Study of Vanadium in Fluid Cracking Catalysts

G. L. Woolery, A. A. Chin, G. W. Kirker, and A. Huss, Jr.

Paulsboro Research Laboratory, Mobil Research and Development
Corporation, Paulsboro, NJ 08066

X-ray absorption spectroscopy was used to investigate
the oxidation state and local environment of vanadium
in FCC catalysts subjected to conditions simulating
reaction and regeneration in an fluid catalytic
cracking unit (FCCU). Vanadium is found to exist in
the +4 oxidation state after cracking and converts to
the +5 oxidation state during catalyst regeneration.
Identical V-edge spectra were observed using V
naphthenate, V porphyrin, or a high V-containing crude,
indicating insensitivity to vanadium source. V-doped
catalysts deactivated over a wide range of conditions
leads to chemically similar V^{+5} species although
cracking activity decreases with increasing severity.
These results suggest that oxidation state is not
solely responsible for catalyst deactivation but that
other factors such as V location and mobility may play
an important role. Basic alkaline earth oxide
passivators such as MgO, admixed to the catalyst,
interact strongly with vanadium during the regeneration
period. Although the oxidation state of vanadium is
essentially unaffected, MgO structurally modifies V as
evidenced by a unique X-ray absorption spectrum.

Processing of resids and heavy oils in an FCCU is becoming
increasingly prevalent in the modern day refinery. However, the high
metals content of these petroleum feedstocks has a deleterious effect
on the performance of cracking catalysts (1-3). These metal
contaminants, in particular nickel and vanadium, deposit on the
catalyst and promote dehydrogenation reactions which result in
increased formation of coke and light gases at the expense of
gasoline production. Vanadium also causes zeolite degradation and
irreversible activity loss. While antimony passivation of nickel is
now widely practiced, there is much ongoing research activity to
fully comprehend the poisoning effect of vanadium (4-8).
Understanding the interaction of vanadium with the catalyst is an
important step in the development of technology to passivate

0097–6156/88/0375–0215$06.00/0
© 1988 American Chemical Society

vanadium. It is generally accepted that the decrease in catalyst
activity results from the interaction of vanadium with the zeolite
subsequent to V_2O_5 (V^{+5}) formation (5-8). Yet different mechanisms
have been proposed for the effect, perhaps due to the inordinately
high V levels used in some of the studies (7-8).

X-ray absorption spectroscopy (XAS) is a very powerful tool that
can provide useful information concerning the interaction of V with
FCC catalysts. This technique refers to the ejection of an inner
core electron (photoelectron) from an atom as a result of x-ray
absorption (9). Since each element has its own characteristic
binding energy, it is possible to examine a specific element in the
presence of many others by tuning the x-ray energy to the proper
absorption edge. The resulting x-ray absorption near edge structure
(XANES), within 100 eV of the threshold binding energy, is rich in
chemical and structural information (10). XAS is well suited for
studies of amorphous or poorly crystalline systems, such as may be
found in zeolite destruction by vanadium, since it does not rely on
long range ordering. Furthermore, XAS is extremely sensitive. With
the availability of high intensity x-ray sources (synchrotron
radiation), this technique is capable of providing chemical
information on metals at the hundred ppm concentration level.

In this paper, the type of information that can be obtained from
the application of XANES to metal-containing systems is demonstrated.
Examples are discussed from V absorption edge studies undertaken to
improve understanding of: the mechanism of V deactivation, the
effects of processing conditions, and the chemistry of known V
passivators. Supplemental data were provided by bench unit
evaluations of the V-containing FCC catalysts.

EXPERIMENTAL

CATALYST PREPARATION AND TESTING. The V-containing catalysts
examined in this study were prepared either by: 1) a microunit
accelerated metals laydown technique or 2) by a simulated
deactivation procedure involving hydrothermal treatment of V-doped
catalysts.

In the accelerated metals laydown technique, vanadium deposits
on the catalyst from a V-doped FCC feed in a cyclic laboratory
microunit. Each cycle consists of cracking a V-doped feed at 1000°F,
steam stripping at 1000°F, and regenerating at 1300°F. By examining
catalyst samples following each of these steps, the state of vanadium
was determined through the simulated riser/regenerator cycle.
Feedstocks used include blends of vanadium naphthenate (ICN
Pharmaceuticals), vanadyl IV mesotetraphenylporphine - VOTPP
(Midcentury), or Boscan crude (130 ppm Ni, 147 ppm V) with a low
metals gas oil. The blends were prepared such that approximately 500
ppm V deposited on the catalyst per cycle. A laboratory prepared,
steam equilibrated USY catalyst containing no rare earths was used
for these studies (catalyst A). To study passivator effects, this
catalyst was blended with 15% MgO (Fisher) as basic alkaline earth
oxides are known to effectively scavenge V, thereby reducing the
extent of deactivation (4,6).

In the simulated deactivation procedure, 5000 ppm V was
deposited on the fresh catalyst or on a 15% MgO/catalyst blend by
either physical admixture with V_2O_5 powder (Fisher) (6) or

impregnation with a V naphthenate/xylene mixture to incipient wetness
(11). In both cases, the V-containing catalysts were steam
deactivated at 1450°F and evaluated in a bench unit test. Both
procedures simulate vanadium deactivation of FCC catalysts as
evidenced by comparison with the catalyst activity, surface area, and
zeolite crystallinity of commercially equilibrated catalysts of
comparable V levels. At these higher V loadings, a commercial REY
catalyst containing 2.6% rare earths (catalyst B) was also examined.
Although La, the primary rare earth constituent on REY, has an L_{III}
adsorption edge (~5490eV) only 20 eV past the K edge of V,
qualitative comparisons can still be made on similar catalysts (same
La content). The results on examination of USY and REY catalysts
suggest that the oxidation state of V is not affected by the presence
of these pre-exchanged rare earths.

X-RAY ABSORPTION MEASUREMENTS. High resolution x-ray absorption data
were collected at the National Synchrotron Light Source in
Brookhaven, New York. The x-ray storage ring was operating at 2.52
GeV at currents of 45-125 mA. The FCC catalysts were examined in the
fluorescence mode at room temperature. Interpretation of the data
was performed by comparison to the x-ray absorption characteristics
of a variety of reference compounds with known structure and valence
(Table I). The absolute height of the vanadium K edge absorption was
normalized to the nodes in the EXAFS region of the spectrum (12).
The absolute K edge energy was determined by reference to V_2O_5, which
was run repeatedly to confirm edge position. The identity and
crystallographic purity of the reference samples (both purchased and
in-house preparations) were confirmed by x-ray diffraction and were
used without further treatment.

Table I
Reference Vanadium Compounds Used For Spectral Comparisons

Compounds		
VO	Mg_2VO_4	Na_2VO_4
V_2O_3	MgV_2O_6	Na_3VO_4
V_2O_4	$Mg_2V_2O_7$	V naphthenate
V_2O_5	$Mg_3V_2O_8$	VOTPP
		VSi_2

RESULTS

K EDGE ABSORPTION SPECTRA. The absorption of x-rays in the vicinity
of the K absorption edge of transition metals gives information on
both oxidation state and coordination geometry of the central
absorbing atom. The energy positions of various absorption features
have been demonstrated to be correlated to the formal valence of V in
an extensive series of oxides, vanadates and intermetallics (13).
For illustration, the K edges of three V-oxide reference compounds
are shown in Figure 1. As the V oxidation state increases from +2 to

+5, the entire spectrum shifts to higher energies. These energy shifts, or so-called chemical shifts, vary linearly with oxidation state. The positive shift in threshold energy can be understood conceptually to be due to an increase in the attractive potential of the nucleus on the 1s core electrons and a reduction of the repulsive core Coulomb interaction with all other electrons in the compound.

Other features in the absorption spectrum are due to local site symmetry about the absorber that dictates the intensity of the various molecular transitions. Figure 2 compares two V^{+4} compounds, V_2O_4 and V naphthenate. The considerable differences in peak intensities, particularly in the pre-edge absorption at ~5465 eV, are due to symmetry changes resulting from different local geometries. The pre-edge peak, which arises from a 1s→3d transition, is formally forbidden. However, geometries which lack inversion centers allow for orbital mixing which break down the selection rules governing transition probability. V in V_2O_4 is in a distorted octahedral environment; the distortion gives rise to the small peak intensity at 5465 eV. V-naphthenate, a vanadyl compound, is square pyramidal with a very short V-O bond. This symmetry lowering gives rise to the increased pre-edge absorption as well as changes in the overall edge profile. In the case of VO, which has a NaCl structure with perfect octahedral symmetry, the pre-edge exists only as a very weak shoulder (Figure 1).

The principal absorption peak is due to the dipole-allowed transition 1s→4p. Differences in the shape of the absorption spectrum in this region can be attributed to splitting of the degenerate energy levels of the atom, which is an indication of asymmetrical metal-ligand bonding (10). Features can also arise from transitions to higher np states, shape resonance, and multiple scattering. These effects are usually more difficult to analyze. However, since the edge profile provides a fingerprint of the compound in question, identification of the structure can usually be obtained when suitable reference materials are available.

VANADIUM OXIDATION STATES IN FCC CATALYSTS. USY catalyst samples (catalyst A) containing 500 ppm V, which was deposited by the microunit accelerated metals laydown technique using a V naphthenate-doped feed, were examined after the reaction and regeneration periods. Comparison of the absorption edge following cracking with V naphthenate indicates that V remains in the +4 oxidation state (Figure 3). Conversion of V to the +3 valence does not occur within the reducing atmosphere of the FCC riser. During catalyst regeneration, V oxidizes primarily to the +5 state (Figure 4) though some residual +4 may remain.

Similar experiments were conducted to examine the effect of vanadium source. Impregnation of naphthenates is usually used to simulate high V-containing equilibrium FCC catalysts although the majority of V compounds in crudes exists as porphyrins or porphyrin-like complexes. Investigators have pointed out that the metal behavior of porphyrins and naphthenates on catalyst performance is similar despite their structural differences (11). Our microunit studies show that after catalyst regeneration, the resultant V oxidation state (V^{+5}) is independent of V source contained in the crude. Identical edge data were obtained using feeds doped with V naphthenate, VOTPP, and Boscan crude (Figure 5). The edges after

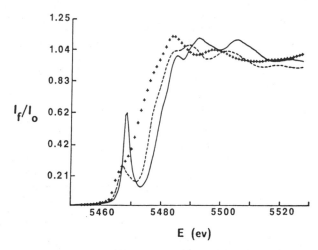

Figure 1. Effect of oxidation state on K-edge absorption spectrum of V: $V_2O_5(V^{+5})$ (——), $V_2O_4(V^{+4})$ (---), $VO(V^{+2})$ (+++).

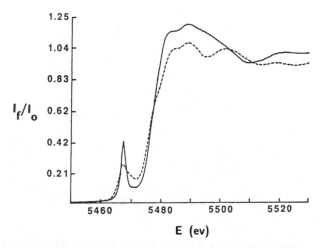

Figure 2. Effect of coordination geometry on V XANES spectrum: V naphthenate (——), V_2O_4 (---).

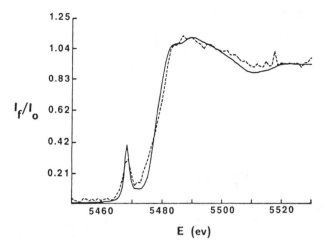

Figure 3.   Comparison of V XANES spectrum of V naphthenate (——)
with Catalyst A containing 500 ppm V after microunit cracking
(---).

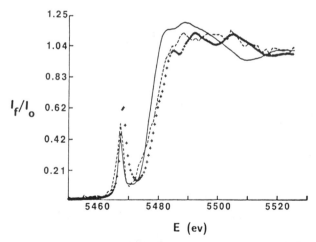

Figure 4.   Comparison of V XANES spectrum of V naphthenate (——)
and V_2O_5 (+++) with Catalyst A containing 500 ppm V after
microunit regeneration (---).

cracking (V^{+4}) differ slightly suggesting that complete decomposition of the V feed does not occur until after catalyst regeneration (Figure 6). The samples treated with VOTPP and Boscan crude were similar as expected.

VANADIUM DEACTIVATION UNDER SIMULATED CONDITIONS. The degree of catalyst deactivation was measured by comparing the activity of the catalyst or catalyst/passivator blend containing 5000 ppm V to that of the corresponding sample with no V added after similar treatment conditions (Table II). For the USY catalyst (catalyst A), steaming with V_2O_5 at 1450°F resulted in a 68% decline in activity. Examination of the V edge indicates the formation of a V^{+5} species that is structurally different from bulk V_2O_5 (Figure 7).

Deactivation severity significantly affects catalyst performance. With either the V_2O_5 (V^{+5}) addition or V naphthenate (V^{+4}) impregnation technique, similar activity losses of 60-70% were obtained on a commercial REY catalyst (catalyst B) steam treated at 1450°F. At 1350°F steaming, only 1/3 of this activity loss was observed. However, the V absorption edges for these catalysts are identical (Figure 8), indicating the same +5 oxidation state and coordination geometry about V at both deactivation temperatures. Air calcination of the V naphthenate-treated REY catalyst at 1450°F, where only a small drop in activity occurred, also results in a V edge that completely overlaps the other samples. V location in the catalyst (matrix vs. zeolite) could not be determined from the edge data alone; V on pure USY zeolite and an amorphous matrix gave identical V edges. Hence, the wide variations in catalyst activity after deactivation may be due to dissimilar V locations resulting from different V mobility during treatment.

Table II
Vanadium Deactivation of FCC Catalyst : Effect of
Thermal/Hydrothermal Treatment and V Source

Base Catalyst	V Source (5000 ppm)	Treatment	Treatment Temp., °F	Activity Retention
A	V_2O_5	Hydrothermal	1450	32
B	V_2O_5	Hydrothermal	1450	39
	Naphthenate	Hydrothermal	1450	30
	V_2O_5	Hydrothermal	1350	80
	Naphthenate	Hydrothermal	1350	73
	V_2O_5	Thermal	1450	94
	Naphthenate	Thermal	1450	87

A - Laboratory prepared catalyst using commercial USY
B - Commercial REY catalyst

Activity Retention = 100 x $\dfrac{\text{Conversion with V}}{\text{Conversion with no V added}}$

Conversion = Vol% of feed converted to <430°F products

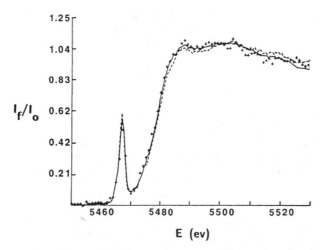

Figure 5. Effect of V source on V XANES spectrum of Catalyst A containing 500 ppm V after microunit regeneration: Boscan (——), VOTPP (---), V naphthenate (+++).

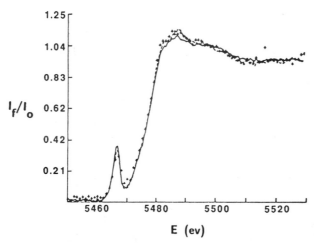

Figure 6. Effect of V source on V XANES spectrum of Catalyst A containing 500 ppm V after microunit cracking: Boscan (——), VOTPP (---), V naphthenate (+++).

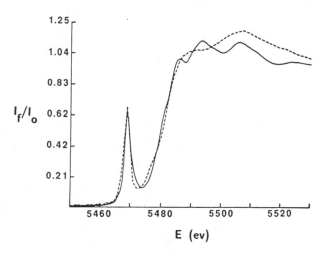

Figure 7. Comparison of V XANES spectrum of bulk V_2O_5 (——) with Catalyst A containing 5000 ppm V (from V_2O_5) after steam deactivation at 1450°F (---).

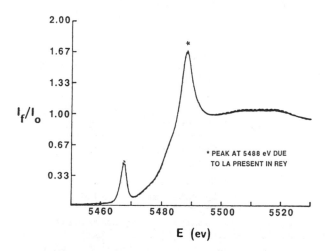

* PEAK AT 5488 eV DUE TO LA PRESENT IN REY

Figure 8. Effect of steaming temperature on V XANES spectrum of Catalyst B containing 5000 ppm V (from V_2O_5): 1450°F (——), 1350°F (---).

A different absorption spectrum was observed for the V_2O_5-containing catalyst B sample following air calcination. This catalyst has nearly complete activity retention. The distinguishing feature in this case lies in the La rather than the V edge region (Figure 9), and is due to a more intimate association of La and V in the steamed sample relative to the calcined sample. Since La is located predominantly in the zeolite for REY catalysts, this is further evidence that V mobility during the deactivation process is a necessary condition for zeolite destruction.

MAGNESIUM OXIDE PASSIVATION EFFECTS. Experiments were conducted with 15% MgO admixed to catalyst A in the cyclic microunit. After reaction with the V naphthenate-doped feed, no change in the V edge profile due to the added MgO was observed (Figure 10). However, after catalyst regeneration, the MgO-containing sample exhibits an edge profile shifted to higher energy than the catalyst without MgO (Figure 11) along with increased intensity in the pre-edge absorption. The increase in strength of the pre-edge transition can be understood conceptually by considering the "molecular cage" defined by the nearest neighbor ligands coordinating to vanadium (13-14). Such an interaction with Mg would cause a reduction in the average bond distance and lead to stronger 3d-4p orbital mixing and a relaxation of selection rules governing the 1s→3d pre-edge transition. Thus, the influence of MgO appears only after regeneration, and then the effect is to partially increase V valence concomitant with modification of the local structure about V.

High activity retentions were achieved in bench unit testing of V_2O_5/steam deactivated catalysts blended with 15% MgO (Table III).

Table III
Vanadium Deactivation of FCC Catalyst : Effect of
MgO Passivation

Base Catalyst	V Source (5000 ppm)	Treatment	Treatment Temp.,°F	Activity Retention
A	V_2O_5	Hydrothermal	1450	32
B	V_2O_5	Hydrothermal	1450	39
15% MgO/A	V_2O_5	Hydrothermal	1450	79
15% MgO/B	V_2O_5	Hydrothermal	1450	98

A - Laboratory prepared catalyst using commercial USY
B - Commercial REY catalyst

Activity Retention = 100 x $\dfrac{\text{Conversion with V}}{\text{Conversion with no V added}}$

Conversion = Vol% of feed converted to <430°F products

A comparison of the absorption edge of catalyst A with and without MgO shows considerable differences (Figure 12). Though the oxidation state of V is essentially the same, the edge fine structure induced by MgO indicates that the local environment about V had been altered significantly. As with the cyclic microunit studies, the

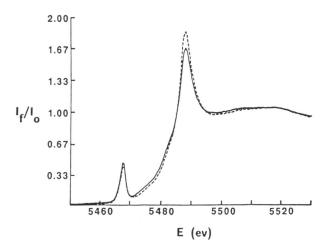

Figure 9. Effect of steam treatment on V XANES spectrum of Catalyst B containing 5000 ppm V (from V_2O_5): 1450°F steaming (——), 1450°F air calcination (---).

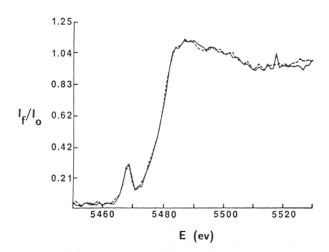

Figure 10. Effect of MgO on V XANES spectrum of Catalyst A containing 500 ppm V after microunit cracking: 0% MgO (——), 15% MgO (---).

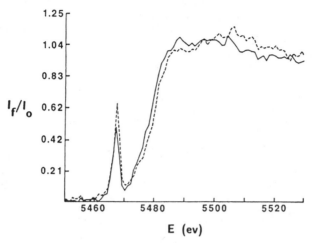

Figure 11. Effect of MgO on V XANES spectrum of Catalyst A containing 500 ppm V after microunit regeneration: 0% MgO (———), 15% MgO (---).

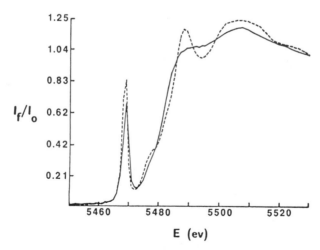

Figure 12. Effect of MgO on V XANES spectrum of Catalyst A containing 5000 ppm V (from V_2O_5) after steam deactivation at 1450°F: 0% MgO (———), 15% MgO (---).

precursor was proposed by Wormsbecher et al. (7). According to this
ism, vanadic acid is formed under FCC regenerator conditions by the
n:

$$V_2O_5 \text{ (s)} + 3 H_2O \rightleftharpoons 2 H_3VO_4 \text{ (v)}$$

anadic acid is a strong acid analogous to phosphoric acid it can destroy
lite by hydrolysis of the zeolite SiO_2/Al_2O_3 framework. Recently
(8) has shown that vanadium deposited on catalyst particles is able to
to particles of a metal scavenger (sepiolite), which initially does not
vanadium, where it can form stable vanadates. Stability together with
pectra of (hydrothermally aged) V-loaded FCC were used to show that
like $H_4V_2O_7$ was more likely to be the volatile specie formed (8).
ost laboratory deactivation studies the catalyst is impregnated with
m compounds and then treated for many hours (5-10 hrs.) at high
tures (1300°-1500°F) with high steam partial pressures. As the
is of V_2O_5 increases rapidly with increasing temperature as well as
reasing water partial pressure (9), these conditions promote the
n of an acid which permanently destroys the catalyst. However, the
n chemistry is different in a commercial FCCU in which the
tor temperature usually is in the range 1250-1400°F, the steam
ressure in the range 0.1-0.4 atm and in which the total residence time
atalyst is widely distributed as catalyst is continuously added to and
n from the unit. At these conditions, part of the vanadium induced
ion is temporary and can be reversed by the Demet procedures (10-

aper gives an example of the response of one equilibrium catalyst to
basic Demet procedures and to modified versions of these
s. The catalysts are evaluated by elemental analysis and by their
performance, as determined by the micro activity test (MAT).

ntal

The catalyst used in this study is an equilibrium Octacat fluid
catalyst from a US refinery. The metal analysis of this catalyst and
racking performance are given in Table I and Table II, respectively.

treatment. The gas phase treatment in the Demet III procedure
r to that described by Burk et al. (12). The catalyst was first
720°C for 4 hrs. in a fluidized bed reactor. After cooling to 340°C
w of nitrogen, the catalyst was oxidized with air at this
re for 30 min.
New Demet procedure, the catalyst was first calcined in air at
hrs. in a fluidized bed reactor. The catalyst was then sulfided at
hrs. After cooling down the catalyst to 320°C under a flow of
was chlorinated at this temperature for 1 hr.
phase treatment in the Demet X procedure simply consisted of
e catalyst in air in a fluidized bed reactor at 720°C for 4 hrs.

cedures. The aqueous phase treatments used for the different
cussed in this paper are schematically shown in figures 1-3.
et III wash consisted of two reductive washes followed by two
ashes. In the reductive wash, approximately 40 g. of treated
dispersed in 250 ml of deionized water. The temperature was
70°C and SO_2 was bubbled through the dispersion for 5 min. In the
sh, the catalyst was first dispersed in 250 ml of deionized water

presence of MgO causes an increase in the pre-edge intensity. The
greater degree of splitting of the main absorption peak is indicative
of a decrease in coordination symmetry and is further evidence of the
interaction of V with MgO. The formation of a magnesium vanadate
compound when V_2O_5 reacts with MgO in the presence of steam has been
proposed previously (6). Through the use of XAS coupled with x-ray
diffraction, positive identification of the magnesium vanadate
species is now possible.

DISCUSSION

Based on the results reported herein, the following interpretation is
presented to explain the mechanism by which V deactivates FCC
catalysts. V is deposited on FCC catalysts from V-porphyrin
complexes present in the FCC feed. Since the matrix accounts for
typically 50-80% of the catalyst and since the V-porphyrin complexes
are generally too large to enter zeolite Y, the V is initially
located on the matrix. In order to destructively interact with the
zeolite, two essential changes are required: 1) V must be oxidized to
V^{+5} and 2) V must be mobile. Oxidation readily occurs when the V-
containing catalyst comes in contact with air at regenerator
temperatures. Yet temperature alone is not sufficient to mobilize
the V^{+5} species formed. The presence of steam provides the necessary
mobility. The V^{+5} entity formed can attack both matrix and zeolite.
Whether this occurs via aluminum removal (vanadic acid mechanism (6))
or oxygen abstraction, the site of reaction for zeolites probably
centers around the framework Al (the Si-OH-Al oxygen would be the
most susceptible). The result is removal of framework Al (possibly
as $AlVO_4$) which can further react to regenerate the original V^{+5}
species. Thus destruction of the zeolite is nonstoichiometric in V.
Both mechanisms discussed above involve an acidic V^{+5} species,
and differ primarily in whether that species behaves as a Bronsted or
Lewis acid. The vanadic acid approach treats the V species as a
proton donor whereas the oxygen abstraction implies electrophilic
attack by V. In either case, it is easy to see how oxygen rich,
basic oxides such as MgO function as V passivators.

CONCLUSIONS

X-ray absorption spectroscopy can provide information concerning
oxidation state and local structure of metals deposited on FCC
catalysts and related supports, even at the several hundred ppm
level. This information is valuable towards the understanding of
catalyst deactivation and passivation mechanisms, and ultimately will
lead to the development of new passivation routes.

ACKNOWLEDGMENTS

The XAS portion of this research was performed at Beam Line X-11 at
the NSLS and is supported by the Division of Materials Science of the
U.S. Department of Energy under Contract No. DE-AS05 80ER10742. The
authors would also like to acknowledge L. J. Altman, M. S. Sarli, P.
Chu, and D. E. Sayers for helpful discussions and W. J. Rohrbaugh and
W. S. Borghard for assistance in data collection at NSLS.

LITERATURE CITED

1. Cimbalo, R. N.; Foster, R. L.; Wachtel, S. J. Oil and Gas Journal May 15, 1972, 112-122.
2. Campagna, R. J.; Krishna, A. S.; Yanik, S. J. Oil and Gas Journal Oct 31, 1983, 128-134.
3. Masuda, T.; Ogata, M.; Yoshida, S.; Nishimura, Y. International Chemical Engineering 1985, 25, 340-345.
4. Masuda, T.; Hiraoka, S.; Ogata, M.; Sato, G. Sekiyu Gakkaishi 1985, 28, 398-402.
5. Occelli, M. L.; Psaras, D.; Suib, S. L. Journal of Catalysis 1985, 96, 363-370.
6. Wormsbecher, R. F.; Peters, A. W.; Maselli, J. M. Journal of Catalysis 1986, 100, 130-137.
7. Pompe, R.; Jaras, S.; Vannerberg, N. G. Applied Catalysis 1984, 13, 171-179.
8. Lars, S.; Andersson, T.; Lundin, S. T.; Jaras, S.; Otterstedt, J. E. Applied Catalysis 1984, 9, 217-325.
9. Sandstrom, D. R.; Lytle, F. W. Annual Review of Physical Chemistry 1979, 30, 215-238.
10. Srivastava, U. C.; Nigam, H. L. Coordination Chemistry Reviews 1972, 9, 275-310.
11. Mitchell, A. N. Industrial & Engineering Chemistry – Product Research and Development 1980, 19, 209-213.
12. Mansour, A. N. Ph.D. Thesis, North Carolina State University, 1983.
13. Wong, J.; Lytle, F. W.; Messmer, R. P.; Maylotte, D. H. Physical Review B 1984, 30, 5596-5608.
14. Kutzler, F. W.; Natoli, C. R.; Misemer, D. K., Doniach, S; Hodgson, K. O. Journal of Chemical Physics 1980, 73, 3274-3288.

RECEIVED February 25, 1988

Chapter 14

Processes for Demetaliz of Fluid Cracking Cat

F. J. Elvin[1], J.-E. Otterstedt[2], and J

[1]ChemCat Corporation, P.O. Box 29866, New
[2]Department of Engineering Chemistry 1, Cl of Technology, Fack, S—412 96, Göteb

Three processes, Demet III, Demet X and Ne demetalization of metal poisoned octacat fl were investigated. These processes removed V (30-40%) from the catalyst. The New Dem very effective in removing Ni (88% and 80% practically no Ni could be removed by Dem procedures also proved effective in removir like Fe and Cu. All Demet methods resulte activities as determined by the micro activ increased from 65% for the untreated cata samples treated according to the different increase in activity was accompanied by a gasoline yield of 5.0-6.5%.

The control of the activity and selectivity of cra optimum yields and profitability. Currently, refi methods of control: the addition of fresh catalys quality equilibrium catalyst. Onsite FCCU catal Demet, is a third alternative which was original then improved by ChemCat Corporation worker are used to remove active metal contaminants f catalysts, thus improving catalyst activity and s are applicable to all types of amorphous and ze

Under FCCU operating conditions, almost l in the feed (such as nickel, vanadium, iron and decomposed and deposited on the catalyst (2). contaminants are vanadium and nickel. The del vanadium on catalyst performance and the mar deposited on the cracking catalyst differ from vanadium on the catalyst performance is prim activity while the major effect of nickel is a s increased coke and gas yields (3). Recent labo nickel distributes homogeneously over the cat preferentially deposits on and reacts destruct mechanism for vanadium poisoning involving

0097–6156/88/0375–022
© 1988 American Chemi

poison mecha reacti

Since the ze Occell migrat contai raman an acid

In r vanadiu temper. hydroly with ind formati vanadiu regener partial for the withdra deactiv. 11).

This the thre procedur cracking

Experime

Catalyst. cracking its MAT

Gas phas was simil sulfided under a f temperat

In the 730°C for 730°C for nitrogen,

The ga calcining

Washing p samples di

The De oxidative catalyst w adjusted to oxidative

and the temperature was adjusted to 70°C. To this dispersion, 20 and 5 ml of H_2O_2 (35%) was added in the first and second oxidative wash, respectively. The catalyst was treated with these solutions for 3 min.

The RE-exchange was carried out by treating the catalyst at 90°C for 1 hr. with a rare earth chloride solution having a concentration of 110 g RE_2O_3/l. The NH_4^+-exchange was performed by treating the catalyst at 90°C for 1 hr. with a solution containing 130 g/l $(NH_4)_2SO_4$.
After each wash or ion exchange, the catalyst was separated from the solution by filtration.

Elemental analysis.   Elemental analysis was performed with atomic absorption spectroscopy (AAS). Solid samples were first solubilized according to the procedure described by March and Meyers (13).

Catalytic cracking.   The cracking studies were carried out using a fixed bed reactor constructed according to ASTM method D 3907-80 "Micro Activity Test for Fluid Cracking Catalysts" (MAT). In this method a known amount of oil is fed to a bed of cracking catalyst. The gas and liquid products are collected and analyzed by gas chromatography. The boiling point range of the liquid products is determined by simulated distillation. The activity of the catalyst in catalytic cracking is defined as the weight-% of the feed that is converted into coke, gas and gasoline. The gasoline fraction is the portion of the product boiling between 36° and 216°C. The light cycle oil (LCO) is not included in the conversion but is calculated from the simulated distillation as the fraction boiling between 216° and 344°C.

The cracking tests were performed using a hydroprocessed mixture of North Sea and Arabian light HVGO, and a reactor temperature of 500°C. A material recovery balance was calculated for each run. All tests with a recovery of less than 97% were discarded. For each sample, duplicate runs were made in order to ensure reproducible results.

Results and Discussion

Metals removal.   The results of the metals removal for some relevant samples are shown in Table I. As seen, all Demet procedures removed a significant part of the vanadium (30-40%) from the catalyst surface. For the removal of Ni, both the New Demet and Demet III procedure was very effective. The New Demet process removed 88% of the nickel while the corresponding value for Demet III was 80%. However, nickel could not be removed by the Demet X procedure. While the gas phase treatment in the

TABLE I.   Results of metals analysis of demetalized samples

Catalyst designation	V (ppm)	Ni (ppm)	Fe (ppm)	Sb (ppm)	Cu (ppm)	Na (ppm)
Oct-0	3667	1477	4966	823	45.8	3954
A2a	2199	170	1840	179	19.8	3039
B1a	2348	287	3050	296	29.6	3436
C2c	2330	1337	5380	395	37.8	3118

Demet X procedure simply consists of an oxidation at elevated temperature, both the New Demet and the Demet III process has a sulfiding step which transforms the metal oxides to insoluble sulfides. In Demet III the sulfiding step is followed by a partial oxidation step. This oxidation is carefully controlled to produce metal sulfates and sulfides which can be directly removed by washing or be transferred into soluble compounds by the reductive and oxidative washes used in this procedure. In the New Demet process the sulfiding step is followed by chlorination which results in a transformation of the sulfides into washable chlorides. Since vanadium chlorides are volatile, most of the vanadium removal using this procedure occurs in the gas phase. In the Demet X procedure, the vanadium oxides formed are water soluble or can be transformed into water soluble forms by aqueous treatments. In contrast the nickel oxides are insoluble in water.

The tendency for the different procedures to remove iron and copper was similar to that for nickel removal in the sense that these metals were removed by the New Demet and the Demet III processes but not by Demet X. The total removal of these metals was lower than that of nickel. In the case of iron, this could be explained by the fact that some of the iron is incorporated into the clay matrix and therefore probably more difficult to remove by these treatments. The untreated catalyst contained about 800 ppm antimony which has been added in the commercial cracking operation to passivate Ni. The Demet processes tested removed a significant part of antimony from the catalyst. The efficiency of the different procedures for antimony removal is similar to that for vanadium removal. This may seem somewhat strange as the antimony associates with the nickel. The antimony oxides formed upon calcination in the Demet X procedure are, however, slightly soluble in water. The Demet procedures also remove a large fraction of the sodium from the catalysts. This may not be clearly seen in the case discussed here as the starting catalyst has a very low sodium content. For other equilibrium catalysts, investigated by us, the sodium removal has been in the 20-50% range. It should also be noted that the values given in Table I represent the sodium content prior to ion exchange. Upon exchange with ammonium or rare earth, the sodium content is further reduced. In addition to metals, the Demet procedures remove minor fractions of aluminum and rare earth metals from the catalyst. The Al dissolution in the New Demet process corresponds to a decrease in alumina content of 0.01-0.1 wt%, depending on the washing procedure, while the corresponding range for the Demet III process is 0.05-0.3 wt%. Most of the Al is dissolved in the low pH washes, i.e. the first water wash in the New Demet process and the SO_2-washes in the Demet III.

Cracking performance.   Micro activity test results for the different preparations are given in Table II. Variants of all three basic Demet procedures (see Fig. 1-3) can be used to improve the performance of this equilibrium catalyst.

The most successful New Demet preparation, A4, showed a MAT conversion of 77.1% compared to 65.2% for the untreated equilibrium catalyst. This increase in conversion was accompanied by an increase in gasoline yield from 46.8 to 52.3% and a decrease in coke yield from 4.5 to 4.3%. These results were achieved by subjecting the catalyst to a series of treatments after the basic gas phase reactions, involving oxidative and reductive washes, and ion exchange with NH_4^+ and RE (see Fig. 1). Each of these treatments resulted in a successive improvement of catalyst performance.

In the Demet III series, sample B3 gave the best results, showing a MAT conversion of 76.2%. The gasoline yield of this sample was 53.2%, up from 47.0% in the untreated sample. In the Demet III series all samples except B1b

Table II.   MAT-cracking results for demetalized samples

catalyst designation	conv (wt%)	gasoline (wt%)	coke (wt%)	gas (wt%)	LCO (wt%)
octacat 0	65.2	46.8	4.5	13.9	16.5
A1a	70.0	48.7	4.3	17.0	14.6
A1b	71.5	49.8	5.0	16.8	14.9
A1c	67.6	47.2	4.0	16.4	15.2
A1d	66.3	46.4	4.2	15.7	16.3
A2a	72.2	50.7	3.5	18.0	13.7
A2b	70.4	47.5	5.2	17.7	14.0
A2c	69.7	49.0	4.1	16.7	14.2
A3a	71.9	50.1	3.8	18.0	14.8
A3b	75.2	50.3	4.4	20.5	12.5
A3c	70.6	47.6	4.7	18.2	14.5
A4	77.1	52.3	4.3	20.6	12.0
B1a	66.5	45.0	5.2	16.3	17.1
B1b	53.8	37.8	3.9	12.2	16.9
B2a	73.0	51.2	4.4	17.4	14.0
B2b	70.5	48.0	5.0	17.4	14.6
B3	76.2	53.2	4.2	18.8	13.4
C1	60.3	41.4	4.8	14.0	17.4
C2a	69.1	46.2	5.1	17.8	15.3
C2b	69.1	47.2	4.3	17.7	15.9
C2c	70.8	49.2	4.1	16.9	14.0
C3a	70.6	46.7	5.2	18.7	14.6
C3b	71.4	48.6	5.3	17.5	14.3
C3c	72.9	51.3	4.1	17.5	12.7
C4	76.0	51.7	4.7	19.8	11.5

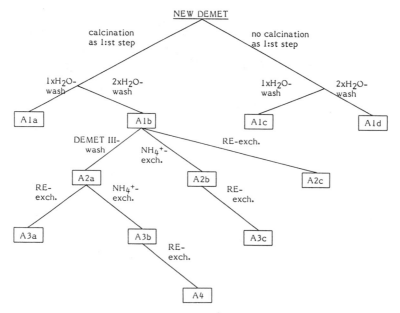

Figure 1.   Schematic representation of modifications used in the gaseous (top level) and in the aqueous phase treatments in the New Demet preparations.

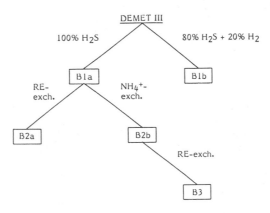

Figure 2.   Schematic representation of modifications used in the gaseous (top level) and aqueous phase treatments in the Demet III preparations.

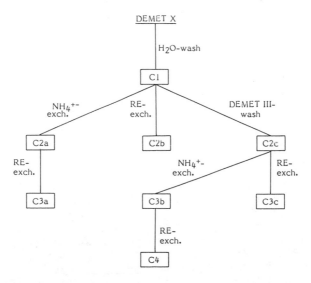

Figure 3.   Schematic representation of modifications used in the aqueous phase treatments in the Demet X preparations.

showed an improved cracking performance relative to the untreated equilibrium catalyst. The treatment of sample B1b differs from the treatments of the other samples in that H_2 was used together with H_2S in the sulfidation step.The addition of H_2 obviously had a negative effect on catalyst performance.

In the Demet X series, the most successful results were obtained for preparation C4. The MAT conversion for this sample was 76.0% and the gasoline yield 51.7%.

Conclusion

From the data given in Table I and Table II, it is clear that, for this particular equilibrium catalyst, all the Demet processes investigated were effective in removing metal poisons from the catalyst surface and restoring a significant part of its original cracking activity. The catalyst responded in a similar manner to all three processes, showing an increase in conversion of more than 10 MAT numbers accompanied by an increase in gasoline yield of 5-6.5 MAT numbers.

Due to the similar nature of the processes, it was possible to design a flexible Demet unit which can be used, with minor modifications, for all the processes. The design of this unit and its incorporation into the flowsheet of the refinery was discussed in a previous paper (1). This paper also discussed the commercial benefits of using Demet processing under different operation conditions (1).

Literature Cited

1.   Elvin, F. J., Otterstedt, J-E., and Sterte, J., Paper no. AM-86-41, NPRA Annual Meeting, Los Angeles, California, March 1986.
2.   Skinnerm, D. A., I.& E. C., 1959, 44(5), 1159.
3.   Järås, S., Appl. Cat., 1982, 2, 207.
4.   Nishimura, Y., Masuda, T., Sato, G., and Egashira, S., Preprints, ACS Div. Petr. Chem., 1983, 28, 707.
5.   Occelli, M. L., Psaras, D., and Suib, S. L., J. Catal., 1985, 96, 363.
6.   Woolery, G. L., Chin, A. A., Kirker, G. W., and Huss, A., Preprints, ACS Div. Petr. Chem., 1987, 32, 663.
7.   Wormsbecher, R. F., Peters, A. W., and Maselli, J. M., J. Catal., 1986, 100, 130.
8.   Occelli, M. L., Preprints, ACS Div. Petr. Chem., 1987, 32, 658.
9.   Yannopoulos, L. N., J. Phys. Chem., 1968, 72, 3293.
10.   Elvin, F., Paper no. AM-87-44, NPRA Annual Meeting, San Antonio, Texas, March 1987.
11.   Elvin, F., Oil & Gas J., 1987, 85(9), 42.
12.   Burk, E. H., Erickson, H., and Anderson, A. D., U.S. Patent, 3,122,510, 1978.
13.   Marsh, W. W., and Myers, G., Anal. Chim. Acta, 1968, 43, 511.

RECEIVED March 30, 1988

Chapter 15

Influence of Preparation Conditions on the Catalytic Properties of Al-Pillared Montmorillonites

D. Tichit[1], F. Fajula[1], F. Figueras[1], C. Gueguen[2], and J. Bosquet[2]

[1]Laboratoire de Chimie Organique Physique et Cinétique Chimique Appliquées, UA 418 du Centre National de la Recherche Scientifique, Ecole Nationale Supérieure de Chimie, 8 Rue Ecole Normale—34075, Montpellier Cédex, France
[2]Centre de Recherches, Elf-Solaize, 69360 St. Symphorien d'Ozon, France

The preparation of montmorillonites pillared by Al-hydroxy cations has been investigated. The thermal and hydrothermal stabilities depend on the type of clay and mode of preparation. The collapse of the structure occurs by sintering of the pillars. The controlling factor for stability is the distribution of the pillars within the particle of clay. Steaming converts the Lewis acidity into Bronsted acidity; the strength of these sites can be controlled by the conditions of steaming. Molecular sieving is preserved, even after steaming at 650°C. High activity is observed for the cracking of heavy gasoil, with a high selectivity to coke which, in the presence of S contaminants, depends on the Fe_2O_3 content of the clay. Model experiments using cumene dealkylation suggest that the detrimental influence of iron is due to the introduction of a dehydrogenation function in the catalyst.

Pillared intercalated clays (PILC) are obtained by exchanging the original cations of a smectite by inorganic cationic polymers. Swelling of the clay permits the introduction of bulky cations which create a porosity with an homogeneous distribution of pore openings. The size of the pillaring species determines then the porosity of the resulting material. Pore openings of 8–17A can be obtained with many cations including Al(1–4), Zr(1,6), Si(7), Cr(8,9) and Ti(3,10). Interest in pillared clays was increased by the report (11) that they were more active than Y zeolites for the catalytic conversion of bulky molecules. Indeed, Lussier et al (12) observed a good activity for cracking of a heavy gas oil, and Occelli (13) reported a gasoline yield comparable to that of zeolites using a

0097–6156/88/0375–0237$06.00/0
© 1988 American Chemical Society

lighter charge. In both cases however the selectivity for coke was high. There are controversial interpretations of this high selectivity for coke: Lussier et al (12) attributed the high amount of coke to iron impurities, whereas Occelli (13) attributed the high coke make to the clay strong Lewis acidity and reported that iron impurities play a minor role on the ease with which pillared clays deactivate during gas oil conversion (13a). Some discrepancies also appear concerning the thermal stability of these pillared clays. Clear differences of stability are reported for Al-PILC (1,14) or Zr-PILC (1,15) which have been widely investigated. We present here some of our results concerning the preparation, characterization and testing of montmorillonites pillared by $Al_{13}O_4(OH)_{24}(H_2O)_{12}^{7+}$ polymers, including the influence of particle size of the original clay on the properties of the resulting PILC.

Experimental

1) Materials. Two montmorillonites of different origins were used in their original forms. Their chemical compositions are reported in Table 1. Sample G, from Greece, is a powder, with particle size in the range 0.1-14 microns . Suspension B is a Volclay montmorillonite, refined by CECA, and formed of particles smaller than 0.5 micron. XRD patterns of these clays made on oriented films showed no detectable contamination with mica.

2) Preparation of the PILC : The pillaring species was produced by partial hydrolysis of $AlCl_3,6H_2O$ by a NaOH solution, following the procedure described by Lahav et al.(2). We mixed 0.2M solutions to obtain a ratio OH/Al=2. The intercalating agent was added dropwise to 10g of clay previously dispersed in 2 L of water. The final pH was adjusted by adding ammonia. The slurry was then stirred for 3 hours at 80°C, then filtered, washed chlorine free in hot deionized water, and dried at 60°C in air. Drying in a thick bed compacts the clay to hard agglomerates that are degraded by subsequent grinding (18). In the present work, the pillared clays were dried in thin beds, typically 1 mm, to obtain a product which was easily crushed to a fine powder without any loss of cristallinity. The characterizations were performed on these powders, with grain sizes   0.1 mm.

A further calcination of the clay above 500°C induces a dehydroxylation of the solid and results in a stabilization of the porous network. However, by this point, the samples have lost their ion exchange capacity. This can be restored using 4.10^{-3}M solution of K_2CO_3 at 80°C, as described by Vaughan (16). Ce^{3+} can then be introduced by ion exchange from a $CeCl_3$ solution.

3) Characterization measurements. Surface areas and pore size distributions were obtained from N_2 adsorption isotherms, using BET and BJH methods. The pore size distribution was computed from the

Table 1 : Chemical analyses and basal spacing of the original clays and of the PILC calcined at 300°C. The chemical composi- tions, on a dry basis, are referred to the silica content of the original clay.

Sample	G	G2	G5	G10	B	B4	B6
Al/clay (mM/g)	–	2	5	10	–	5	5
final pH	–	6	6	6	–	4	6
composition wt% oxides							
SiO_2	61.74	61.74	61.74	61.74	58.62	58.62	58.62
Al_2O_3	20.1	29.77	39.71	41.24	20.45	29.35	45.51
Fe_2O_3	7.39	6.61	6.58	7.01	3.35	–	4.27
CaO	1.98	–	0.09	–	0.02	–	–
MgO	3.86	–	4.98	–	1.88	–	1.57
Na_2O	0.24	–	0.11	–	3.06	0.12	–
K_2O	3.58	–	1.66	–	0.2	–	–
TiO_2	0.87	–	–	–	0.33	–	–
%Al_2O_3fixed	0	9.6	19.6	21.16	0	8.9	25.06
d(001)A	15.4	17.6	17.6	17.6	12.5	17.6	17.6
Sm^2/g	42	180	330	310	–	–	360

desorption branch of the isotherm, assuming a cylindrical pore shape.

X-ray diffraction powder patterns were recorded on a CGR Theta 60 instrument, using monochromated CuKα radiation. The adsorption capacities for several adsorbates were measured at room temperature by gravimetry, using a Cahn RH microbalance as proposed by Vaughan and Lussier (18). The samples were first treated in air for 5 hours at 480°C. The experiment was performed by passing, over the sample, a stream of nitrogen saturated by the vapor pressure of the sorbate at room temperature, the relative pressure P/Po was then equal to 1.

4) Catalytic testing. The samples were exchanged by Ce^{3+} ions, then calcined at 680°C in dry air. In two types of catalytic tests, a commercial zeolitic catalyst (super D from Grace Davison) was taken as reference.

a) For microactivity tests, a deactivation in 100% steam was done at different temperatures. Steam was passed during 5 or 17 h through a fixed bed of PILC. The conditions of the test were: 530°C for the temperature, $WHSV=30h^{-1}$, cat/oil = 6 and contact time = 20 sec. The feed was heavy gas oil ; boiling range was 210–525°C, gravity was 21°API, carbon residue was 0.29wt% ; sulfur content was 2.46wt%, aniline point was 77.8°C. The material balance of the reaction was $100 \pm 3\%$. The conversion was defined by the fraction of products boiling below 210°C. The selectivity for product i is the ratio of the weight of fraction i to the weight of cracked feed. Gasoline is defined as the fraction C_5-C_{11} and gases include hydrogen and C_1 to C_4 hydrocarbons. The amount of coke is determined on the catalyst after the microactivity test.

b) The model reaction of cumene dealkylation was studied at 300°C in a flow microreactor operated at low conversion. Nitrogen saturated by the reactant at 0°C was passed over the catalyst at a WHSV of $0.27h^{-1}$. The products of the reaction were first identified by GC–MS analysis after condensation in a cold trap, then routinely quantified every 20 minutes by on line gas chromatography.

Results

1) Preparation of the PILC. As seen in Table 1, two factors determine the extent of Al fixation (% Al_2O_3) by the clay: the final pH of the solution and the size of the clay particles. The influence of pH is readily explained by the equilibrium of formation of the polymer and by a competitive exchange with the protons. The surface area increases from 42 to $180-360m^2/g$ upon intercalation, as reported on Table 1, and seems to be determined by the amount of Al fixation. It appears that on sample G the extent of Al fixation reaches a plateau at Al/clay=5. After this, diffusional limitations control the exchange on the large particles.The N2 adsorption gives a typical type IV isotherm, with 70% of the surface area localized in micropores smaller than 20A, after dehydration at 300°C.

2) Thermal stability of the PILC. Upon calcination, there is
a small contraction of the d(001) spacing from 18.6 on the dried
sample to 17.6A at 300°C. The main modification above 500°C is a
gradual degradation of the (001) line, with no change of the (060)
line. The (001) line disappears at 800°C on sample G5 and at 850°C
on sample B6. The presence of the (060) line on the samples calcined
at 750°C shows that the structure of the clay sheet is still
preserved at that temperature. Figure 1 shows the evolution of the
surface areas. The temperature at which the surface area begins to
decrease depends on the density of the pillars, as reported earlier
(17), and on the clay particle size. Sample B6 retains a surface
area of 180m^2/g at 800°C, compared to 125m^2/g for sample G5. The
pore size distribution is gradually shifted to larger pores of
30-60A, as reported previously (17) reflecting the collapse of the
pillared structure upon calcination. Steaming decreases the thermal
stability by 150-200°C, as shown, in Table 2.

3) Accessibility of the PILC. The adsorption capacities for a
series of adsorbates reported in Table 3, determined on sample G5
treated under different conditions, agree with earlier work (18,19)
stating that the Al-PILC dried in air and calcined at 500°C behave
like wide pore zeolites, while excluding molecules larger than 8A.
Calcination at high temperatures and steaming create large pores,
but do not decrease the molecular sieving effect towards large
molecules. The large pores created by steaming are probably occluded
by the migration of alumina from the pillars to the entrance of the
pores.

4) Acidity of the PILC. Acidic properties were studied by
infrared spectrometry adsorbing pyridine as probe molecule on self
supported wafers prepared by pressing the PILC into thin films (15
mg/cm^2). Figure 2 shows the spectra obtained on a G5-Ce sample
calcined at 680°C, after pyridine adsorption and subsequent
evacuation at different temperatures. Several authors (4, 17, 20)
have reported that Al-PILC calcined above 500°C exhibit mainly a
Lewis acidity. The Bronsted acidity is weak and disappears above
300°C, but the Lewis sites are strong and retain pyridine at 480°C.
The exchange of the residual clay cations by Ce^{3+} gives a Ce-PILC.
This has a weaker Bronsted acidity, since the pyridine band
disappears by outgassing at 180°C. After steaming at 550°C, the
spectra of Figure 3 show the presence of a strong Bronsted acidity,
stable to vacuum at 480°C. Bronsted acidity is still detected after
steaming at 650°C, but the sites are weaker and not detected after
outgassing at 300°C. The clay steamed at 650°C exhibits an IR
spectrum of pyridine similar to that of a FCC zeolitic catalyst
steamed at 775°C (Figure 4).

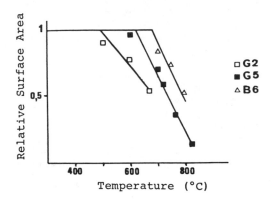

Figure 1 : Evolutions of the relative surface areas $(S_T/S_{300}\,^{\circ}C)$ for three samples.

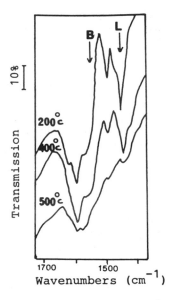

Figure 2 : Infra-red spectra of pyridine after evacuation at increasing temperatures. Sample G5-Ce calcined at 680°C and pyridine adsorption at room temperature.

Table 2 : Surface areas (m^2/g) of sample G5 exchanged by Ce after calcination in dry air or steaming.

Treatment Temperature	500°C	550°C	600°C	650°C	700°C
dry air 5h	320				270
100% steam 17h		93	72	29	

Table 3 : Adsorption capacities, in ml/g for some adsorbates, at room temperature ; sample G5 calcined or steamed in different conditions. H Ω is given as a reference of wide pore zeolite.

Treatment	500°C dry air	680°C dry air	550°C steam 17h	650°C steam 17h	H Ω 500°C dry air
surface area (m^2/g)	310	260	93	29	
adsorbate nitrogen (σ=4A)	0.23	0.2	0.11	0.04	0.19
n-hexane (σ=4.6A)	0.166	0.119	0.09	0.024	0.145
1,3,5,TMB[a] (σ=7.6A)	0.150	0.092	0.068	0.02	0.124
1,3,5TIPB[b] (σ=9.2A)	0.030	0.005	0.011	0	0

a) trimethylbenzene
b) triisopropylbenzene

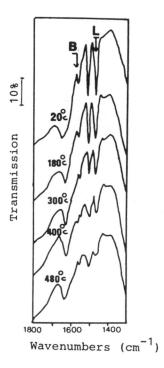

Figure 3 : Infra-red spectra of pyridine on sample G5-Ce, steamed
at 550°C. Adsorption of pyridine at room temperature,
then evacuation at different temperatures.

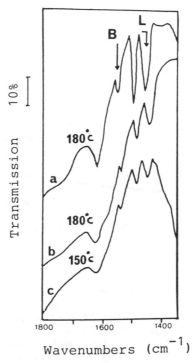

Figure 4 : Infra-red spectra of pyridine adsorbed on sample G5-Ce
steamed at 550°C (spectrum a) and 650°C (b) and on a
FCC commercial catalyst steamed at 775°C (c). Pyridine
adsorption at 25°C and desorption at different
temperatures.

5) Catalytic properties. The results are reported in Table 4. As reported earlier (12,13,14), high conversions can be reached with PILC. The hydrothermal stability of the PILC depends dramatically on the mode of preparation. After steaming at 650°C for 17 hours the conversion is 42% for sample G5 and 82% for sample B6. Hydrothermal stability at 700°C, from MAT results, can be obtained by simply decreasing the size of the particles of the original clay. The selectivity for coke is high, as expected, and changes with conversion (see on Figure 5).

The conversion of cumene has been determined at 300°C on sample G5, either fresh or regenerated after reaction. The regeneration was a calcination at 500°C in dry air. Conversion decreases steadily as a function of time, following a Voorhies law $\alpha_{(t)} = \alpha_o t^{-n}$, where $\alpha(t)$ in the conversion at time t and α_o the initial conversion. The value of n can be taken as an estimation of the rate of deactivation. Reaction products were identified by GC-MS analysis as propene, benzene, and α-methylstyrene. The selectivity of the reaction clearly changes with the thermal treatment of the sample. With the fresh catalyst. The main reaction is dealkylation, as reported in Table 5, whereas the regenerated sample is essentially a dehydrogenating catalyst. As expected, the propene/benzene ratio in the products does not correspond to the stoichiometry of the reaction. An average of 50% of the propene is converted into coke. All the clay samples, either fresh or regenerated, and the commercial zeolitic catalyst behave identically from that point of view. Therefore, the different amounts of coke are not related to different levels of conversion of propene into oligomers.

Discussion

Several factors appear to have an influence of the thermal properties of PILC. Vaughan et al (1) first emphasized the importance of using small particles of the original clay, but gave no justification. From the present results it appears that the final sample exhibits a single (001) line, and, that the cations are randomly exchanged in the clay. The changes of the chemical compositions suggest that diffusion controls the exchange of the Al_{13} cations. The situation found here is very similar to that known for the exchange of noble metals (21). In that case, the distribution of the metal within the particle affects the stability of the metallic dispersion because the rate of sintering is correlated to the average distance between the particles. We can then postulate that thermal stability will depend on the distribution of the cations. This, in turn, depends on the experimental conditions, including the size of the particles. This model predicts a more homogeneous distribution with the smaller particles, which show a better stability. A variety of experimental conditions have been used to improve the thermal stability of the pillared clays: dilution of the solution of Al used for pillaring

Table 4 : Catalytic properties of pillared clays in the cracking of an heavy gas oil. Selectivities are expressed in wt%.

Catalyst	G5	G5	G5	G5	B6	B6	B6	Super D
Treatments	dry air 680°C 5h	steam 550°C 17h	steam 600°C 17h	steam 650°C 17h	steam 550°C 17h	steam 650°C 17h	steam 700°C 17h	steam 775°C 17H
conversion	73.1	81.6	67.9	42.6	91.6	81.7	64.4	72.5
gasoline	37.7	39.8	36.6	25.6	43.9	43.3	41.8	51.3
coke	17.6	19.3	15	6.9	19.7	15.2	6.7	3.3
gases	17.8	22.8	16.5	10.1	27.8	23.4	15.8	17.9
hydrogen	0.6	0.64	0.6	0.3	0.47	0.32	0.21	0.03

Table 5 : Selectivities of the conversion of cumene on the clay catalysts at 300°C.

Sample	Cumene % conversion	Selectivities		Deactivation rate (n)
		Dealkyl	Dehydrogen	
Fresh	5	58	26	0.49
	20	44	44	
Regenerated	5	0	94	0.56
	20	15	82	

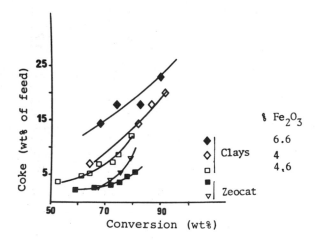

Figure 5 : Amount of coke formed on the catalyst in function of
the conversion. Charge 1 : light gas oil, from Occelli
(14) (■,□); charge 2 : heavy gas oil, ∇,◊,♦).

Reproduced with permission from reference 26. Copyright
1988 Marcel Dekker.

(1), refluxing the solution of the pillaring agent in contact with the clay (1,15), and competitive ion exchange (1). All of them tend to increase the homogeneity of the distribution of the pillaring cations. The observation of the (060) line on the samples calcined at 760°C supports the proposal that the collapse of the PILC is not due to the structural degradation of the clay sheet itself.

The influence of the K_2O content of the PILC can be investigated, comparing the present results with those reported for an Al-PILC prepared from a similar clay and containing a lower amount of K_2O (18b) (see Table 6).

The aluminium content of the two samples is comparable, when referred to the silica content of the original clay, and the two PILC have comparable surface areas after calcination at 300°C. The ACH bentonite was formed into small extrudates and flash-dried, whereas sample G5 was dried in a thin cake. In both cases, crushing to a fine powder was easy. Sample G5 retains a higher surface area at 800°C in spite of a higher potassium content. Therefore the K_2O content of the PILC is not the predominant factor for the thermal stability.

Steaming increases the molecular sieving effect. The accessibility of molecules having a kinetic diameter larger than 8A is restricted even after steaming at 650°C. The cracking catalyst, steamed at these high temperatures, still behaves as a wide pore zeolite from the point of view of adsorption of hydrocarbons, even if N_2 adsorption indicates the presence of large pores.

The acidity of these PILC appears stronger than that of Y zeolites (22), since they retain pyridine at 500°C (13b, 17). Steaming decreases the number and strength of the acid sites yielding a surface comparable to that of an FCC catalyst, at least for the acid properties. MAT results indicate that the catalytic activity is increased by a moderate steaming, in spite of the decrease of the surface area, when the acidity has been shifted to the Bronsted form. This constancy of catalytic activity when the surface area decreases, most probably reflects the importance of diffusional limitations when converting heavy fuels. The higher activity of sample B6, prepared from small particles also supports this hypothesis. Pillared clays are as active as zeolites for the cracking of heavy gas oil, even after steaming at 650-700°C. The main point is that the pillared clays yield less gasoline and more coke than the Y zeolite. As reported elsewhere (23), the selectivity for gasoline depends on the type of charge which is processed, and the heavy charge used here gives much lower selectivities than light hydrotreated feeds. Coke selectivity increases with the iron content of the clay, as reported by Lussier et al.(12), who used heavy gas oil (gravity 23.9°API) of unspecified sulfur content and pillared clays of type B, steamed 3 hours at 732°C. By contrast, Occelli (13) observed no influence of the iron content on the coke make when using a light gas oil and a PILC comparable to sample G, obtained from an unrefined clay and hydrothermally stable at 650°C. The comparison of our results with those reported by Occelli, (Figure

Table 6 : Influence of the K_2O content on the thermal stability of
clays. (1) this work : original clay and sample G5.
(2) ACH bentonite from flash dried extrudates ([18])

Sample		% SiO_2	% Al_2O_3	% K_2O	BET Surface Area		
					300°C	700°C	800°C
Original Clays	(1)	61.7	20.1	3.58	42		
	(2)	62.9	20.0	2.32	50		
PILC	(1)	61.7	39.1	1.66	330	225	157
	(2)	62.9	35.5	0.5	398	282	60

5), shows that the type of feed and the iron content of the clay have an influence on the selectivity for coke. The influence of the charge has been reported for zeolite containing catalysts : the heavier charge produces more coke, (24). The same tendancy appears when comparing the sample used by Occelli, containing 4.6wt% Fe_2O_3 and sample B6. With the heavy charge, iron oxide has a clear effect on carbon selectivity. These results agree with the work of Mills (25) showing that iron on the catalyst was detrimental mainly when using sulfur rich feedstocks. Fe_2O_3 is then converted to the sulfide. The high amount of hydrogen produced by the clays indicates the presence of a dehydrogenation function. Mössbauer spectrometry shows that iron is partly reduced to Fe^{2+} in the MAT test and then participates in the complex process of cracking. Model experiments using cumene as probe molecule support this hypothesis. On the fresh sample, calcined in air, the main reaction is dealkylation to benzene and propene. On a regenerated or steamed catalyst, the main product is α-methylstyrene, a product of cumene dehydrogenation. Deactivation is accelerated on this steamed sample, compared to the fresh sample. A high concentration of olefins favors the building of coke, then the old ideas developed for natural clays can be applied to PILC as well.

It must be recognized however that iron free clays produce more coke than zeolites (12, 13a, 23) whatever type of charge is converted. Therefore the nature of the acidity (13a) or the density of acid sites of these pillared clays may be responsible for this higher coke make.

In conclusion, pillared clays catalysts are not as good as initially predicted for the cracking of heavy gas oils, mainly because of the iron contamination of natural clays. There is a probability that they could be applied for the conversion of hydrotreated gas oils, giving a slightly lower gasoline yield, but higher octane number than REY zeolites.

References

1. Vaughan,D.E.W.,Lussier,R.J.and Magee,J.S.,US Patent,1979, 4176090
2. Lahav,N.,Shani,U.and Shabtai,J.,Clays Clay Miner,1978,26,107.
3. Jacobs,P.,Poncelet,G.and Schutz,A.,French Patent,1983,251 2043.
4. Occelli,M.L.and Tindwa,R.M.,Clays Clay Miner.,1983,31,22.
5. Plee,D.,Borg,F.,Gatineau,L. and Fripiat,J.J.,J.Amer.Chem.Soc. 1985,107,2362.
6. Yamanaka,S.and Brindley,G.W.,Clays Clay Miner.,1979,27,119.
7. Lewis,R.M.,Ott,K.C.and Van Santen,R.A.,US Patent,1985,4510257.
8. Shabtai,J.and Lahav,N.,US Patent,1980,4216188.
9. Pinnavaia,T.J.,Tzou,M.S.and Landau,S.D.,J.Amer.Chem.Soc.,1985, 107,4783.
10a. Yamanaka,S.,Nishihara,T.,Hattori,M.,M.Suzuki,M.,Preprints Poster Papers,7th Intern.Zeolite Conf.,Tokyo,1986,p 29.
10b. Sterte, J. Clays Clay Miner., (1986), 34, 658.

11. Shabtai,J.,Lazar,R.,and Oblad,A.G.,Proc.7th Intern.Congr.
    Catalysis,Tokyo,1980,Elsevier-Kodansha (1980),p 828.
12. Lussier,R.J.,Magee,J.S.and Vaughan D.E.W.,7th Canadian Symp.
    Catalysis,(S.E.Wanke and S.K.Chakrabarty Ed), Chem.Inst.Canada,
    1980,p 88.
13a.Occelli,M.L. and Finseth,D.H.,J.Catal.,1986,99,316.
13b.Occelli, M.L. and Lester, J.E., Ind. Eng. Chem. Prod. Res.
    Dev., 1985, 24, 27.
14. Occelli,M.L.,Ind.Eng.Chem.Prod.Res.Devel.,1983,22,553.
15. Bartley,G.J.J.and Burch,R.,Applied Catal.,1985,19,175.
16. Vaughan,D.E.W.,Lussier,R.J.and Magee,J.S.,US Patent,1981,
    4271043.
17. Tichit,D.,Fajula,F.,Figueras,F.,Bousquet,J.and Gueguen,C.,
    "Stud. Surf. Sci. Catal"., (B.Imelik et al.Ed) Elsevier,
    1985,20, p 351.
18a.Vaughan,D.E.W., and Lussier,R.J.,Proc.5th Intern.Conf.Zeolites,
    Naples 1980, (L.C.Rees Ed), Heyden,London,1980,p 94.
18b.Occelli, M.L., Proceed. Intern. Clay Conf.,Denver 1985,
    The Clay Minerals Society, Bloomington, 1985, p. 319.
19. Pinnavaia,T.J.,Tzou,M.S.,Landau,S.D.and Raythatha,R.H.,
    J.Molecular Catal.,1984,27,195.
20. Shabtai,J.,Massoth,F.E.,Tokarz,M.,Tsai,G.M.and Mc Cauley,J.,
    Proc.8th Intern.Congr.Catal.,Berlin (1984),Verlag Chemie 1984,
    Vol 4,p 735.
21. Ribeiro,F.and Marcilly,C.,Rev.Inst.Français Petrole,1979,
    34,405.
22. Ward,J.W.,in "Zeolite Chemistry and Catalysis",chap 3, ACS
    Monograph 171, (J.A.Rabo Ed) 1976,p.118.
23. Tichit, D., Fajula F., Gueguen, C. and Bousquet, J.,
    9th Intern. Congr. Catal., Calgary (1988).
24. Magee,J.S.and Blazek,J.J.,in "Zeolite Chemistry and Catalysis",
    ACS Monograph 171, (J.A.Rabo Ed),1976,p 615.
25. Mills,G.A.,Ind.Eng.Chem.,1950,42,182.
26. Figueras, F.,Cat.Rev.-Sci.Eng.,1988(in press).

RECEIVED June 14, 1988

Chapter 16

Effect of Aging of Pillaring Reagent on the Microstructure and Cracking Activity of Pillared Clay

J. R. Harris

Phillips Petroleum Company, Bartlesville, OK 74004

Aging of hydroxyaluminum polycation solutions used to prepare pillared clays affects the properties, including surface area and cracking activity, of these pillared clays. The effects were correlated with the state of hydrolysis of the aged solutions. Dilution of the pillaring reagent, Chlorhydrol, causes depolymerization of polycations present in this reagent and the formation of new polycations which react to form the pillared clay. An optimum dilution level was established, 0.06M Al. Lower dilution levels did not allow sufficient depolymerization and higher dilution caused excessive depolymerization in the aged solutions. Pillared clays prepared from aged dilute solutions had an enhanced microstructure which showed an increased activity for selectively cracking large molecules to the light cycle oil range. This microstructure is lost in the presence of steam which also reduces the formation of catalytic coke. Addition of rare earth zeolite to pillared clay can partially overcome the effects of this loss of microstructure.

Pillared interlayer clays (PILC) are formed by exchanging large hydroxyaluminum polycations into the interlayer of a smectite clay such as montmorillonite, a clay mineral, which consists of sheet-like silica/alumina layers. Calcination of the exchanged clay gives a well dispersed array of metal oxide clusters (i.e., pillars) bonded top and bottom to the silica/alumina layers of the clay. The permanent separation of the clay layers gives an 8 to 10-fold increase in surface area, from 30 to 250-300 m^2/g, and a microporous structure similar to but less constrained than that of zeolites. Recently, there has been an increased interest in the use of these clays as cracking catalysts. For example, pillared clays have been shown to be active cracking catalysts for both single component [1] and gas oil feeds [2,3]. They generate both higher light cycle oil (LCO) and coke yields and they are less hydrothermally stable than conventional cracking catalysts [2,3].

0097–6156/88/0375–0253$06.00/0
© 1988 American Chemical Society

Aluminum polycations are obtained by the controlled hydrolysis of Al(III) solutions; the extent of the hydrolysis reaction can be monitored with pH measurements. The products of the hydrolysis reactions, i.e. the successive generation of polycations of increasing degree of polymerization with increasing extent of hydrolysis, must be inferred from non-equilibrium measurements. Thus, equilibria between many polycationic species, i.e. $[Al_2(OH)_2]^{+4}$, $[Al_{24}(OH)_{60}]^{+12}$, etc., were proposed. More recently, ^{27}Al NMR has identified only three species in solution, the monomer $[Al(H_2O)_6]^{+3}$, the dimer $[Al_2(OH)_2]^{+4}$ and the spherical cation $[Al_{13}O_4(OH)_{24}]^{+7}$ (4).

The approach to equilibrium of these hydrolyzed polycation solutions is known as aging. During the aging process certain polycationic species disappear from the solution and new ones are formed. For this reason, the aging process can have a significant influence on the properties of the pillared clays.

The basal spacing (d_{001}) of the PILC depends on the age of the pillaring reagent, the degree of hydrolysis of the reagent and the amount of reactants (i.e. Al/clay ratio) (5). XRD patterns of PILC dried at 110°C and prepared at an Al/clay ratio of 1.96 mM/gr (from a base hydrolyzed aluminum chloride solution with OH/Al of 1.85 and aged at 25°C for 0-6 days) showed an increase in basal spacing from 14.6 A to 17.5 A. No additional increase in basal spacing occurred on further aging to 30 days. The aging period was also extended to 18 months without any further effect (6). The possibility of accelerating the aging process by refluxing the polycation solutions at 95-100°C has been considered (7). The aging time was shortened from days to hours. Aging up to 6 hours yielded PILC with increased surface area. No improvement was found on extending the aging period to 48 hours. Similar polycation solutions aged at 25°C were used to pillar hectorite clay (8). The largest surface area and basal spacing were found for an intermediate aging period of 15 days.

In all of these investigations the PILC was prepared by injecting the aged polycation solution into a dilute (0.2-0.8 g/l) clay colloidal dispersion. Generally these reactant concentrations are too low to produce practical quantities of PILC catalysts. PILC can, of course, be prepared from more concentrated clay slurries. In this case, aging of the washed PILC (9) or of the clay-pillaring reagent slurry (10) have been recommended. The specific effects of these aging processes or of aged pillaring reagents on concentrated clay slurries have not been reported.

Commercially available metal hydrolyzed hydroxyaluminum solutions containing Chlorhydrol have been used as one source of the polycation solution (10). The major objective of this work was to determine how the physical and catalytic properties of pillared clay depend on the aging of the dilute Chlorhydrol solutions.

EXPERIMENTAL

Hydroxyaluminum polycation solutions were prepared by dilution of Chlorhydrol 50% w/w solution, Reheis Chemical Company. It is a clear colorless, viscous (50 cps) solution containing 50 weight percent of a complex identified by the salt, $Al_2(OH)_5Cl.2H_2O$. Chlorhydrol solution, 6.43 molar in aluminum, was approximately diluted by factors of 10, 100, and 1000 to provide the desired pillaring reagent. The actual molar concentrations of aluminum in the dilute solutions, as determined by plasma emission using an Applied Research Laboratories Instrument Model ICPQ1-37000, were 0.005, 0.040, 0.058, 0.061, and 0.467. The solutions were aged in covered beakers and the pH was monitored using an Orion Research 601A Ionalyzer and 91-04 combination electrode.

The aged pillaring reagents were heated to 65°C and 325 bentonite, American Colloid Company, whose major constituent is the layered clay mineral, montmorillonite, was added. There was always a 5-fold excess of aluminum in solution and the volume of solution per gram of clay was always 45 cc/g or more. The reaction was carried out for 2 hours. The slurry was filtered and the solids washed two times with water, dried, sized, and calcined at 500°C for 2 hours in air.

When rare earth Y-zeolite (REY) was added to the PILC or to the parent clay, the dried PILC or "as received" clay was reslurried in water and the calcined REY added to the 10 wt % level. This slurry was then mixed, filtered, dried, and calcined at 500°C for 2 hours in air. The calcined REY was obtained from Union Carbide and contained 14.1 wt % rare earth elements, primarily lanthanum and cerium. Portions of the PILC were pretreated by one of the methods listed below prior to the microactivity testing.

A - Heated in nitrogen for 4 hours at 732°C
B - Heated in steam (1 atm) for 1 hour at 732°C
C - Heated in steam (1 atm) for 2 hours at 732°C
D - Heated in steam (1 atm) for 4 hours at 732°C
E - Heated in steam (1 atm) for 7 hours at 787°C

Surface areas of the pillared clays were obtained from nitrogen adsorption isotherms on a Micromeritics Accusorb unit. The BET equation was used. All samples were outgased at 200°C for one hour. X-ray diffraction (XRD) patterns of calcined powder samples were obtained on a Philips 3100 XRG unit using a copper tube and Norelco goniometer equipped with a graphite monochromator. Only first order reflections are reported here which are the sum of the pillar height and the height of the silica-alumina clay layer, 9.6A. Line broadening measurements were made on these first order reflections and are uncorrected for instrument broadening. The microactivity tests (MAT) were carried out using a procedure similar to ASTM test D-3907-80 (5 grams of catalyst and a cat/oil ratio of 3/1). Two different feeds were used in this study: a narrow cut of a North Sea gas oil (API of 26.8) with boiling range between 390 and 480°C, and a hydrotreated resid (API of 18.0) with 50 % boiling above 550°C.

The MAT tests using North Sea gas oil were run at 482°C while the hydrotreated resid was run at 510°C. Simulated distillations on the recovered liquid products were run using 217 and 343°C gasoline and LCO cut points. All data have been normalized to a 100% material balance.

RESULTS AND DISCUSSION

The effect of dilution on the polycations present in the Chlorhydrol solution can be understood by considering two types of reactions - hydrolysis and olation. A typical hydrolysis reaction is illustrated by Equation 1.

$$[Al(H_2O)_5(OH)]^{+2} + H_2O \rightleftharpoons [Al(H_2O)_4(OH)_2]^{+1} + H_3O^+ \qquad (1)$$

Polycations result from the concurrent process of polymerization or olation. An example of an olation reaction is given by Equation 2 where the basic complexes react with each other via hydroxyl bridges to form polycations.

$$2[Al(H_2O)_4(OH)_2]^{+1} \rightleftharpoons [Al_2(H_2O)_7(OH)_4]^{+2} + H_2O \qquad (2)$$

These polycations can be further hydrolyzed or react with each other to give a large number of possible polycations. The olation reaction occurs without a change in solution acidity but does change the concentration of hydrolyzed species in solution. Dilution causes the reversal of reaction 2 (i.e., depolymerization) and the introduction of new hydrolyzed species into solution. The new species formed can then re-equilibrate through the hydrolysis reaction. The kinetics of aging depend on the relative rates of the olation and hydrolysis reactions.

   In this section we first describe the results of measurements made on fresh and aged solutions. Potentiometric, pH, measurements, which indicate the extent of hydrolysis of the aluminum ions, were made on all solutions during the aging process. Next, we report surface areas of pillared clays made from the aged solutions. Finally, we will discuss the cracking activities of some selected pillared clay samples.

Effects of Aging. Chlorhydrol was diluted in the range 10 to 1000-fold to obtain pillaring solutions 0.005-0.467M in Al. These solutions were either used immediately (0 day solutions) or aged for periods of time (i.e., 10 and 25 day solutions) before being used to pillar the clay. The dilution range was extended to 1000-fold in an attempt to observe rapid rehydrolysis at the low (0.005M) Al concentration. Fifteen minutes after dilution, the pH of the solution was measured and the value obtained was taken as the zero day aged value. A pillared clay was immediately prepared from a portion of the solution and the remaining solution was allowed to age further. Additional pillared clays were prepared after aging for 10 and 25 days.

   In Figure 1, the pH of the batch diluted solutions is plotted against the dilution ratio, C/Co, where C is the molar concentration of Al in the dilute solution and Co is the molar concentration of Al in Chlorhydrol (6.43 M). The pH of the most concentrated solution was still increasing after ten days aging. (The higher viscosity of the concentrated solutions may contribute to the slower equilibriation). At higher dilution (lower C/Co values), new equilibria can be introduced due to depolymerization reactions. For the zero day curve, pH continuously increases with dilution. For the 10 day curve, a maximum is observed, see Figure 1. The position of the maximum most likely depends on the degree of hydrolysis of the starting solution. If this is so, then solutions diluted in this range might be expected to contain polycations uniquely suitable for forming a pillared clay.

The progress toward re-equilibration of all of the dilute solutions aged for up to 25 days at 23°C is shown in Figure 2. The most dilute solution, 0.005M Al, was highly depolymerized initially and rapidly returned to an equilibrium pH of 4.72 in 10 days. The most concentrated solution, 0.467M Al, depolymerized slowly to an apparent maximum pH of 4.49 at about 15 days and then the pH declined to 4.44 at 25 days. The 0.058 and 0.061M solutions continued to depolymerize throughout the 25 day period while the slightly more dilute 0.040M solution reached a maximum pH at about 10 days and then the pH declined to 4.71 after 25 days. After 53 days the pH of this solution was 4.57 and still decreasing, indicating that equilibrium had not been reached. These results suggest that the kinetics of re-equilibration are very slow at 23°C except for the most dilute solution.

Pillared Clays. The surface areas of the calcined pillared clays derived from the various dilute solutions under study are shown in Figure 3 as a function of solution age. The curves for the more concentrated solutions (0.058 to 0.467M) are similar to those obtained from the pH measurements (Figure 2) for the same solutions. The 0.061M solution produced the highest surface area pillared clays, 300-335 m^2/g; aging to 25 days only resulted in a 10% increase in surface area. Over a similar aging period, the surface area produced by the 0.058M solution increased from 250 m^2/g to 320 m^2/g. The most dilute solution, 0.005M, produced very low surface area pillared clays, 200-225 m^2/g, insensitive to the age of the solution used. The low surface area produced by the highly depolymerized (pH=4.93) zero day aged 0.005M solution was unexpected and indicates that excessive depolymerization can produce polycations unsuitable as pillaring agents. The 0.04M solution also yielded a low surface area material, 160 m^2/g, after zero days aging but the surface area increased to 260 m^2/g after aging the solution for 25 days.

In Figure 4, the surface areas of all the pillared clays prepared from solutions aged at 23°C are plotted against the logarithm of the Al concentration used. The maximum surface areas are produced from the 0.058-0.061M solutions. The highest surface areas are also associated with the maximum pH in the aged pillaring reagent. Less dilute solutions did not produce high surface area material because they are very slow to depolymerize and probably tend to relax back to the state of hydrolysis of the original solution. This could indicate that the highly polymerized polycations in the original Chlorhydrol solution are not good pillaring agents. On the other hand, very dilute solutions may be too highly depolymerized to produce high surface area PILCs.

The pillared clays were also characterized by XRD. The [001] reflection characteristic of the expansion of the clay is due to insertion of the hydroxyaluminum polycations between the clay layers. In Figure 5 the traces of the [001] reflection are shown

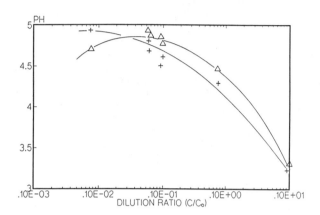

Figure 1.   pH of dilute Chlorhydrol, Co=6.43M Al, aged 0 days
(+) and 10 days (Δ).

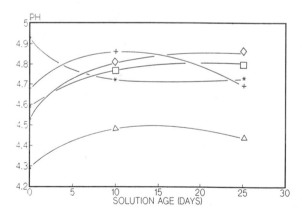

Figure 2.   Solution pH versus solution age. Aluminum concentration (C), 0.005M (*), 0.040M (+), 0.058M (□), 0.061M (◊),
0.467M (Δ).

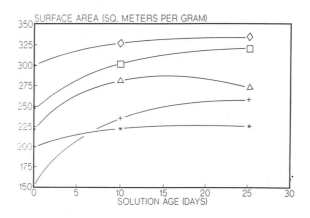

Figure 3. PILC surface area versus solution age. See Figure 2 for symbols.

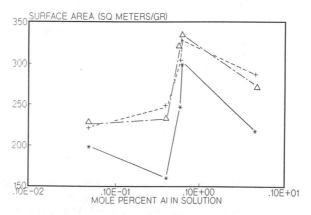

Figure 4. Surface area versus Al concentration. Solutions aged for 0 days (*), 10 days (+) and 25 days (Δ).

for pillared clays prepared from unaged dilute solutions. The
peak width at half height, $w_{1/2}$, is also shown. The maximum d_{001}
value, 18.4 A, was found for the PILC prepared from the 0.04M
solution. This indicated a pillar height of about 8.8 A. Other
dilute solutions produced pillared clays with only slightly
smaller d_{001} values. The peak intensity was highest and peak
width at a minimum for the PILC prepared from the 0.061M solution.
This solution also produced the PILC with maximum surface area at
zero days aging. The near equivalent fresh 0.058M solution yielded a PILC with a much broader (001) reflection and lower surface
area. It is likely that for fresh solutions these differences are
associated with the susceptibility of the more dilute solutions to
reaction variables, particularly temperature, during the preparation of the pillared clay. The sharper more intense peaks are an
indication of more extensive exchange of polycations with formation of pillars thermally stable at 500°C.

The aging process was followed using XRD measurements for the
0.04M solution and the x-ray diffractograms are shown in Figure 6.
The d_{001} value remained almost constant at 18.4 A over the entire
53 day aging period. Thus, aging did not change the clay pillar
height. However, the peak became narrower with increasing age of
the solution until a minimum peak width was observed when using
solutions aged for 10 days. A slight broadening occurred on further aging to 53 days. Similar results were observed from surface
area measurements.

Cracking Activity. In the previous section, we demonstrated that
aging conditions affect the surface area of pillared clays. Here,
we discuss the cracking activities of some selected aged PILCs.
In particular, we are concerned with the high coke yields and high
LCO selectivity reported elsewhere (2,3).

In order to reduce the high coke level found for calcined
PILC, a sample of aged PILC was pretreated under progressively
more severe thermal (pretreatment A) and hydrothermal (pretreatments B to D) conditions. Microactivity tests were made using a
narrow cut of North Sea gas oil which contained no material in the
LCO range. The results are shown in Table I. Conversion decreases monotonically with surface area, obtained after regeneration at 593°C in air, due to the increasing severity of the pre-
treatments, A to D. The decrease in gasoline yield and the corresponding decrease in the LCO/HCO ratio reflect the loss of
cracking activity with surface area. Coke selectivity increased
slightly as surface area declined through treatment B and then
decreased after treatment C and D. Each of the catalysts was run
three additional times with a regeneration step after each run.
Conversion, coke yields, selectivities, and surface areas after
the fourth and final regeneration are also shown in Table I. Conversion and surface area decreased, however, catalysts initially
pretreated by methods C and D retained their initial low surface
area and the decrease in cracking activity is possibly due to
residual coke deposits after regeneration.

After the initial thermal pretreatments, conversion is directly related to the nature of the microstructure developed in aged
PILC. In the early stages of collapse of the microstructure,

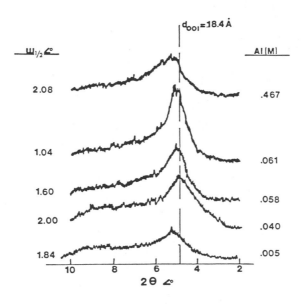

Figure 5. XRD line broadening ($w_{1/2}$). Fresh, 0 day, solutions.

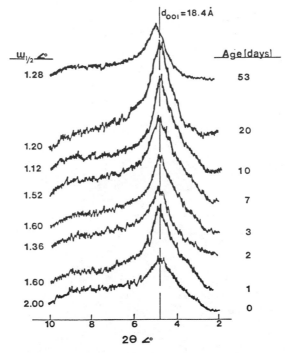

Figure 6. XRD line broadening ($w_{1/2}$). Al concentration = 0.04M.

Table I. Effect of Pretreatment on Cracking Activity

Pretreatment	None	A	B	C	D
S.A. (m^2/g), 1st regen.	203	149	113	88	74
Conversion, Wt%	78.2	62.1	49.0	46.0	39.5
C_5^+ Gasoline, Wt%	53.2	42.4	32.4	33.4	28.6
C_5^+ Gasoline/Conv.	0.68	0.68	0.66	0.73	0.72
Light Cycle Oil, Wt%	17.0	19.3	20.5	20.2	18.3
Heavy Cycle Oil, Wt%	4.8	18.6	30.5	33.8	42.2
LCO/HCO	3.5	1.0	0.7	0.6	0.4
Light Gas, Wt%	14.4	9.2	8.1	6.2	5.1
Coke, Wt%	10.5	10.5	8.6	6.3	5.6
Coke/Conv.	0.13	0.17	0.18	0.14	0.14
- - - - - - - - - - - -	- - - -	- - - -	- - - -	- - - -	- - - -
S.A. (m^2/g), 4th regen.	172	106	105	90	75
Conversion, Wt%	52.8	43.4	37.5	27.8	18.7
Coke, Wt%	10.7	7.4	6.7	--	5.5
Coke/Conv.	0.20	0.17	0.18	--	0.29

Catalyst: PILC from 0.3M Al solution aged 7 days, calcined S.A. = 270 m^2/g.
Feed: North Sea gas oil.
Conditions: See Text.

selectivity to LCO is lost and coke yields and selectivities are
decreased by steam most probably due to a reduction in pillar
heights and partial collapse of the pillared structure.

To promote the activity of steam deactivated PILC and to
evaluate PILC as a matrix component in cracking catalysts, REY-
PILC and REY-clay containing 10 wt % REY were deactivated by method D. The MAT conversions, using North Sea gas oil, and surface
area after regeneration are compared with calcined PILC below.
The results show that REY-PILC yields a higher conversion than
PILC or REY-clay.

	Surface Area (m^2/g)	MAT (wt% Conversion)
PILC	74	39.5
REY-PILC	89	64.9
REY-clay	51	28.8

In Table II, the product yields of REY-PILC are compared with
PILC, a commercial equilibrium catalyst, and with the same commercial catalyst that had been deactivated in the laboratory to near
constant conversion. The addition of REY to PILC maintained activity in the presence of steam while coke yield was reduced and
the LCO/HCO ratio was slightly higher than for either of the commercial catalysts. This suggests that the microstructure of the
PILC after pretreatment D will still convert large molecules into
gasoline range products instead of generating coke as seen in PILC
alone.

Finally, PILC, REY-PILC, and a commercial equilibrium catalyst
were evaluated at near constant conversion using a heavier feed,
hydrotreated resid. The product yields are shown in Table III.
Steam deactivated (D), REY-PILC, produced the same gasoline selectivity, LCO/HCO ratio, and coke yield as calcined PILC. The equilibrium catalyst which represents a more severely deactivated (E)
sample had higher gasoline selectivity, lower coke yield, and lower HCO/LCO ratio. The higher coke yield of REY-PILC could be due
to occlusion of high molecular weight hydrocarbons in the microstructure of the pillared clay.

CONCLUSIONS

The surface areas of pillared clays prepared from dilute Chlorhydrol solution depend on the extent of dilution and age of the dilute solution. Dilution produces polycations favorable to the
production of pillared clays by depolymerizing larger polycations
present in the Chlorhydrol solution. Aging is the re-
equilibration of these depolymerized solutions.

In the most dilute solutions, depolymerization is very rapid
and, in some cases, the solutions rehydrolyze. The lower surface
area PILCs formed from these solutions indicate that the polycations formed during rehydrolysis are different from the original
polycations. In the most concentrated solutions, depolymerization
was slow and less extensive. These solutions were also less
favorable pillaring reagents. Thus, we find an optimum pillaring
reagent exists at an intermediate dilution. This reagent can be

Table II. Product Distributions from Cracking North Sea Gas Oil

Catalyst	PILC	REY-PILC	Commercial	Commercial
Pretreatment	A	D	Equilibrium	E
Conversion, Wt%	62.1	64.9	62.0	64.3
C_5^+ Gasoline, Wt%	42.4	47.2	46.8	49.3
C_5^+ Gasoline/Conv.	0.68	0.73	0.75	0.77
Light Cycle Oil, Wt%	19.3	19.4	19.5	17.8
Heavy Cycle Oil, Wt%	18.6	15.7	18.5	17.9
LCO/HCO	1.0	1.2	1.1	1.0
Light Gas, Wt%	9.2	11.2	10.3	9.2
Coke, Wt%	10.5	6.5	5.0	5.7

See text for conditions.

Table III. Product Distributions from Cracking Hydrotreated Resid

Catalyst	PILC	REY-PILC	Commercial
Pretreatment	None	D	Equilibrium
Conversion, Wt%	74.3	78.2	70.9
C_5^+ Gasoline, Wt%	42.8	47.0	47.9
C_5^+ Gasoline/Conv.	0.58	0.60	0.68
Light Cycle Oil, Wt%	19.4	16.3	19.1
Heavy Cycle Oil, Wt%	6.3	5.5	10.0
LCO/HCO	3.1	3.0	1.9
Light Gas, Wt%	15.5	16.4	14.3
Coke, Wt%	18.1	18.5	12.6

See text for conditions.

further improved by aging. The production of the optimum pillaring reagent will depend on the Al concentration in the initial solution and the initial state of hydrolysis of the solution. In the case of Chlorhydrol, the optimum solution would be 0.06M in Al and aged 5 to 10 days at 23°C.

PILC prepared from aged pillaring reagent has an enhanced microstructure which shows an increased activity for selectively cracking large molecules to the light cycle oil range. This microstructure is lost in the presence of steam which also reduces the formation of catalytic coke. Addition of REY-zeolite to PILC can overcome the effects of loss of microstructure if the gas oil has a narrow boiling range. Heavier resids still produce large amounts of coke possibly by diffusion of liquid into the micropores.

LITERATURE CITED

1. Shabtai, J.; Lazar, R.; Oblad, A. G. Proc. 7th Intl. Cong. Catal., 1981, pp 828-837.

2. Lussier, R. J.; Magee, J. S.; Vaughan, D. E. W. Preprints, 7th Canadian Symposium on Catalysis 1980, p. 88.

3. Occelli, M. L. Ind. Eng. Chem. Prod. Res. Dev. 1983, 22, 553-59.

4. Akitt, J.; Farthing, A. J. Chem. Soc., Dalton Trans. 1981, 1624-1628.

5. Lahav, N.; Shani, U.; Shabtai, J. Clays and Clay Minerals 1978, 26, 107-15.

6. Lahav, N.; Shani, U. Clays and Clay Minerals 1978, 26, 116-24.

7. Tokarz, M.; Shabtai, J. Clays and Clay Minerals 1985, 33, 89-98.

8. Shabtai, J.; Rosell, M.; Tokarz, M. Clays and Clay Minerals 1984, 32, 99-107.

9. Reed, M.; Jaffe, J. U.S. Patent 4 060 480, 1977.

10. Vaughan, D. E. W.; Lussier, R. J.; Magee, J. S. U.S. Patent 4 176 090, 1979.

RECEIVED February 25, 1988

Chapter 17

Catalytic Cracking of Heavy Oils

J.-E. Otterstedt, B. Gevert, and J. Sterte

Department of Engineering Chemistry 1, Chalmers University
of Technology, Fack, S–412 96, Göteborg, Sweden

The effects of composition of heavy oils derived from petroleum and
biomass, on their response to cracking over catalysts of various
composition were investigated. The contribution to the conversion
from different types of cracking was estimated and the effect of
temperature on the product distribution was studied.
Heavy fractions of Wilmington crude contained more aromatics and
polars compared with a conventional HVGO. The conversion of the
Wilmington fractions increased with boiling point range. The zeolitic
contribution to the conversion decreased while the matrix
contribution remained constant and the contribution from thermal
cracking increased.
The low H/C-ratio of FCC feed derived from liquefied biomass led
to low conversion and poor gasoline selectivity. Addition of alumina
to the matrix resulted in a catalyst more active for heavy oil
cracking but with a poor selectivity. Alumina-montmorillonite
catalysts showed activities for heavy oil cracking comparable to
that of a conventional, zeolite based, cracking catalyst. Effects of
matrix composition and zeolite type on the heavy oil cracking
performance are discussed.

Of the many factors which influence product yields in a fluid catalytic
cracker, the feed stock quality and the catalyst composition are of particular
interest as they can be controlled only to a limited extent by the refiner. In
the past decade there has been a trend towards using heavier feedstocks in the
FCC-unit. This trend is expected to continue in the foreseeable future. It is
therefore important to study how molecular types, characteristic not only of
heavy petroleum oil but also of e.g. coal liquid, shale oil and biomass oil,
respond to cracking over catalysts of different compositions.

Heavy oils have high specific viscosities and contain components, boiling
above 525°C, which are not necessarily distillation bottoms but can also be
vacuum gasoils boiling above the normal range of such oils (350-525°C). The
hydrogen to carbon ratio is generally lower for heavy oils and their contents of
heteroatoms and metals, such as vanadium, nickel and iron, are higher. Heavy
oils contain large molecules of which some have polar character (resins) or are
large clusters (asphaltenes). Normally, synthetic oils derived from coal, shale

0097–6156/88/0375–0266$06.00/0

or biomass also have the characteristics of heavy oils since they may contain large amounts of metals, have low hydrogen to carbon ratios and high specific densities (see Table I).

In the fluid catalytic cracking (FCC) process the metals and the ash will be deposited on the catalyst, causing catalyst deactivation and cracking to higher production of coke and gas. The higher sulfur content results in higher sulfur emissions while the high nitrogen contents lower the conversion, as part of the nitrogen compounds are basic and neutralize the acid sites on the catalyst.

Deactivation of the catalyst is reflected by a higher tendency for production of gas and coke on the catalyst. The effects of the increased coke on catalyst are:
- an increase in regeneration temperature which can cause catalyst deactivation, metallurgical problems and higher emissions of NO_x
- a lower catalyst to oil ratio, required in order to maintain heat balance in the reactor
-a risk for inadequate regeneration if the capacity of the airblowers is insufficient.
-high gas velocities in the regenerator which will increase the amount of fines in the flue gas.

The larger amounts of coke on the catalyst can be handled by more effective steam stripping, regeneration with heat removal, or using a two-step regenerator. Improved temperature tolerance of the catalyst and of the construction materials in the regenerator also contributes to the handling of the coke problem.

The effects of heavy oils on cracking can be met by process modifications, feed pretreatment or by the use of specially designed catalysts.

The most important pretreatment steps of the feed are proper desalting and hydroprocessing. The latter step will reduce the content of heteroatoms, asphaltenes and metals, and raise the hydrogen to carbon ratio of the feed. In other words, hydroprocessing significantly reduces the heavy oil character of the feed oil.

The selectivity problem caused by nickel contaminants can be reasonably well handled by adding nickel passivators, usually containing antimony, to the feed (6). Although passivators have been reported to decrease the deactivation effects of vanadium, a more promising way to handle this problem is to introduce vanadium "traps", which prevent the vanadium from migrating and destroying the zeolite. Catalysts designed to have a high metals tolerance are available on the market (7-9). Another interesting way to solve the metals problem is to restore the activity by removing the metals deposited on the catalyst using the NEW DEMET process (10). This process can also be used in combination with passivators and/or metal tolerant catalysts.

In order to decrease sulfur emissions, sulfur transferring catalysts containing Al_2O_3 or MgO (11-13), can be used.

The large molecules found in heavy oils can not penetrate the zeolite structure but must initially be cracked on the surface of the zeolite crystals, on the matrix surface or thermally (14). The intermediate products can then be cracked in the zeolite to desirable products. In order to increase the activity in the cracking of heavy components it is thus possible to use a catalyst having an active matrix or to crack at higher temperatures. A third approach is to substitute some or all of the Y-type zeolite, currently used in commercial cracking catalysts, with a zeolitic component having a larger pore-size, e.g. a pillared smectite. The potential of smectites, pillared or cross-linked with inorganic polycations, as cracking catalysts was first demonstrated by Vaughan et al. (15). The main obstacle for the use of these materials in commercial catalysts is their lack of thermal and hydrothermal stability. At the

Table I. Properties of Oils of Different Origins

Property	North Sea[1]	Tia Juana[2]	Coal oil[3]	Shale oil[4]	Biomass[5]
H/C-ratio[6]	1.7	-	1.4	1.5	1.0
N(wt%)	0.2	0.33	0.8	2.1	<.02
O(wt%)	-	-	3.8	1.2	15.1
S(wt%)	0.5	1.8	0.3	0.7	0.01
Ash(wt%)	-	-	.004	.03	-
Metals (ppm)	6	238	-	100	-
Specific gravity	0.92	0.95	0.9	0.93	1.1
Conradson carbon (wt%)	4.5	9.3	-	-	-
Pour point (°C)	-	7	19	32	35

[1]Statfjord atmospheric resid (1). [2]Atmospheric resid (2). [3]SRC II (3). [4]Prahoe shale oil (4). [5]Directly liquefied oil from wood chips using the PERC process (5). [6]Molar ratio adjusted assuming that ammonia, water and hydrogen sulfide are formed by the heteroatoms.

temperature of the regenerator, the materials of this type reported to date rapidly break down and lose their activity.

This paper reports results of cracking heavy vacuum gasoil from Wilmington crude, a hydroprocessed oil derived from biomass and a hydroprocessed mixture of North Sea and Arabian light HVGO. The cracking was performed at two temperatures using commercial, laboratory prepared, and alumina-montmorillonite catalysts.

Experimental

Most of the experimental techniques have been reported elsewhere and will therefore be described only briefly.

Feed oils. Crude from the Wilmington oil field in California was distilled into four fractions of vacuum gasoil boiling between 360-502 (No. 4), 381-496 (No. 5), 445-541 (No. 6) and 483-73% off at 548°C (No. 7).

The oil derived from biomass was liquefied with the PERC process, extracted with decalin, hydroprocessed at 370°C, and the fraction boiling above 350°C (BMO) was separated by distillation (16). A hydroprocessed mixture of North sea and Arabian light vaccum gas oil (HVGO) was used as a "base line", i.e. a typical FCC feed stock.

Some important characteristics of these oils are given in Table II and further information is provided in references (16-18).

Feed stock characterization. The compositions of the feeds expressed in different molecular types were determined by bonded phase chromatography. The distributions of carbons in different structures were calculated from NMR spectra of the feedstocks. Detailed procedures for the characterization of feedstocks are described in reference (18) .

Commercial catalysts. Two commercial catalysts made by Katalistiks b.v. were used. The first, EKZ-4, was steam aged at 750°C for 18 hrs prior to use and the second, an EKZ-2 equilibrium catalyst from a European refinery, was heated at 300°C in air for 3 hrs prior to use. Alpha alumina, heated at 300°C in air for 3 hrs, was used in order to estimate the contribution to conversion from thermal cracking.

Catalytic cracking. The cracking studies were carried out using a fixed bed reactor constructed according to ASTM method D 3907-80 " Micro Activity Test for Fluid Cracking Catalysts" (MAT). In this method a known amount of oil is fed to a bed of cracking catalyst. The gas and liquid products are collected and analyzed by gas chromatography. The boiling point range of the liquid products is determined by simulated distillation and the gas product distribution is analyzed by gas chromatography. The activity of the catalyst in catalytic cracking is defined as the weight-% of the feed that is converted into coke, gas and gasoline. The gasoline fraction is the portion of the product boiling between 36° and 216°C. The light cycle oil (LCO) is not included in the conversion but is calculated from the simulated distillation as the fraction boiling between 216° and 344°C.

The cracking tests were performed using reactor temperatures of 500° and 560°C . A material recovery balance was calculated for each run. All tests with a material recovery of less than 97% were discarded.

Table II. Feedstock analysis.

Analysis	Wilmington fraction No.					HVGO	BMO
	4	5	6	7	8		
Simulated distillation[1] (5% off - 95% off)	360-502	381-496	445-541	483- 73% off at 548°C	519- 28% off at 548°C	346-544	355- 89% off at 540°C
Elementary analysis: (weight %)							
Carbon	84.4	84.6	84.3	84.8	84.4	87.0	89.7
Hydrogen	11.5	11.1	11.1	11.2	11.1	12.5	9.5
Nitrogen	0.53	0.64	0.75	0.84	0.87	0.10	0.02
Sulfur	1.64	1.75	2.05	2.27	2.40	0.40	0.05
Oxygen	0.64	0.61	0.65	0.80	1.02	0.33	0.80
Metals(ppm):							
Nickel	-	-	2	3	19	0.2	-
Vanadium	-	-	-	-	9	-	-
Sodium	-	-	0.6	0.7	7.6	-	-
Density (g/cm^3)[2]	.9510	.9703	.9750	.9789	.9852	.9058	-
Viscosity (cst, 50°C)[3]	97	236	972	2468	7725	34	-
Ramsbottom carbon (wt%)[4]	0.4	0.4	0.9	1.7	3.6	0.4	-

[1]ASTM D 2887-73, [2]ASTM D 1298, [3]ASTM D 445, [4]ASTM D 524

Catalyst preparation. A sample of CREY (calcined rare earth Y) was prepared by repeated ion exchange and calcination of NaY. The zeolite product contained 0.58% Na_2O, 19.3% RE_2O_3 and had a surface area of $610m^2/g$. A catalyst was prepared by spray drying a slurry of this zeolite together with kaolin and aluminum chlorohydrate. The slurry contained 17% CREY, 73% kaolin and 10% aluminum chlorohydrate (Chlorohydrol, Reheis) (calculated as Al_2O_3). A second catalyst was prepared using the same procedure and a slurry containing 17% CREY, 48% kaolin and 35% colloidal alumina (Disperal, Condea). These catalysts (designated H2 and H6, respectively) were steam treated at 790°C for 18 hrs. prior to the cracking experiments.

Al_2O_3-montmorillonite complexes were prepared according to the procedure described by Sterte and Otterstedt (19). The samples used in this study were prepared from untreated aluminum chlorohydrate and from aluminum chlorohydrate hydrothermally treated at 120° and 140°C (catalyst designations M1, M2 and M3). The catalysts were air dried and ground in a ball mill. The fraction 40-100 microns was separated and steamed in a muffle furnace at 750°C for 18 hrs. As a reference, a sample containing 20 % REY in a kaolin-binder matrix was prepared and treated in the same manner (catalyst M4).

Results and discussion

Feedstock characterization. Table III shows the distributions of carbons in different structures, calculated from NMR spectra. Table IV shows the contents of saturated, aromatic and polar components, as determined by HPLC (18), for the different feedstocks used in this study. As boiling point increases the paraffinic carbon decreases, the aromatic carbon increases while the naphthenic carbon remains nearly constant. The Wilmington fractions and the biomass oil contain considerably more aromatics and polars than the HVGO. The amount of saturates in the Wilmington fractions decreases with increasing boiling point range and is generally much lower than that of the HVGO. The contents of aromatics and polars, on the other hand, increase with boiling point range and are much higher than that of HVGO.

Catalytic cracking of Wilmington heavy vaccum gasoil over EKZ-4. Nilsson et al. (18) have investigated the response of heavy vacuum gasoils of different compositions and different distributions of molecular types to cracking over EKZ-4, a commercial cracking catalyst containing rare earth zeolite Y in a clay-binder matrix.

The fractions were cracked at 560° and also at 500°C, with the exception of fraction 7 which did not vaporize completely at the lower temperature. The contributions of thermal and matrix cracking to the product yield were determined by cracking over   -alumina and matrix respectively. Figure 1 shows that the zeolitic contribution to conversion decreases due to poorer access to zeolite pore structure, the thermal contribution decreases with increasing boiling point range, whereas the matrix contribution remains constant.

Tables V and VI show that the distribution of molecular types in the liquid products after cracking at 500° and 560°C shifts towards more aromatics, particulary monoaromatics, and polars with increasing boiling point range of the feed. The yields of monoaromatics increase at the higher temperature since they are favoured thermodynamically as dehydrogenation products of naphthenes. Polyaromatics are rejected to coke. The conversion of polars decreases with increasing boiling point of the feed at 500°C, but increases

Table III. Distribution of Carbons in Different Structures Calculated from the
           NMR Spectra of the Feedstocks/Weight %

Structure	Fraction					
	4	5	6	7	HVGO	BMO
Paraffinic (%C_p)	78.1	75.5	74.9	78.9	82.1	57.0
Aromatic (%C_A)	21.9	24.5	25.1	21.1	18.9	43.0
-alkyl	12.4	13.5	13.7	10.3	9.5	16.7
Naphtenic (%C_N)[1]	33.2	31.2	30.7	30.2	23.8	20.7
Degree of substitution[2]	56.5	55.3	54.8	48.9	50.4	38.9

[1]%C_N = 54.3 (H_{CH_3} / H_{-CH_2-} + 0.100) (3)
[2]%C -alkyl / %C_A x 100

Table IV. Molecular type separation by HPLC/weight %.

	Feed oil					
	4	5	6	7	HVGO	BMO
Saturates	55.8	53.9	37.9	31.0	66.7	20.3
Aromatics	33.9	34.6	42.0	42.4	28.9	67.8
Polars	10.3	11.5	20.1	26.6	4.4	11.8

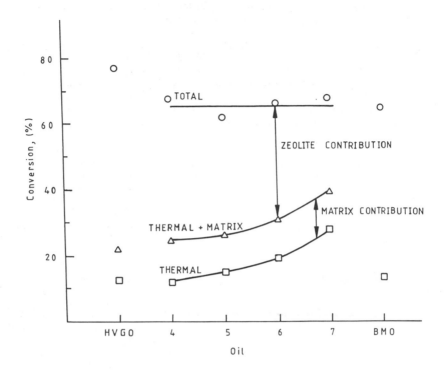

Figure 1. Contribution to the conversion from different types of cracking using the EKZ-4 catalyst.

Table V. Product distribution from catalytic cracking at 560°C in weight %

	4	5	6	7	HVGO
Saturates	55.8	53.9	37.9	31.0	66.7
Monoaromatics	32.8	32.4	45.4	52.1	23.3
Diaromatics	4.5	3.8	4.4	4.8	5.1
Fluorene	.37	.35	.35	.36	.34
3-ring compounds	1.7	1.8	1.8	1.9	1.9
4-ring compounds	1.4	1.5	1.8	1.8	1.2
Polars	3.2	5.9	8.7	8.2	1.6
Polars in feedstock	10.3	11.5	20.1	26.6	4.4
Difference	-7.1	-5.6	-11.4	-17.8	-2.8

with boiling point at 560°C, indicating that polars are readily converted by thermal reactions to products in the gasoline range.

Catalytic cracking over CREY in two different matrices. The MAT-results for cracking of fraction No. 6 and HVGO over CREY in a kaolin (H2) and in a kaolin-alumina (H6) matrix are given in Table VII. For each oil, the results are shown at the same level of conversion. For the HVGO, this conversion level was obtained using essentially the same c/o-ratio (catalyst to oil ratio), indicating similar activities of the two catalysts for cracking this oil. Somewhat lower gasoline and higher coke and gas yields were observed for H6 compared with H2.

For the cracking of fraction No.6, a higher c/o-ratio was required for H2 compared with H6 in order to obtain a given conversion level. This reflects the additional activity supplied by the alumina part of the matrix. The contribution of the alumina in the matrix is also seen when fraction No. 6 is cracked over spray dried samples of the matrices only. At a c/o-ratio of 3.0, conversions of 33% and 44% were obtained using the kaolin and the kaolin-alumina matrix, respectively. The tendency for higher coke and gas production at the expense of gasoline over catalyst H6 compared with H2 is also seen for oil No. 6.

Catalytic cracking over alumina-montmorillonite complexes. The cracking experiments over the alumina-montmorillonite complexes were performed using fractions No. 4 and No. 6. The results of these experiments are shown in Table VIII together with that of the reference catalyst containing 20% REY in a kaolin matrix. Due to collapse upon steaming, the conversion over the conventional pillared smectite (M1) is very low for both types of feed. The higher stability of the materials prepared from the hydrothermally treated aluminum chlorohydrate is reflected in higher conversions over these catalysts. For the lighter feed (No. 4), the sample prepared from the solution treated at 140°C (M3) show a somewhat lower conversion compared with the REY catalyst (M4) while the reverse situation is observed for the heavier feed (No. 6). This is attributed to the larger pores in the alumina-montmorillonite complex compared with those in the zeolite based catalyst. No major differences in gasoline yield between the different catalysts were seen. The montmorillonite based catalysts did, however, produce somewhat more coke and less gas than the REY-catalyst.

Catalytic cracking of biomass oil over EKZ catalysts. The BMO showed higher stability than the HVGO towards thermal cracking at 560°C while the opposite was found at 500°C .

Table IX shows that cracking of the BMO with the EKZ-4 catalyst at 500°C resulted in a higher coke yield (16%) compared to the HVGO under the same conditions (8%). This reflects the higher boiling point range, higher aromatic content and higher amount of polar components of the BMO compared to the HVGO. The molar ratios of hydrogen to carbon were 1.3 and 1.7 in the BMO and in the HVGO, respectively (Gevert, B.S.; Otterstedt, J-E. Submitted to Biomass) . At 560°C, the yields of gas and coke increased while the gasoline yield decreased. This indicates that both the BMO and the HVGO are sensitive to overcracking; and more so than, for instance, Wilmington fraction No. 6.

Cracking of the BMO under mild conditions, i.e. using EKZ-2 instead of EKZ-4 and 500°C, resulted in a lower amount of coke and a lower conversion (50%). The yield of gasoline was, however, about the same as when cracking with EKZ-4 and thus the milder conditions improved the selectivity.

Table VI.   Effect of Temperature on Product Distribution

| | Weight % at 560°C - Weight % at 500°C | | | | |
	4	5	6	7	HVGO
Saturates	-	-	-	-	-
Monoaromatics	8.6	8.3	14.8	-	2.9
Diaromatics	-3.6	-4.6	-3.6	-	-1.0
Fluorene	-.19	-.26	-.19	-	-.10
3-ring compounds	-1.0	-1.4	-.50	-	-.44
4-ring compounds	-1.1	-.74	-1.5	-	-.53
Polars	-2.9	-1.8	-9.2	-	-.70

Table VII. Catalytic cracking over CREY in different matrices

Catalyst Designation	Oil	Conversion (wt%)	Gasoline (wt%)	Coke (wt%)	Gas (wt%)	c/o-ratio
H2	HVGO	77.7	55.5	4.4	17.8	3.08
H6	HVGO	77.7	54.3	5.3	18.1	3.05
H2	no.6	64.2	38.1	8.1	18.0	3.23
H6	no.6	64.2	36.2	9.9	18.2	3.04

[1]A reactor temperature of 560°C was used when cracking oil no.6

Table VIII. Catalytic cracking over alumina-montmorillonite complexes

Catalyst Designation	Oil	Conversion (wt%)	Gasoline (wt%)	Coke (wt%)	Gas (wt%)
M1	no.4	21.3	12.6	4.2	4.5
M2	no.4	42.9	24.2	9.8	9.0
M3	no.4	50.0	28.9	10.7	11.0
M4	no.4	56.0	31.8	10.2	14.0
M1	no.6	23.3	13.2	5.4	4.7
M2	no.6	46.4	24.6	12.6	9.2
M3	no.6	51.1	25.5	15.3	10.3
M4	no.6	47.6	22.6	12.7	11.7

Table IX.   Cracking of BMO over EKZ-4

| | 500°C | | 560°C | |
	BMO	HVGO	BMO	HVGO
coke	16	8.3	19.2	9.8
gas	16	22	18.5	27.8
gasoline	30.5	52.6	27.3	46.0
gasoil	20.1	14	17.8	9.6
conversion	62.5	82.9	65	83.6

Discussion. Characterization of biomass oil with bonded phase chromatography could only be done after deoxygenation. This resulted in an FCC-feed stock with a high content of aromatics. Similar results have been obtained by Elliot and Baker (20).

Catalytic cracking at higher temperatures is generally associated with higher octane numbers due to increased olefins production (21). The higher temperature, 560°C, used in this work to ensure complete vaporization of Wilmington fraction No. 7, reduced polynuclear aromatics and especially polars to aromatic compounds in the gasoline range, which will give an additional boost to the octane number. Cracking resid containing feeds at higher temperatures (530°C) also produce gasoline with high octane numbers due to increased production of aromatics (22).

The nature of the matrix containing REY or CREY does not play a significant role in cracking conventional vacuum gas oils like the HVGO used in this study. Conversion of heavy vacuum gas oil, on the other hand, like Wilmington fraction No. 7 can be significantly increased by combining zeolites with high surface area, diffusion enhancing matrices such as clay+alumina which a fortiori has been found to be the case for bottoms cracking (14). This increase in activity is, however, accompanied by an increase in coke selectivity. UOP has developed a new concept for the evaluation of the performance of a cracking catalyst, in a commercial FCCU, from MAT-results (23). Application of their model on the results obtained for the catalysts prepared with and without addition of alumina to the matrix indicates that, due to the high coke make of the former, the latter would perform better when cracking heavy oils in a commercial unit (Otterstedt, J-E.; Yanming, Z.; Sterte, J. Submitted to Appl. Catal.). The surface of boehmite which has been exposed to the temperatures of the regenerator, typically 700-800°C, will contain predominantly Lewis acid sites (24). Such sites are catalytically active with preponderance for coke making in processes like catalytic cracking (25). The high surface area alumina component of the active matrix is therefore responsible for the non-selective cracking behaviour, i.e. high coke make and gas yields, characteristic of such a matrix.

Alumina as an active component of the catalyst matrix is one example of the approach to cracking heavy oils involving incorporation of various types of zeolite Y in active matrices. According to Takatsuka (26), the first step in the conversion will involve precracking of the large molecules on the matrix surface or on the surface of the zeolite crystals. The precracked molecules can undergo further cracking in the zeolite to desirable products or on the matrix surface to products which may or may not be desirable depending on the make of the matrix surface. With the right contributions of external surface of zeolite crystals and properties of the matrix surface, for instance total acidity and ratio between Lewis and Bronsted acid sites, an optimum selectivity in the precracking step can be achieved. The results of this study indicate that the properties of the alumina surface do not lead to an optimum selectivity for desired products.

In another approach, more reliance is put on the ability of the zeolite component to crack heavy molecules, although it is well known that the pore opening of such zeolites, about 8 Å, are too small to admit the large molecules present in heavy oils. Nevertheless, it has been reported that cracking catalysts containing USY are more efficient "bottoms" catalysts than those containing REY (27). Moreover, Rabo (28) has recently discovered that significant changes occur in the crystal structure of USY and dealuminated-silicon enriched zeolites of the type LZ-210 (Union Carbide) upon hydrothermal treatment. During the steam treatment aluminum ions are removed from the framework sites and replaced by silicon ions. The effect of the redistributions of framework silicon ions is to reduce the high concentration of defect sites (Al-vacancies). Ultimately, this steam induced recrystallization results in the formation of near defect free, silicon rich lattice segments, and 20-300 Å size intra-crystalline cavities, i.e. a secondary pore structure, throughout the zeolite crystals. The debris, consisting of amorphous alumina or alumina-silica, is deposited in the secondary pores where it can affect cracking of large molecules. The contributions of different zeolites and matrices to the cracking of large molecules or aggregates of molecules in heavy oils are being investigated in this laboratory.

The importance of diffusion enhancement to heavy oil cracking is further illustrated by the alumina-montmorillonite complexes which crack heavier feeds, i.e. Wilmington fraction No. 6, more effectively than REY. When used as matrices for REY, the alumina-montmorillonites results in considerably more active catalysts, at the same zeolite content, compared with a catalyst having a kaolin-binder matrix, while the selectivity properties differs very little between the two types of catalysts (Sterte, J.; Otterstedt, J-E. Submitted to Appl.Catal.).

The cracking of the BMO gave a poor result mainly due to the low H/C-ratio (see Table III). Hemler and Wilcox (29,30) catalytically cracked coal liquids, hydroprocessed at different severities, and found that the conversion increased and the selectivity improved with increasing severity of hydroprocessing. Hydroprocessing the BMO at more severe conditions should improve the cracking properties of this oil.

Acknowledgements

The authors acknowledge the financial support from the Swedish Board for Technical Development (STU) and the Swedish National Energy Administration (STEV).

Literature Cited

1.   Andersson, S-I.; Otterstedt, J-E. Paper presented at Katalistiks 8th Annual Fluid Cat Cracking Symposium, Budapest, Hungary, June, 1987.
2.   Speight, J. G. The Desulfurization of Heavy Oils and Residue; Marcel Dekker: New York, 1981.
3.   Frumkin, H. A.; Sullivan, R. F.; Stangeland, B. E. ACS Symposium Series, 1981, 156, 75.
4.   Sullivan, R. F. Paper presented at the SAE West Coast International Meeting, San Fransisco, Aug., 1982.

5.   Gevert, B. G.; Otterstedt, J-E. Preprints, IGT Conference on Energy from Biomass and Wastes X, Washington DC, April, 1986.
6.   Parks, G. D. Preprints, ACS Div. Petr., Houston, March, 1980.
7.   De Jong, J. I. U. S. Patent 4 519 897, 1984.
8.   Otterstedt, J-E.; Järås, S. G.; Pudas, R.; Upson, L. L. U. S. Patent, 4 515 903, 1984.
9.   Wear, C. Oil & Gas J. 1985, 106, March 4.
10.   Elvin, F.; Otterstedt, J-E.; Sterte, J. Preprints, ACS Div. Petr. Chem. 1987, 32, 694.
11.   McArthur, D. P.; Simpson, H. D.; Baron, K. Oil & Gas J. 1981, 55, Feb. 23.
12.   Aitken, E. J.; Baron, K.; McArthur, D. P. Paper presented at Katalistiks 6th Annual Fluid Cat Cracking Symposium, Munic, May, 1986.
13.   Baron, K.; Wu, A. H.; Krenzke, L. D. Preprints, ACS Div. Petr. Chem. 1983, 28.
14.   O´Connor, P.; Houtert, F. Paper F-8, 4th Ketjen Catalyst Symposium, Kurhaus, Scheveningen, The Netherlands, May, 1986.
15.   Vaughan, D. E. W.; Lussier, R. J.; Magee, J. S. U. S. Patent 4 176 090, 1979.
16.   Gevert, S. B. Preprints, IGT Conference on Energy from Biomass and Wastes XI. Orlando, March, 1987.
17.   Nilsson, P.; Massoth, F. E.; Otterstedt, J-E. Appl. Cat., 1986, 26, 175.
18.   Nilsson, P.; Otterstedt, J-E. Appl. Cat., 1987, 33, 145.
19.   Sterte, J.; Otterstedt, J-E. In Studies in Surface Science and Catalysis, Delmon, B.; Grange, P.; Jacobs, P.A.; Poncelet, G., Eds.; Elsevier Science Publishers: Amsterdam, 1987.
20.   Elliot, D. C.; Baker, E. G. Preprints, IGT Conference on Energy from Wastes and Biomass X, Washington D.C., April, 1986.
21.   Venuto, P. B.; Habib, E. T. Fluid Catalytic Cracking with Zeolite Catalysts; Marcel Dekker: New York, 1978.
22.   Henz, H. F.; Fusco, J. M. Paper F-4, 4th Ketjen Catalyst Symposium, Kurhaus, Scheveningen, The Netherlands, May, 1986.
23.   Mott, R. W. Oil & Gas J. 1987, 85, (4), 73.
24.   Linsen, B. G.; Steggerda, J. J. Physical and Chemical Aspects of Adsorbents and Catalysts; Linsen, B.G, Ed.; Academic Press: London and New York, 1970.
25.   Hall, W. K.; Lutinsky, F. E.; Gerberich, H. R. J. Catal. 1964, 3, 512.
26.   Takatsuka, T. "Bottoms Cracking Capability of Resid FCC Catalysts", translation of Japanese Publication, November 1984.
27.   Ritter, R. E.; Creighton, J. E.; Roberie, T. G.; Chin, D. S.; Wear, C. C. Paper AM-86-45, NPRA Annual Meeting, San Antonio, March, 1986.
28.   Rabo, J. A.; Pellet, R. G.; Risch, A. P.; Blackwell, C. S. Paper presented at the Katalistiks 8th Catalytic Cracking Symposium, Budapest, Hungary, June, 1987.
29.   Hemler, C. L.; Wilcox, J. R. Proc. Am. Petr. Inst., Refin. Dep., 1981, 60, 203.
30.   Hemler, C. L.; Wilcox, J. R., Pet. Int. (Milan), 1981, 28, (11), 30.

RECEIVED February 25, 1988

Chapter 18

Catalytic Cracking of a Wilmington Vacuum Gas Oil and Selected Hydrotreated Products

Jan W. Wells[1]

IIT Research Institute, National Institute for Petroleum and Energy Research, P.O. Box 2128, Bartlesville, OK 74005

The catalytic cracking of a Wilmington vacuum gas oil and the products from mild hydrotreating and severe hydrotreating of this gas oil were evaluated over a low metal equilibrium catalyst in a microconfined bed unit (MCBU). Two levels of catalytic cracking severity were evaluated for these three samples. The results indicated that a level of hydrotreating exists above which the quality of the liquid products and the yields of coke and heavy cycle oil are not affected significantly by the severity of the catalytic cracking process. The sulfur and nitrogen content of the liquid products (gasolines, light cycle oil, and heavy cycle oil) were found to decrease as the severity of the feed hydrotreating increased. The distribution of sulfur and nitrogen in the liquid products was found to be independent of cracking conditions or product yields for a given level of hydrogenation. Analysis of the gas products shows that the degree of hydrogen transfer increases with the severity of hydrogenation.

Background

In the modern refinery, upgrading of "the bottom of the barrel" is a critical part of the refining process. One of the most successful unit operations used in this upgrading process is fluidized catalytic cracking (FCC). In catalytic cracking, a zeolite catalyst is used to "crack" a residue or gas oil cut to lighter products--hopefully gasoline range material. In addition, carbon is formed on the catalyst surface, and light gases are also produced. These latter products are less desirable than the

[1]Current address: Phillips Petroleum Company, Bartlesville, OK 74004

0097–6156/88/0375–0279$08.25/0
© 1988 American Chemical Society

gasoline fraction because of their lower value. Successful operation of a catalytic cracker depends on the proper combination of the catalyst, the catalytic cracking hardware, and the feedstock to produce the desired products.

A recent review by Corma and Wjcieckowski (1), concluded that the chemistry of gas oil cracking is at present poorly defined. For this reason, much of the literature addressing the effect of feedstock composition is limited to performance measurements and general chemical characterizations. The behavior of heavy feeds in catalytic cracking has been found to depend to a large extent on the nature of the feed (2). The cracking of aliphatic or naphthenic feed is much easier and results in a better product slate than the cracking of aromatic cuts. Specifically, the more aromatic a feedstock, the lower the gasoline yield and the greater the coke yield. The more aliphatic or naphthenic the feed, the higher the gasoline yield and the lower the coke.

Also, the performance of the feed depends on the molecular weight. For paraffinic feeds, the higher the average molecular weight, the larger the yield of gasoline. For aromatic feeds, the higher the average molecular weight, the lower the gasoline yield. The performance of the catalytic cracker is also affected by the presence of polynuclear aromatic hydrocarbons (PNA). These rather large PNA molecules have a greater affinity for the acid sites on a typical zeolite cracking catalyst. As a result, the PNAs block the active sites for the cracking reaction and allow the aliphatic and naphthenic molecules to pass through the reactor with low conversion. In general, the zeolite catalyst, which is strongly acidic, is particularly susceptible to temporary deactivation by the presence of PNAs (3).

The presence of heteroatoms also affects catalytic cracker performance and product quality. The sulfur compounds crack and distribute the sulfur to the catalytic cracker products. A study by Huling, et al. (4), has shown that the largest percentage of the feed sulfur is found in the light gas as hydrogen sulfide (usually over 50 percent of the feed sulfur). The remainder of the sulfur distributes to the light cycle oil (LCO), heavy cycle oil (HCO), coke, and gasoline. The least sulfur is usually found in the gasoline fraction (3 to 5 percent of the feed sulfur). The gasoline fraction sulfur tends to be contained in acidic mercaptans which must be removed to ensure fuel quality. This is normally done by caustic treatment which neutralizes the mercaptan. The specific distribution of sulfur among the catalytic cracking products has been found to vary with feedstock. This is especially true of the distribution of the feedstock sulfur within the LCO, HCO, and coke products. The distribution of the feedstock sulfur in these products has been shown to vary from 2.8 to 28 weight percent. The reason for these dramatic differences is thought to be variation in the structure of the sulfur molecules in the feedstock.

Another heteroatom in the feed which affects performance and product quality is nitrogen. Basic nitrogen in the feed tends to lower cracking activity by adsorbing onto the acid sites of the surface of the cracking catalyst. The work of Wu and Schaffer (5), showed that not all nitrogen compounds were equally harmful. They found that poisoning could be related to the structure and the size of the nitrogen-containing molecule. Proton affinity was found to be useful in explaining and predicting the deactivating effects of various nitrogen compounds adsorbed on the catalyst surface. The nitrogen compounds tend to decompose on the catalyst surface and thus increase the yield of coke. The nitrogen contained in the coke may be oxidized in the regenerator to form potentially troublesome NO_x when the regenerator is operated to convert all of the CO to CO_2. When the regenerator is operated in the partial CO combustion mode, ammonium chloride and ammonium sulfate may form in the regeneration off gas. In addition to the nitrogen compounds adsorbed on the catalyst surface, other nitrogen compounds crack and appear in the light gas as ammonia and in the liquid products. Nitrogen compounds such as ammonia and cyanides also appear in the sour water product. Information on the distribution and the structure of nitrogen compounds in the liquid products is quite limited. In the LCO from the catalytic cracker, pyrroles and pyridines have been identified (6). These compounds, when oxidized, are believed to cause sediment formation and color problems in refinery products.

Another type of problem compound in the feedstock is organo-metallics. Of primary interest in catalytic cracking are compounds containing nickel and vanadium. When the organometallic compounds decompose on the catalyst, the contained metals tend to remain quantitatively on the surface when the catalyst is regenerated. The metals block active catalyst sites, permanently reducing the action of the catalyst. The detailed mechanism of the effects of the metals has been described by Upson, et al. (7). In summary, the presence of vanadium on the catalyst surface leads to the permanent deactivation of the zeolite site, while nickel does not cause a loss of surface activity but does result in nonselective cracking and excessive light gas and coke production. If the overall content of these metals in the feed is greater than 15 ppm, the rate of catalyst deactivation will be excessive, and the process will require the replacement of catalyst at a rate which makes the process uneconomical.

As can be seen in the above discussion, the presence of heteroatom and organometallic compounds can cause pollution problems, catalyst deactivation problems (permanent or temporary), and product stability problems. One way of controlling these factors is to hydrotreat the feedstock prior to catalytic cracking. In the hydrotreating step, the objective is to remove the sulfur, nitrogen, and metal-bearing compounds. The sulfur and metal compounds are relatively easy to remove at mild hydrotreater conditions, while nitrogen compounds are more difficult to remove and may require more severe hydrotreating conditions. At mild hydrotreating conditions, there is sometimes an increase in the basic nitrogen content, resulting in a lower catalytic activity when the material is fed to the catalyic cracker.

In addition, hydrotreating converts polynuclear aromatic (PNA) compounds and other potential coke-forming material to more easily cracked naphthenes and paraffins. Like the removal of nitrogen compounds, the saturation of PNAs also requires more severe conditions than removal of sulfur or metals and results in a significant increase in hydrotreater hydrogen consumption.

As reported by Venuto and Habib (8) and Decroocq (3), hydrotreating generally improves the reactivity of the catalytic cracker feedstock. The degree of improvement is usually directly proportional to the amount of hydrogen consumed. Thus, higher conversions, gasoline yields, and lower coke make are generally reported as a result of cracking hydrotreated feedstocks. Also, product quality is significantly better for all products from light gases to coke because of the removal of metals and the reduction of the sulfur and nitrogen content of the final products. In this study, the effects of upstream hydrotreating on the crackability of a 650° to 1000° F nominal boiling range Wilmington distillate are evaluated.

Bench-scale catalytic cracking unit

A schematic of the bench-scale cracking unit is shown in Figure 1. The quartz reactor in a three-zone temperature-controlled furnace is charged with about 35 g of sized and aged catalyst (the procedure used in aging and sizing the catalyst will be discussed in a subsequent section). Water-saturated nitrogen is used to fluidize the bed during the cracking reaction. The oil is injected via a hand-held syringe through a movable tube at about two to three inches above the expanded bed. The injection is timed to last 30 seconds. After the injection of the oil feed, the fluidized catalyst bed is stripped with nitrogen gas for 4.5 minutes, while the gaseous products are collected in a plastic bag immersed in a full water displacement tank. The total volume of the gas collected is determined from the weight of the water displaced and the temperature of the water displacement tank. This gas is then analyzed using a previously calibrated gas chromatograph (Hache Model 400 AGE) to determine the volume percent composition of the gas. The liquid products are weighed and then analyzed via the ASTM D 2887 simulated distillation technique to determine the boiling point curve of the liquid products. The specific gravity of the liquid products is also determined via ASTM D 4052.

After the cracking run is complete, the coked catalyst is regenerated by passing air saturated with water at room temperature over the catalyst at an elevated temperature (1250° F). The amount of coke deposited on the catalyst is determined by the difference in reactor weight before and after the regeneration.

Catalyst preparation

The catalyst chosen for this study was a low metal, equilibrium, commercial zeolite-containing cracking catalyst obtained from Phillips Petroleum Company. No specific characterization of the catalyst is available.

In order to prepare the low metal equilibrium catalyst for the bench-scale cracking unit evaluation, the catalyst must be sized, dried, and conditioned. In the following, each of these steps is described.

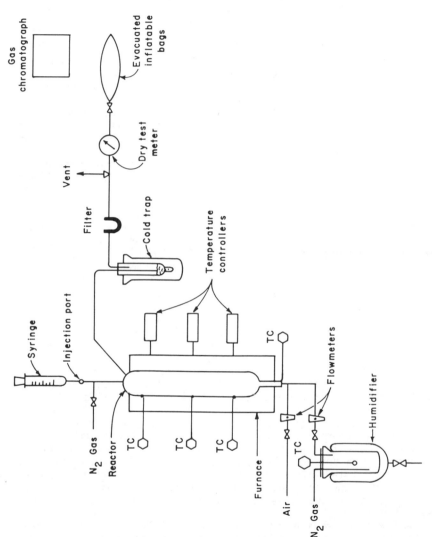

Figure 1. Schematic of bench-scale catalytic cracking unit.

The catalyst samples were screened to give a 200- by 325-mesh particle size sample. This was done to remove fines and coarse particles and hence assure good fluidization characteristics with minimal entrainment of fines. As a result, the majority of the particles in the sample has a particle size between 44 and 53 microns. Dry ice was used to eliminate plugging of the screen due to static electricity.

Next, the catalyst was weighed into the reactor. A sample size of about 35 grams was used for all evaluations. The rationale for this was an attempt to maintain reasonable gas residence times and fluidization behavior. After the reactor was placed into the furnace, the catalyst was fluidized with nitrogen, and dried for 30 minutes at 400° F. The reactor then was cooled and reweighed. Next, the catalyst was conditioned by exposure to two reducing and oxidizing cycles. The reactor was fluidized with nitrogen and heated to about 950° F (510° C). The oil to be cracked was injected into the bed (reducing cycle), and the bed was stripped with nitrogen gas for a short period. The reactor temperature was then raised to 1250° F (677° C), and the bed was fluidized with air (oxidation cycle).

Feedstock Characterization. The feedstocks studied in this effort were a Wilmington vacuum gas oil and two hydrotreated products of this gas oil. The specific samples considered were sample No. 1693, an untreated Wilmington vacuum gas oil, a low severity hydrotreated product from sample No. 1693 (sample No. WM-2-2R, hydrotreated at 375° C, 1.5 LHSV, and 1500 psig), and a high severity hydrotreated product (sample No. WM-2-9, hydrotreated at 425° C, 0.5 LHSV, 1500 psig). The available physical properties for each of these feedstocks are given in Table I.

A review of the feedstock characteristics shows that the vacuum gas oil (1693) is a good cracker feed material because of the low metals content (below level of detection) and the low carbon residue, a good indication of little asphaltic material in the oil. The low asphaltic content of this gas oil indicates that the majority of the oil will vaporize, diffuse to the zeolite site, and be catalytically cracked. In addition, the simulated distillation results imply that very little of this gas oil will remain as a liquid to be thermally cracked to coke and light gas on the external surface of the catalyst. The total nitrogen content of the untreated vacuum gas oil (0.56 weight percent) is greater than the level of total nitrogen which is known to affect catalytic cracker performance (greater than 0.03 to 0.09 weight percent) (8). Hence, some reversible poisoning of the cracking catalyst may be expected.

The hydrotreated feedstock samples (WM-2-2R and WM-2-9) could be expected to be more readily cracked. The nitrogen and sulfur levels are lower, and this implies that asphaltic material, where these heteroatoms are normally concentrated, has been greatly reduced. The lower nitrogen level also implies a reduction in deactivation due to nitrogen poisoning of the active sites. For example, in WM-2-2R (low severity hydrotreating) the nitrogen level, while significantly reduced (0.33 versus 0.56 weight percent), is still high enough to affect cracking performance; but, for the high severity sample (WM-2-9), the level of total nitrogen

Table I. Catalytic cracker feedstock characteristics

Property	Sample 1693	Sample WM-2-2R	Sample WM-2-9
API gravity	13.3	19.1	31.3
Specific gravity @ 60°F	0.977	0.939	0.869
Viscosity, cSt			
@ 130° F	311.7	64.6	2.89
@ 180° F	51.9	NM	NM
Carbon residue, wt %			
(Conradson)	0.68	NM	NM
Metals, ppm	BDL	NM	NM
Elemental analysis, wt %			
Carbon	86.23	NM	87.14
Hydrogen	11.23	NM	13.16
Sulfur	1.97	0.236	0.016
Nitrogen	0.56	0.327	0.002
Molecular weight			
(estimated)	390	380	245
Simulated distillation, °F			
IBP	545	277	176
10%	715	642	320
25%	792	739	438
50%	850	822	584
75%	918	882	719
90%	979	932	813
EBP	1032	1015	956

BDL - Below detection limits.
NM - not measured.

has been reduced to a level (0.002 wt. pct.) which will not affect catalytic cracker performance. As with the vacuum gas oil, the simulated distillations for the hydrotreated catalytic cracker feedstocks imply that the majority of the oil fed will vaporize and efficiently contact the active sites on the catalyst. Both hydrotreated samples contain some gasoline boiling range (below 430° F) hydrocarbons. The cracking reaction rate for these lower boiling components is very low, and they may serve mostly as an oil feed diluent in FCC units.

The distribution of nitrogen compounds in the polar fraction of these feedstocks is given in Table II. This table is based on work currently being performed by J. B. Green (Private Communication, NIPER, September 1986). In the nonhydrotreated feed (1693), the most common polar nitrogen compounds are the acidic pyrrolic benzologs. These include compounds such as pyrroles, indoles, and carbazoles. The next most common nitrogen compounds in the untreated feed (1693) are basic azaarenes. Examples of these compounds are pyridines and quinolines. The compound types present in the lowest levels are basic N-H compounds (e.g., 9,10-dihydrophenanthridine) and basic arylamines (e.g., anilines). As can be seen in Table II, mild hydrotreating (WM-2-2R) causes the pyrrolic concentration to increase slightly, the basic azaarenes concentration to drop, and the levels of basic N-H and arylamines to remain about the same. Severe hydrotreating (WM-2-9) causes a dramatic drop in concentration of all polar nitrogen compounds with only the acidic pyrrolic compounds surviving at a significant level. It can be expected that significant reversible deactivation of the cracking catalyst will occur for the nonhydrotreated feedstock (1693) and the mildly hydrotreated feedstock (WM-2-2R). This will cause lower conversions of the gas oil to desirable products. The extremely low levels of basic nitrogen (and total nitrogen) in the severely hydrotreated feed (WM-2-9) imply that almost no nitrogen compound catalyst deactivation will occur during the cracking of this feed.

Table II. - Distribution of polar nitrogen compounds in the Wilmington vacuum gas oil (1693) and its hydrotreated products (WM-2-2R and WM-2-9)

	Sample Number		
Compound Type	1693	WM-2-2R	WM-2-9
Acidic, wt pct			
Pyrroles	3.7	3.8	0.05
Basic, wt pct			
Azaarene	1.8	1.0	0
Basic N-H	0.40	0.4	0
Arylamine	0.1	0.1	0

Results and Discussion

Performance Analysis. In order to determine the effect of hydrotreating on catalytic cracking performance, the above feedstocks were evaluated at a low severity cracking condition (catalyst-to-oil ratio of 6.0 and reactor temperature of 910° F) and a high severity cracking condition (catalyst-to-oil of 8.0 and reactor temperature of 1010° F). The results from the catalytic cracking of these feedstocks (shown in Tables I and II) are shown in Tables III through V. The results presented in these tables are

the average of three to five replicate runs. In general, the
material balance for all runs closed within ±10 percent.
Conversion in Tables III through V is defined as follows:

$$X = 100 [1.0 - (V_p/V_f)]$$

where X is the conversion in volume percent, V_p is the volume of
the product which boils above 430° F, and V_f is the volume of the
feed. Conversion is the fraction (or percent) of material which
boils below 430° F (light gases or gasoline) plus the coke. The
gasoline yield is the volume of C_5 to 430° F material divided by
the total feed volume expressed as a percentage. The volume of the
gasoline is determined from the total liquid product volume and the
simulated distillation of the liquid products and is corrected by
the gas chromatographic analysis of the light gases for C_5 and C_6
compounds. It should be noted that this definition of the yield of
gasoline assumes all C_5 to 430° F boiling range material, even when
some low boiling material is present in the feed oil. Light cycle
oil (LCO) is the product boiling between 430° F and 650° F, and
heavy cycle oil is the product boiling above 650° F.

In general, the data in these tables show that an increase in
the severity of the hydrotreating increases the conversion and
gasoline yield from the downstream cracking operation. Increasing
hydrotreating severity also decreases the yield of coke and heavy
cycle oil. The yield of the LCO appears to be independent of the
hydrotreating condition. Increasing the severity of the catalytic
cracking step increases the conversion for all samples tested. For
the nonhydrotreated feed material, Table III, the gasoline yield
increases with cracking severity. For the lightly hydrotreated
feedstock (Table IV), the gasoline yield remains relatively
constant for increasing cracking severity, and, for the heavily
hydrotreated feedstock (Table V), the gasoline yield actually
decreases at severe catalytic cracker conditions. This indicates
that the severely hydrotreated feed is more likely to undergo
secondary cracking reactions which lead to overcracking and
decrease in the gasoline yield.

Table III. Catalytic cracking of untreated
Wilmington 650° to 1000° F (1693)

	Catalytic cracking conditions	
	Low severity	High severity
Conversion, vol %	54.5	71.8
Gasoline, vol %	41.0	48.6
Coke, wt %	6.2	6.9
Light cycle oil yield, vol %	21.4	16.5
Heavy cycle oil yield, vol %	24.2	11.6
Ratio of C_4 saturates to olefins	0.9	0.7

Table IV. Catalytic cracking of lightly hydrotreated (511.5 scf/bbl) Wilmington 650° to 1000° F (WM-2-2R)

| | Catalytic cracking conditions | |
	Low severity	High severity
Conversion, vol %	66.8	75.7
Gasoline, vol %	56.4	55.5
Coke, wt %	4.1	5.4
Light cycle oil yield, vol %	19.4	15.0
Heavy cycle oil yield, vol %	13.8	9.2
Ratio of C_4 saturates to olefins	1.3	1.0

Table V. Catalytic cracking of severely hydrotreated (1610.5 scf/bbl) Wilmington 650° to 1000° F (WM-2-9)

| | Catalytic cracking conditions | |
	Low severity	High severity
Conversion, vol %	76.2	79.5
Gasoline, vol %	66.9	61.1
Coke, wt %	2.5	2.5
Light cycle oil yield, vol %	19.8	16.6
Heavy cycle oil yield, vol %	3.9	3.9
Ratio of C_4 saturates to olefins	1.8	1.3

The results given in Tables IV and V are shown in Figures 2 and 3. Specifically, these figures show the conversion, gasoline yield, light cycle oil yield, and heavy cycle oil yield as a function of feed hydrotreating hydrogen consumption for both the low severity cracking (Figure 2) and the high severity cracking (Figure 3). In general, the conversion and gasoline yields increase with hydrogen consumption in the feed pretreatment for both cracking severity levels; but past a hydrogen consumption of about 500 scf/bbl, the gain in conversion and gasoline yield is much less per standard cubic foot of hydrogen added in the pretreatment. As can be seen, the increase in conversion is primarily a result of the cracking of the heavy cycle oil to lighter materials and coke.

Also shown in Tables III through V is the effect of hydrotreating on hydrogen transfer during catalytic cracking. This effect is shown by the ratio of saturated C_4 to olefinic C_4. In catalytic cracking, there are two mechanisms for the formation of saturates. These are the primary cracking reaction, such as

$$\text{Paraffin} \rightarrow \text{Paraffin} + \text{Olefin} \tag{1}$$

and the hydrogen transfer reaction

$$\text{Olefin 1} + \text{Olefin 2} \rightarrow \text{Saturate} + \text{Diolefin}. \tag{2}$$

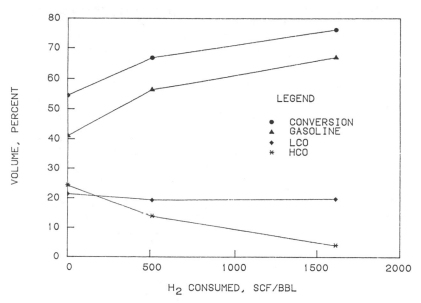

Figure 2. The effects of hydrotreating on catalytic cracking performance -- low cracking severity.

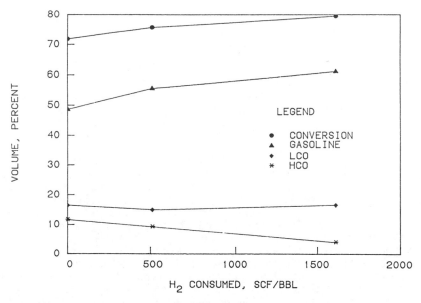

Figure 3. The effects of hydrotreating on catalytic cracking performance -- high cracking severity.

In theory, if only the primary cracking reaction occurred, the ratio of saturates to olefins in the products would be one. A review of the saturate to olefin ratios given in Tables III through V shows that as the severity of the cracking increases, the ratio of the saturated C_4 to olefinic C_4 also increases. This is true at every level of hydrogen pretreatment. These results imply that less hydrogen transfer is occurring at more severe cracking conditions, and hence more olefinic products are being produced. The opposite is true as the severity of hydrotreating pretreatment increases. Specifically, for the low severity cracking condition, the saturate to olefinic ratio starts at 0.9 for the Wilmington 650° to 1000° F fraction catalytic cracker feed and increases to 1.8 for high severity hydrotreated Wilmington catalytic cracker feedstock. This indicates a large increase in the amount of hydrogen transfer when the hydrotreated feed is cracked. If this trend extends to heavier molecules (C_6 to C_{10}), this increase in hydrogen transfer may decrease the octane number of the gasoline.

Another interesting trend shown in Tables IV through V, can be seen by considering the coke, light cycle oil, and heavy cycle oil data. As previously stated, the increase in the degree of hydrotreating generally decreased the yield of these products, except for the light cycle oil which remained constant. Increasing severity of the catalytic cracking in general would be expected to increase the coke and decrease the yields of the light cycle oil and heavy cycle oil [more primary and secondary cracking reactions due to greater residence time and higher temperature (reaction rate)]. These trends hold true for the results shown in Tables III and IV; but, for Table V (catalytic cracking of the severely hydrotreated sample), the coke and the heavy cycle oil remain constant as the catalytic cracking conditions are varied from low to high severity. The light cycle oil yield does decrease (as observed in Tables III and IV). This implies some degree of hydrotreating exists which causes the coke and heavy cycle oil production to be independent of catalytic cracking conditions. This could be caused by the presence of highly stable compounds which are formed or survive during the hydrotreating process. The causes and implications of these preliminary results should be explored.

Product Analysis. In addition to the above performance analysis, the gaseous and liquid products were analyzed in greater detail. The gas analysis was performed during the evaluation runs made to generate the data of Tables III through V. A separate set of runs was conducted to collect liquid products for analysis. This was necessary because of the small amount of liquid generated by a typical bench-scale catalytic cracker run (~1-3 ml). To overcome this small sample size, multiple runs were made until approximately 60 ml of liquid products was obtained. No effort was made to analyze the coke deposited on the catalyst. In the following section, the results of the analysis of the bulk liquids and corresponding fractionated liquid samples will be given along with the light gas analysis. Because of the complex and poorly understood nature of gas oil cracking (1), only limited discussion of these results will be given.

Bulk Liquid Product Analysis

The effect of operating severity on the characteristics of the
liquid products is given in Tables VI through VIII which show that
the catalytic cracking process produces a liquid significantly
lighter (higher API gravity and lower specific gravity) than the
cracker feed.   In addition, the cracking process lowers the
heteroatom content of the liquid product. Cracking reduces the
nitrogen content in the liquid, and the final level appears to be
essentially independent of the severity of the cracking.
     The cracking process also lowers the sulfur content of the bulk
liquid   products.   Like   the   results   for   nitrogen,   the
nonhydrotreated   feedstock   (1693,   Table   VI)   and   the   mildly
hydrotreated   feedstock   (WM-2-2R,   Table VII)   show   no   significant
difference in the sulfur levels of the low severity cracking liquid
product and the high severity cracking liquid product. For the
severely hydrotreated feedstock (WM-2-9, Table VIII), the sulfur
content of the liquid product decreases, but the higher severity
cracking condition produces a liquid with an apparently higher
sulfur concentration than the low cracking severity case (100 ppm
versus 50 ppm). This increase may be an analytical artifact caused
by the low sulfur concentrations, and these levels may well be
equal.

Table VI. - Liquid product analysis from cracking of
Wilmington vacuum gas oil (Sample No. 1693)

Property	Catalytic Cracker Feedstock Sample No. 1693	Liquid Product	
		Low Severity Sample No. 2123	High Severity Sample No. 2124
API gravity	13.5	25.6	26.2
Specific gravity @ 60° F	0.9758	0.9004	0.8975
Elemental Analysis			
Carbon	86.23	87.44	87.35
Hydrogen	11.23	10.77	10.26
Nitrogen	0.56	0.40	0.40
Sulfur	1.97	1.12	1.08
Hydrogen to carbon molar ratio	1.56	1.48	1.41
Molecular weight (API Proc. 2B2.1)	390	172	146
Bromine number	7.3	34.5	35.4

Table VII. - Liquid product analysis from cracking of low
severity hydrotreated product
(Sample No. WM-2-2R)

| Property | Catalytic Cracker Feedstock Sample WM-2-2R | Liquid Product | |
		Low Severity Sample No. 2125	High Severity Sample No. 2126
API gravity	19.1	34.4	33.5
Specific gravity @ 60° F	0.9398	0.8531	0.8574
Elemental Analysis			
Carbon	NM	88.30	88.48
Hydrogen	NM	11.42	10.79
Nitrogen	0.33	0.19	0.22
Sulfur	0.24	0.09	0.13
Hydrogen to carbon molar ratio	NM	1.55	1.46
Molecular weight (API Proc. 2B2.1)	380	150	130
Bromine number	NM	24.0	29.6

Table VIII. - Liquid product analysis from cracking of severely
hydrotreated product (Sample No. WM-2-9)

| Property | Catalytic Cracker Feedstock Sample No. WM-2-9 | Liquid Product | |
		Low Severity Sample No. 2127	High Severity Sample No. 2128
API gravity	31.3	42.6	42.1
Specific gravity @ 60° F	0.8691	0.8107	0.8155
Elemental Analysis			
Carbon	87.14	87.92	88.99
Hydrogen	13.16	11.48	11.16
Nitrogen	0.002	0.00174	0.00128
Sulfur	0.0158	0.00515	0.01044
Hydrogen to carbon molar ratio	1.81	1.57	1.51
Molecular weight (API Proc. 2B2.1)	245	135	132
Bromine number	NM	12.2	18.1

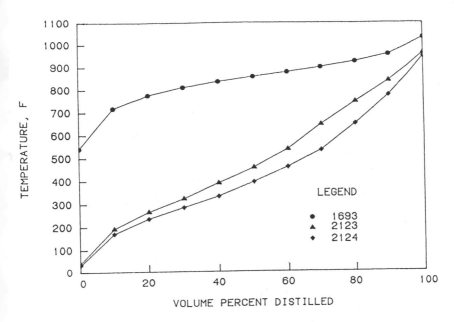

Figure 4. Simulated distillation of sample No. 1693 and bulk products from catalytic cracking of low severity (2123) and high severity (2124).

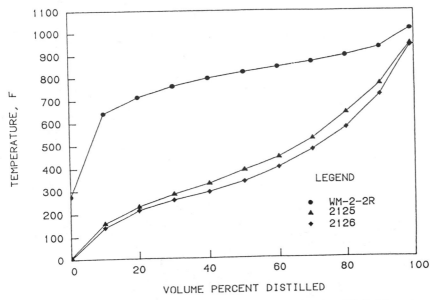

Figure 5. Simulated distillation of sample No. WM-2-2R and bulk products from catalytic cracking at low severity (2125) and high severity (2126).

The analysis of the molecular weight data given in Tab
through VIII shows that cracking results in significant mol
weight reduction. Also, the molecular weight of the liquid p
decreases as the severity of hydrotreating increases. Fc
nonhydrotreated feedstock (1693) and the mildly hydroti
feedstock (WM-2-2R), increasing the severity of the cri
conditions results in lower molecular weight liquid products.
the severely hydrotreated cracker feedstock (WM-2-9), the mole
weight of the liquid product does not vary with cra
severity. As discussed earlier, this indicates the presen
highly stable compounds in this feedstock.

The bromine number results indicate that increasing
severity of hydrotreating prior to catalytic cracking lowers
olefinic content of the product liquids. The severity of
cracking process had minimal effect on the bromine number of
product liquids from the nonhydrotreated feedstock (i.e.,
sample No. 1693, both were essentially the same). This indi
that the olefinic content of liquid product from the crackir
the nonhydrotreated feedstock (1693) does not depend on crac
severity, which is a surprising result and cannot be ea
explained. It may be due to the hydrogen transfer reactio
heavier molecules. More typically, the hydrotreated feedst
showed a significantly higher bromine number (hence, ol
content) for the high severity product than the low severity li
product.

The simulated distillation results (ASTM D 2887) for
samples presented in Tables VI through VIII are given in Figure
through 6. Figure 4 shows the simulated distillation for
nonhydrotreated Wilmington vacuum gas oil (1693) and the li
products from the low severity cracking (sample No. 2123) and
high severity cracking (sample No. 2124). As can be seen,
cracking process generates a significantly lighter liquid produ
and, as the severity of the cracking increases, the liquid proc
boiling point curve shifts to the right, indicating a lower boil
material. A similar trend is observed in Figure 5 for the liq
products from the cracking of the mildly hydrotreated feedst
(WM-2-2R). A comparison of the boiling point curves of the liq
products from the low severity cracking (2125) and the high sev
ity cracking (2126) shows that the differences are less th
observed for the nonhydrotreated sample (see Figure 4). Figure
for the severely hydrotreated feedstock again shows a significa
shift in the boiling point curves indicating lighter product
However, the curves for the low severity cracking liquid produ
(2127) and the high severity liquid product (2128) are essential
identical. A review of Table IX shows the only significa
difference between the two liquid products is the bromine numbe
The high severity cracking liquid has a higher bromine number the
the low severity liquid sample (18 versus 12). Sevel
hydrotreating appears to have resulted in a cracked liquid produc
whose properties, except for bromine number, are not significantl
affected by cracking severity.

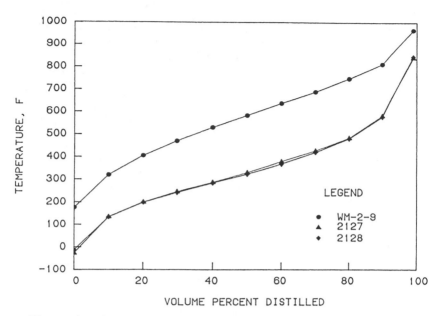

Figure 6. Simulated distillation of sample No. WM-2-9 and bulk products from catalytic cracking at low severity (2127) and high severity (2128).

Table IXa. - Analysis of liquid product fractions from low severity cracking of Wilmington vacuum gas oil (sample No. 1693)

| | Low severity catalytic cracking | | | |
Property	Liquid product sample No. 2123	Gasoline (IBP-430° F) sample No. 2176	LCO (430-650° F) sample No. 2177	HCO (650°+ F) sample No. 2178
API gravity	27.4	47.4	14.5	4.9
Specific gravity @ 60° F	0.8904	0.7911	0.9690	1.0371
Molecular weight (API Proc. 2B2.1)	175	118	190	330*
Elemental analysis				
Carbon	87.44	87.06	88.9	87.72
Hydrogen	10.77	12.70	9.65	9.36
Nitrogen	0.404	0.040	0.311	0.732
Sulfur	1.119	0.472	1.50	1.62
Bromine number	34.5	52.6	15.0	NM

Table IXb. - Analysis of liquid product fractions from high
severity cracking of Wilmington vacuum gas
oil (sample No. 1693)

| Property | High severity catalytic cracking | | | |
	Liquid product sample No. 2124	Gasoline (IBP-430° F) sample No. 2179	LCO (430-650° F) sample No. 2180	HCO (650°+ F) sample No. 2181
API gravity	27.5	46.2	10.6	0.10
Specific gravity @ 60° F	0.8899	0.7964	0.9957	1.0752
Molecular weight (API Proc.2B2.1)	148 117	182	293*	
Elemental analysis				
Carbon	87.35	87.96	88.82	88.53
Hydrogen	10.26	12.23	8.66	8.47
Nitrogen	0.402	0.060	0.362	0.793
Sulfur	1.080	0.42	1.63	1.66
Bromine number	35.4	50.3	15.0	NM

NM - Not measured
* - VPO molecular weight

Analysis of Liquid Product Fractions

As a result of repetitive runs at both low and high severity
catalytic cracking conditions, sufficient liquid sample was
collected to allow atmospheric and vacuum distillations into a
gasoline fraction (IBP - 430° F), light cycle oil fraction
(boiling 430°-650° F), and a heavy cycle oil fraction (boiling
>650°+ F). The available analyses for these fractions are shown in
Tables IX through XI. Each table has two parts, (a) and (b). Part
(a) corresponds to low severity cracking results, and part (b)
refers to high severity cracking results.

Figures 7 through 12 summarize Tables IXa-XIb showing the
effects of hydrotreating pretreatment on the sulfur and nitrogen
content and on the bromine number of the liquid product
fractions. Figure 7 shows the sulfur content of the gasoline, LCO,
and HCO fractions from the low severity cracking runs. The
hydrotreating of the catalytic cracking feed significantly lowers
the sulfur concentration of all liquid products; and, as the
severity of the hydrotreating increases, the level of sulfur
continues to decrease but at a slower rate. A similar trend is
observed in Figure 8 for the sulfur content of the liquid products
from the high severity cracking test. A comparison of the results,
Figures 7 and 8, shows that the severity of the cracking did not
significantly affect the distribution of the sulfur. This finding
agrees with the total sulfur analysis discussed in the previous
section.

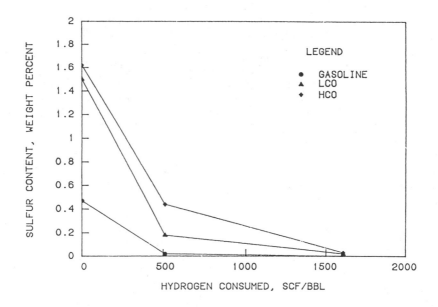

Figure 7. Distribution of sulfur in low severity cracking products as a function of hydrotreating pretreatment.

Table Xa. - Analysis of liquid product fractions from low severity cracking of mildly hydrotreated Wilmington vacuum gas oil (No. WM-2-2R)

Property	Liquid product sample No. 2125	Low severity catalytic cracking		
		Gasoline (IBP-430° F) sample No. 2182	LCO (430-650° F) sample No. 2183	HCO (650°+ F) sample No. 2184
API gravity	34.3	49.1	17.1	8.8
Specific gravity @ 60° F	0.8531	0.7833	0.9520	1.0086
Molecular weight (API Proc.2B2.1)	150 123	195	302*	
Elemental analysis				
Carbon	88.30	87.29	89.88	89.18
Hydrogen	11.42	13.06	9.90	10.21
Nitrogen	0.196	0.033	0.182	0.450
Sulfur	0.094	0.015	0.180	0.44
Bromine number	24.0	32.6	9.0	NM

Table Xb. - Analysis of liquid product fractions from high
severity cracking of mildly hydrotreated
Wilmington vacuum gas oil (No. WM-2-2R)

| | High severity catalytic cracking | | | |
Property	Liquid product sample No. 2126	Gasoline (IBP-430° F) sample No. 2185	LCO (430-650° F) sample No. 2186	HCO (650°+ F) sample No. 2187
API gravity	34.345.6	12.6	6.3	
Specific gravity @ 60° F	0.8536	0.7991	0.9820	1.0266
Molecular weight (API Proc.2B2.1)	130 115	180	310*	
Elemental analysis				
Carbon	88.48	87.99	90.54	89.64
Hydrogen	10.79	12.24	9.00	9.73
Nitrogen	0.224	0.035	0.235	0.472
Sulfur	0.129	0.001	0.253	0.42
Bromine number	29.635.0	10.0	NM	

NM - Not measured.
* - VPO molecular weight.

Table XIa. - Analysis of liquid product fractions from low
severity cracking of severely hydrotreated
Wilmington vacuum gas oil (WM-2-9)

| | Low severity catalytic cracking | | | |
Property	Liquid product sample No. 2127	Gasoline (IBP-430° F) sample No. 2188	LCO (430-650° F) sample No. 2189	HCO (650°+ F) sample No. 2190
API gravity	43.0	52.8	21.6	11.2
Specific gravity @ 60° F	0.8107	0.7667	0.9244	0.9917
Molecular weight (API Proc.2B2.1)	134 118	182	264*	
Elemental analysis				
Carbon	87.92	86.74	89.45	90.48
Hydrogen	11.48	13.74	10.72	10.22
Nitrogen	0.00174	<0.001	<0.001	0.021
Sulfur	0.005	0.001	0.018	0.031
Bromine number	12.2	17.8	2.3	NM

Table XIb. - Analysis of liquid product fractions from high
severity cracking of severely hydrotreated
Wilmington vacuum gas oil (No. WM-2-9)

Property	High severity catalytic cracking			
	Liquid product sample No. 2128	Gasoline (IBP-430° F) sample No. 2191	LCO (430-650° F) sample No. 2192	HCO (650°+ F) sample No. 2193
API gravity	42.1 50.0		20.4	10.3
Specific gravity @ 60° F	0.8149	0.7796	0.9314	0.9980
Molecular weight (API Proc.2B2.1)	132 118	182	294*	
Elemental analysis				
Carbon	88.99	86.90	90.19	89.95
Hydrogen	11.16	13.20	10.61	10.22
Nitrogen	0.00128	<0.001	<0.001	0.022
Sulfur	0.01044	<0.001	0.019	0.070
Bromine number	18.1 24.2	3.8	NM	

NM - Not measured.
* - VPO molecular weight.

Figures 9 and 10 show similar results for nitrogen. Figure 9 shows the nitrogen content of the catalytic cracker gasoline, LCO, and HCO fractions as a function of hydrogen consumption for low severity cracking conditions. The nitrogen level of the cracker products drops as severity of the hydrotreating increases but at a slower rate than observed for sulfur. The high severity cracking results, Figure 10, show a similar trend. Comparison of Figures 9 and 10 shows that the severity of the cracking operation did not significantly affect the levels of the nitrogen in the liquid products. This also agrees with the bulk results discussed above.

The effect of hydrotreating on the bromine number (olefinic content) of the catalytic cracker products is shown in Figures 11 and 12. The bromine numbers for gasoline and LCO fractions were measured directly using ASTM procedure D 1159. For the HCO, the bromine number could not be measured because of procedural problems. For the low severity cracking case, Figure 11, the olefinic content of the products drops as the severity of hydro- treating increases. In general, the gasoline fraction has the highest olefinic content.

A similar trend is observed in Figure 12 for the high severity cracking experiments. A comparison of the results shows that the bromine number for the nonhydrotreated case (hydrogen consumption equal to 0 scf/bbl) and the mildly hydrotreated case (511 scf/bbl) appears not to be affected by the severity of the cracking process. However, for the high hydrogen uptake case (1610.5 scf/bbl), the olefinic contents of the gasoline and LCO are higher for the high severity cracking process than the low severity

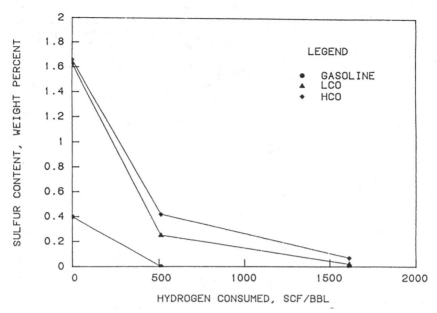

Figure 8. Distribution of sulfur in high severity cracking products as a function of hydrotreating pretreatment.

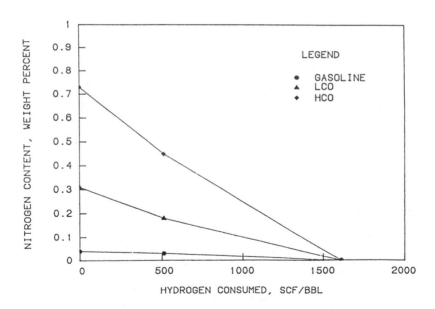

Figure 9. Distribution of nitrogen in low severity cracking products as a function of hydrotreating severity.

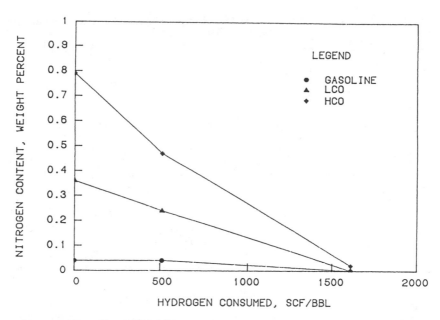

Figure 10. Distribution of nitrogen in high severity cracking products as a function of hydrotreating severity.

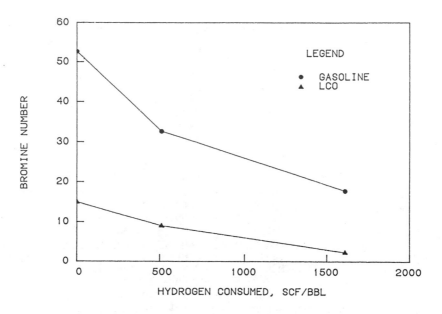

Figure 11. Bromine number distribution in low severity cracking products as a function of hydrotreating severity.

cracking process. These results imply that, at severe cracking conditions, the rate of olefin production via primary and secondary zeolite cracking exceeds the rate of olefin removal via the hydrogen transfer reaction. Increased thermal cracking may also contribute to this trend.

Gas Analysis

The effects of hydrotreating severity on the cracked gas composition are shown in Figures 13 and 14. These figures show the yields of individual hydrocarbons in the cracked gas as a function of the hydrotreating pretreatment for the mild (Figure 13) and the severe (Figure 14) catalytic cracking conditions. The symbols used in the ordinate are defined in Table 12. As can be seen in Figure 13, the yields of the thermal and secondary cracking products (H_2, CH_4, C_2H_4 and C_2H_6) tend to decrease as the hydrotreating severity increases. The catalytic cracking of nonhydrotreated feed (1693) produces significantly more of the above products than the cracking of the mildly hydrotreated feed (WM-2-2R) at the same conditions. This trend is also shown in Figure 14 which gives the hydrocarbon analysis of the gas from the high severity catalytic cracking runs. As expected, the yields of these light products are higher than those shown in Figure 13. This is due to the higher catalytic cracking temperature and residence time used to generate the samples whose analysis is given in Figure 14. These conditions result in higher thermal and secondary cracking rates which lead to the greater yields of these products.

Table XII. - Legend to ordinate Figures 13 through 17

H_2	–	Hydrogen
CH_4	–	Methane
C_2H_4	–	Ethylene
C_2H_6	–	Ethane
C_3	–	Propane
$C_3=$	–	Propene
IC_4	–	Isobutane
nC_4	–	Butane
$C_4=1$	–	Butene-1
$M2C_3=$	–	Isobutylene
$tC_4=2$	–	trans-Butene-2
$cC_4=2$	–	cis-Butene-2
$C_4Di=$	–	Butadiene
IC_5	–	Isopentane
$M3C_4=1$	–	3-Methylbutene-1
nC_5	–	Pentane
$C_5=1$	–	Pentene-1
$M2C_4=1$	–	2-Methylbutene-1
$tC_5=2$	–	trans-Pentene-2
$cC_5=2$	–	cis-Pentene-2
$M2C_4=2$	–	2-Methylbutene-2
C_6+	–	Hexane and heavier

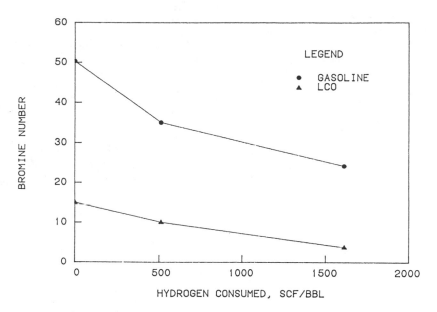

Figure 12. Bromine number distribution in high severity cracking products as a function of hydrotreating conditions.

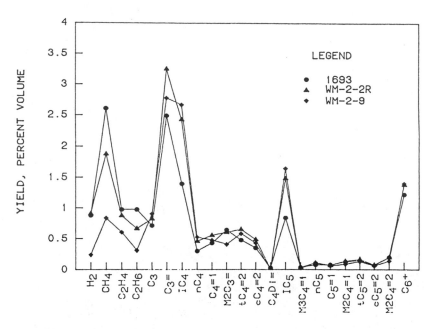

Figure 13. Effect of hydrotreating severity on catalytic cracking light gas composition -- low severity cracking.

Figures 13 and 14 also show that hydrotreating the catalytic cracker feedstock increases the zeolite cracking. C_3, C_4 and C_5+ compounds are possible products of primary zeolite cracking. These figures show that hydrotreating of the feedstock results in larger yields of these primary cracking products and hence more valuable products. This improvement is most likely due to the heteroatom removal and the saturation of aromatic compounds during hydrotreating which tend to block active sites and reduce the activity of the catalyst.

Closer analysis of the C_3 and C_4 compound yields, Figures 13 and 14, shows that the most abundant compounds produced are propylene and isobutane. In general, the highest concentration of saturated C_3 and C_4 compounds occurs in the cracking products from the severely hydrotreated feedstock (WM-2-9). The yield of the olefinic C_3 and C_4 compounds is lowest for the original nonhydrotreated feedstock (1693) and highest for the lightly hydro-treated feedstock (WM-2-2R). The olefinic yields of the severely hydrotreated feedstock (WM-2-9) fall between the olefinic yields from 1693 and WM-2-2R. This is true for all C_3 and C_4 components except isobutylene. For this component the yield is lowest for WM-2-9 and highest for 1693 and WM-2-2R, which are approximately equal. Figures 13 and 14 show that all of the above trends hold for both levels of catalytic cracking with only the magnitude of the yields being different. The reasons for these trends are difficult to isolate because of the complex nature of the catalytic cracking of gas oils. They may be due to increased hydrogen transfer caused by increased active site availability (i.e., less active site blockage by heteroatoms and aromatics) resulting in high saturate yields and lower olefinic yields.

Analysis of the C_5+ light gases, Figures 13 and 14, indicates that isopentane is the major separable component. WM-2-9 produced higher yields of saturates and lower yields of olefins, again indicating the possibility of greater hydrogen transfer.

The effects of catalytic cracking conditions on the product gas for the three feedstocks are shown in Figures 15 through 17. These figures show the yields of the gas products increased or remained about the same as the severity of the cracking process increased. The exceptions to this trend are isobutane and isopentane for the previously hydrotreated feeds (Figures 16 and 17). For these compounds, the yields decrease significantly at high severity cracking conditions. The lower yields of these isoparaffins and the higher level of olefins seem to imply a lower overall rate of hydrogen transfer at the more severe cracking conditions.

Conclusions

The performance analysis and product analysis results confirm previous findings (3,8) that hydrotreating improves the quality of catalytic cracker feedstock and the resultant products. In addition, it was shown that the quality of the liquid products and the yields of the coke and the heavy cycle oil (HCO) from cracking of the severely hydrotreated feedstock (WM-2-9) were independent of the conditions of the cracking process. These results imply that there exists a degree of pretreatment hydrotreating above which

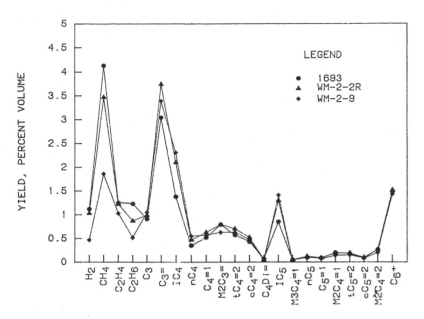

Figure 14. Effects of hydrotreating severity on catalytic cracking light gas composition -- high severity cracking.

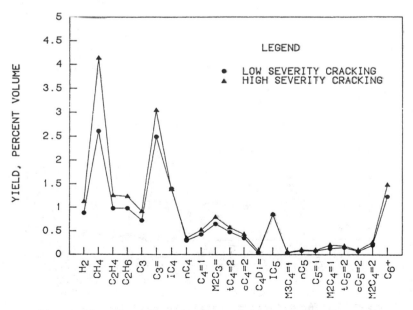

Figure 15. The effects of catalytic cracking operating conditions on light gas yields for sample 1693.

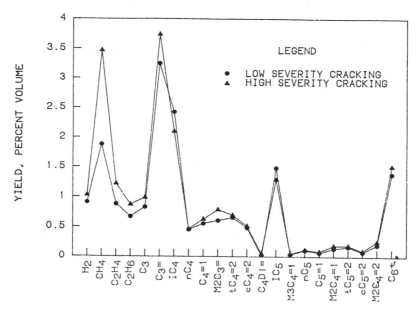

Figure 16.   The effects of catalytic cracking operating conditions on light gas yields for sample WM-2-2R.

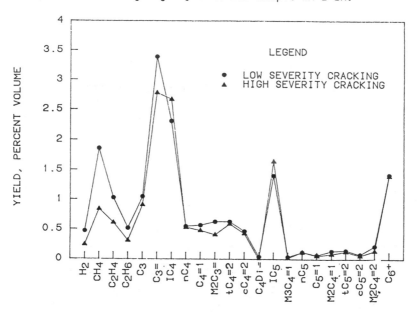

Figure 17.   The effects of catalytic cracking operating conditions on light gas yields for sample WM-2-9.

improvement in catalytic cracker performance is not significant. Unfortunately, the experimental design and the level of analysis performed was insufficient to estimate this hydrotreating level or the nature of the compounds in the liquid products. For the HCO, it is expected that the products are aromatic in nature, extremely resistant to hydrogenation, and thermally quite stable. In addition, they are very low in heteroatom content.

The sulfur and nitrogen content of the liquid products (gasolines, LCO, and HCO) were found to decrease as the severity of the feed hydrotreating increased. The distribution of the sulfur and the nitrogen in the liquid products was found to be independent of cracking conditions or product yields for a given level of hydrogenation pretreatment. This implies that the parent compounds which are generating these cracked heteroatom products are reacting at about the same rate as the hydrocarbon compounds in the feed. The distribution of the nitrogen and sulfur in the coke and gas was not determined.

Analysis of the gas products has shown that hydrotreating significantly reduces the extent of thermal cracking and increases the amount of zeolite cracking which occurs. The analysis also shows that the degree of hydrogen transfer increases as the severity of the hydrogenation increases, indicated by the increase in the saturated compounds in the gas products. As the cracking severity increases, the apparent degree of hydrogen transfer decreases, and the concentration of the olefinic compounds increases relative to the saturated compounds. In general, hydrogen transfer is both detrimental and beneficial to catalytic cracker operation. Hydrogen transfer produces more gasoline range material, but the octane of this fuel is lower, and the formation of dienes by the hydrogen transfer reaction tends to cause the formation of coke with increased catalyst deactivation.

Literature Cited

1. Corma, A., and B. W. Wojciechowski. Catal. Rev.-Sci. Eng. 1985, 27, No. 1, pp 29-150.
2. White, P. J. Hydrocarbon Processing 1968, 47, No. 5, p 103.
3. Decroocq, D. Catalytic Cracking of Heavy Petroleum Fractions. Gulf Publishing Co., Houston, Texas, 1984.
4. Huling, G. P., J. D. McKinney, and T. C. Readal. Oil & Gas J., 73, May, 19, 1975.
5. Wu, C. M., and A. M. Schaffer. Amer. Chem. Soc. Prepr., Div. Petrol. Chem. 1983, 28, No. 4, p 876.
6. Unzelman, G. H. Potential Impact on Cracking on Diesel Fuel Quality. Presented at Katalistiks' Fourth Fluid Catalytic Cracking Symposium, Amsterdam, the Netherlands, May 18-19, 1983.
7. Upson, L., S. Jaras, and I. Dalin. Oil & Gas J., 135, September 20, 1982.
8. Venuto, P. B., and E. T. Habib, Jr. Fluid Catalytic Cracking with Zeolite Catalysts. Marcel Dekker, Inc., New York, 1979.

RECEIVED February 25, 1988

Chapter 19

Development of a Reduced Crude Cracking Catalyst

William P. Hettinger, Jr.

Ashland Petroleum Company, P.O. Box 391, Ashland, KY 41114

Faced with the need of obtaining more transportation
fuels from a barrel of crude, Ashland developed the
Reduced Crude Conversion Process (RCC®). To support
this development, a residuum or reduced crude cracking
catalyst was developed and over 1,000 tons were
produced and employed in commercial operation. The
catalyst possessed a large pore volume, dual pore
structure, an Ultrastable Y zeolite with an acidic
matrix equal in acidity to the acidity of the zeolite,
and was partially treated with rare earth to enhance
cracking activity and to resist vanadium poisoning.
While subsequently replaced by further improved
catalysts, the catalyst achieved high selectivity, was
metal resistant at 7,800 ppm nickel plus vanadium, and
achieved design projections during start-up and two
months of commercial operation. Development of the
catalyst served to stimulate research efforts by the
catalyst industry to introduce other advanced residuum
processing catalysts.

In 1974 OPEC imposed an embargo on oil to the United States,
causing a rapid rise in the price of a barrel of oil. Ashland
Petroleum, a transporter, refiner and marketer of oil, purchases
most of its crude oil. At the time of the embargo, Ashland
imported much of its oil from the Middle East, thus raising the
question of availability.

　　As the problem became severe, Messrs. Myers, Busch and
Zandona (1-4) of our company began to consider alternative
sources of crude and ways of squeezing more product from a given
barrel. After considering many possibilities, including a number
of processes then commercially available, they conceived a new
way to convert the 1050°F+ fraction of the barrel directly to
gasoline. If successful, this inexpensive new process would, in
effect, give them an additional volume of oil for conversion to
gasoline. They also concluded that if vacuum fractionation were
eliminated, the entire 650°F+ (reduced crude) portion of the

0097–6156/88/0375–0308$09.25/0

barrel could be processed in one step, thus also greatly reducing operating costs and investments for intermediate processing equipment. At the same time, the 650 to 1050°F fraction would provide a carrier or diluent for the 1050°F+ residuum.

They began reduced crude cracking experimentation in a small 12,000 barrel per day (B/D) Fluid Catalytic Cracking (FCC) operating unit at Louisville, Ky. The RCC process was born from these goals, concepts and a small operating unit. The development and attributes of this process have been described in a number of articles and patents (1-6).

Figure 1 shows the distribution of 650°F+ volume percent content in reduced crude for some 50 crudes then available to Ashland. Figure 2 indicates the volume percentage of 1050°F+ present in the same crudes, ranging from less than 10% to more than 30%.

Catalyst Development

As work began on the process, it quickly became apparent that the extraordinary catalyst properties required for the process were not then available, and even with a superior catalyst, consumption would undoubtedly be severe. Figure 3 shows how Ramsbottom Carbon and nickel plus vanadium vary in the same reduced crude oils. All levels are very high; far beyond anything normally encountered in a gas oil feedstock.

Although they are not shown here in detail, nitrogen, sulfur, asphaltenes, polynuclear aromatics, and heterocyclics are all also present in significant amounts in reduced crudes. Figure 4, however, does depict the general relationship between $^{\circ}$API gravity, sulfur, asphaltene and total metal content of crudes in general. Certainly none of these ingredients, especially in such large amounts, could be considered "friendly" for catalysts used in normal catalytic cracking.

Hardware modification alone, without simultaneous consideration of how to meet catalyst property requirements, would not be enough to achieve success. Therefore, a catalyst development program was proposed and approved to help formulate new catalysts that could deal with these severe contaminants. Its goal was the simultaneous development of a new process and tailored catalysts, as both were obviously critical to the ultimate economic success of the project.

Of course, there were catalysts on the market in 1977-78 that were being targeted for processing heavier stocks, with higher levels of metals. Catalyst manufacturers such as Davison and Filtrol had already been working along these lines.

However, these stringent new requirements created a need to accelerate the development of specifically targeted catalysts. Ashland decided to initiate its own catalyst preparation program, coupled with installation and development of advanced testing equipment, to speed the evolution of advanced catalysts.

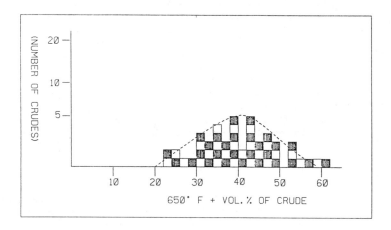

Figure 1.   650°F+ Atmospheric Reduced Crude Oil Vol.% of Crudes
for 50 Crudes

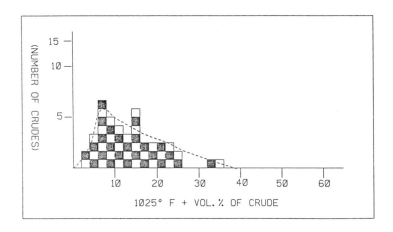

Figure 2.   1025°F+ Bottoms Vol.% of Crude for 50 Crudes

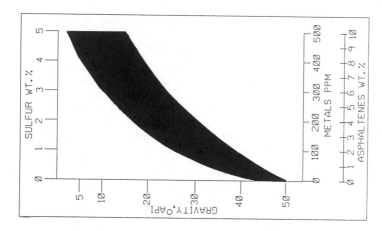

Figure 4. Relationship Between Crude Oil API, Sulfur, Metals and Asphaltenes

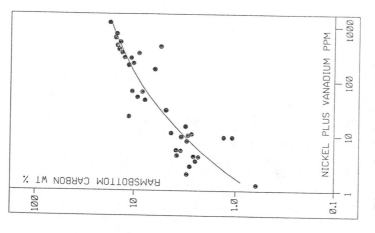

Figure 3. Relationship Between Nickel Plus Vanadium and Ramsbottom Carbon for Reduced Crude

Equipment

Equipment and facilities for batch catalyst preparation and spray drying and ovens for drying and calcining were rapidly acquired and installed. A variety of catalyst testing reactors were also designed, constructed, and placed in operation. Testing began with improved microactivity catalytic cracking testing reactors, modified to operate on reduced crude, to monitor and evaluate developmental, virgin, commercial, and operating catalysts. They functioned remarkably well. Of course, fresh catalysts were also exposed to various severe pretesting conditions to prepare them properly for evaluation. High-purity hydrocarbons and reactors were also used to focus in detail on critical mechanisms.

　　Advanced testing for extensive evaluation of selected catalysts and feedstocks was carried out in a fixed fluid bed of about one liter cracking catalyst capacity. This provided us with representative yields and large volumes for product quality testing including octane numbers. In construction and operation, this test equipment was similar to that used much earlier to develop the semisynthetic catalysts of the 1950s.(7) Considerable modification was required, however, to enable us to process reduced crude rather than gas oil.

　　The better catalysts were further evaluated in two circulating bed operations. The first unit, complete with regenerator, was developed by Ashland pilot plant personnel. It was capable of evaluating specific feedstocks, or processing parameters, and testing fluid catalysts over long periods of operation (days and weeks). The unit permitted continuous catalyst replacement and extensive variation in operating conditions and catalyst treatments, while yielding large volumes of light and heavy products.

　　An even larger one-quarter barrel per day circulating unit came very close to simulating both the 200 B/D demonstration unit and later commercial operations. It also possessed a two-stage regenerator and vented riser (both hallmarks of the RCC process). This allowed simulation and evaluation of additional RCC operating parameters.

　　Finally a 200 B/D 80' tall demonstration unit was used for studying operating parameters, equipment, process variations, and finally catalysts, catalyst treatments, and varying feedstocks. Much of the 200 B/D work has been described in published reports.(8-10) In brief, satisfactory runs with excellent yields and good conversion were made on catalysts containing as much as 12,300 ppm of nickel plus vanadium.(4)

Catalyst Research and Physical Chemical Evaluation

A number of analytical instruments helped us to probe and understand our catalysts in greater detail. Although these may be standard equipment for a large manufacturer or large petroleum research laboratory, we had to acquire them and train our personnel in their use before we could proceed. Some of the more vital instruments included equipment for measuring surface area, pore volume and pore diameter distribution, and X-ray

diffraction, scanning electron microscopy, and energy dispersive
X-ray fluorescence were also utilized. High severity fluid bed
steamers and calciners, and differential thermal and thermal
gravitational analyzers, and micro-calorimetry also were of great
value.

Catalyst Development and Scale-Up

With the challenge well defined, catalyst preparation,
development, and evaluation began. Research and development took
a two-pronged approach.
    We began with examination and evaluation of all catalysts
available on the market. Detailed analysis of catalysts showing
promising performance in our test units gave us insight as to
which properties and ingredients should receive greater
attention and which were contributory or noncontributory.
    Secondly, we began research and development based on our own
knowledge and experience with commercial catalyst manufacture and
compositions. We also drew on many years of personal experience
directing catalyst research and development, as well as our own
speculations as to what properties might be most important.
    As our work gained momentum, we realized that a cooperative
effort with a catalyst manufacturer would be highly desirable.
Therefore, we arranged for a development program which lasted
four years. This work lead to several catalysts which showed
promise and which were prepared commercially in tonnage
quantities and evaluated in the 200 B/D RCC unit.
    Finally, in late 1982, just prior to RCC commercial
start-up, a more advanced catalyst was developed and prepared in
several commercial-size 20-ton batches. It also was tested in
the 200 B/D pilot plant unit, and shown to be an excellent
catalyst. Over 1,000 tons of this catalyst, designated DZ-40,
was produced commercially and used for start-up and two months
successful reduced crude operation.(11)
    As catalyst improvements evolved along with the process, the
yields in the 200 B/D unit from a typical Arabian Light reduced
crude oil at the "knee" conversion level (the point of maximum
gasoline yield) gradually rose from 47-48 volume percent gasoline
to 52% and subsequently to as high as 56-57 volume percent
gasoline, with a corresponding reduction in high-boiling slurry
oil product. These yields have now been well confirmed and
exceeded in the commercial unit (Tables I & II).
    A second catalyst subsequently introduced by a second
manufacturer was also considered acceptable and utilized
successfully. However, the stimulus of our work undoubtedly had
a favorable impact on commercial producers, resulting in
accelerated development and commercial introduction of new and
superior-performing RCC catalysts, and at reduced cost.

Commercial Operation

The RCC process commercial unit has been on-stream for over four
years. Except for a few minor problems during start-up, it has

Table I.   Design and Actual Operating Results
Commercial RCC Unit

Feedstock Inspection	Design	Intermediate $^{\circ}$API And Ramscarbon Feed	Low $^{\circ}$API, High Ramscarbon Feed
$^{\circ}$API	18.6	21.3	19.2
Ni + V, ppm	35.0	44.0	65.0
Ramsbottom Carbon, Wt.%	6.0	4.5	6.9
UOP K-Factor	11.8	11.8	11.8
Product Yields			
Dry Gas, Wt.%	4.1	3.3	4.1
Propane/Propylene, Vol%	2.5/9.3	1.8/8.7	1.8/8.3
Butanes/Butylenes,Vol%	5.9/10.9	4.6/10.1	3.9/9.9
C_5-430°F Gasoline, Vol%	51.5	57.8	55.6
Distillate, 430°-630°F, Vol%	11.3	15.0	15.0
Heavy Oil, 630°F, +, Vol%	10.4	8.4	10.9
Coke, Wt.%	11.5	8.4	10.8
Operating Parameters			
Conv. to 430°F & Coke, Vol%	78.3	76.6	74.1
Conv. to 630°F & Coke, Vol%	89.6	91.6	89.1
C_3 + Equivalent Gaso. + Distillate, Vol%	86.7	93.6	89.1
Total Liquid Yield, Vol%	102.0	106.4	105.4
Gasoline & Distillate Selectivity, %	70.1	79.5	79.2
Gasoline Octane, Ronc	93.0	93.2	93.6
Metals on Catalyst, Ni + V ppm	6,000	7,200	8,000

Table IIA. Catlettsburg RCC Unit Achieves Design Objectives
on Untreated Feedstocks

| Thruput MBPD | °API | Feedstock Properties | | | LPG, Equiv. Gaso.* + Dis. Yd. Vol.% | Gaso.** Select. % |
		K-Factor	Rams Carbon Wt.%	Metals Ni + V PPM		
			Design			
40.0	18.6	11.8	6.0	35.0	86.1	65.0
			Commercial Experience			
47.5	22.1	11.9	4.6	21.0	86.3	69.0
39.8	20.9	11.8	5.8	47.0	88.9	72.0
30.5	21.5	11.9	5.4	55.0	93.2	74.0
28.8	18.5	11.8	7.1	68.0	89.6	77.0

Table IIB. Catlettsburg RCC Unit Achieves Design Objectives
on Untreated Feedstocks

| Octane RONC | Equilibrium Catalyst Ni + V PPM | Carbon Functions | |
		Coke Yield Wt.%	Regenerator Coke Processed MLb./Hr.
	Design		
93.0	6000	11.4	63
	Commercial Experience		
93.4	7200	10.0	67
92.9	7800	10.9	65
92.6	7100	8.4	36
93.6	7700	10.8	44

* Equivalent Gasoline = C_5-430 Naphtha + (0.8)(C_3/C_4 Olefins) + C_4's

** Gasoline Selectivity = {(Vol.% C_5-430 Naphtha) ÷ (Vol.% Gas Oil + Disappearance)} x 100

run almost continuously and has met or exceeded all the design
projections obtained from the 200 B/D unit (Figure 5). In
addition, process modifications made during construction and in
operation have further enhanced the performance of the unit,
exceeding early predictions. Figure 6 shows the flow diagram for
the process. Tables I and II show results obtained while
operating on a range of carbometallic feedstocks. Note the
impressive yield of gasoline and other liquid products.

Catalyst Design

Keeping the properties of the reduced crudes clearly in mind,
we drew upon basic catalyst concepts and previous experience.
The state of the art in 1978 suggested keying in on a number of
catalyst properties. We focused on them individually and
collectively in order to optimize each property in terms of the
overall objective. This meant harnessing and optimizing such
properties as pore volume, pore diameter distribution, zeolite
properties and acidity, rare earth stabilization, metal
resistance, matrix acidity, attrition resistance, burning rate,
and cost. Our goal was to cope with carbon, metals, asphaltenes,
polynuclear aromatics and heterocyclics, n-paraffins, sulfur, and
nitrogen-containing molecules. The following is a detailed
account of how some of the more important problems were
addressed.

Pore Volume and Pore Diameter Distribution

In the recent past, commercial cracking catalysts have tended to be
high in density (low in pore volume) in order to reduce attrition
and avoid air pollution problems, which tend to relate to
catalyst density. Catalysts for FCC application are not
considered to be diffusion limited; and, therefore, higher-
density catalysts are quite acceptable.

   For RCC application, we soon concluded that a higher pore
volume catalyst which could act as a sponge in picking up
nonvolatile or only partially volatile residuum liquid, could be
desirable for resid processing. Development of a dual pore
structure with feeder pores to the zeolite crystals would enhance
accessibility of the much higher molecular weight reactants,
found in the $1050°F+$ bottom portion of the reduced crude barrel,
to the zeolite "portal surface area"* and internal acidity. In
addition, such means might avoid pore passageway blockage by
highly adsorbing super-large asphaltene colloidal particles and
high molecular weight aromatic and basic nitrogen-contaminating
molecules. Figure 7 portrays this objective in an exaggerated
fashion and Figure 8 shows how this relates to the overall
composition of our preferred residual cracking catalyst.

   When cracking catalysts are prepared with a silica or
silica-alumina gel base, the pore volume and average pore

* The term "portal surface area" has been proposed by the author
   to convey the concept of the outer surface of a zeolite crystal
   providing entrance to the strong acid sites within the crystal.

Figure 5.   Ashland RCC Process Demonstration Unit

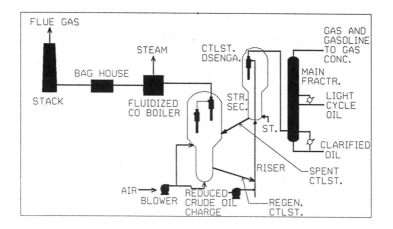

Figure 6.   Process Flow Diagram RCC Unit

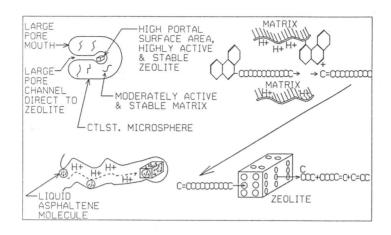

Figure 7. Catalyst Structure

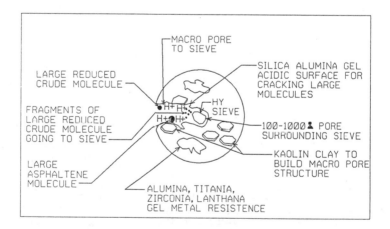

Figure 8. Reduced Crude Catalyst

diameter can be readily varied by control of gel concentration,
time, temperature, and pH. To obtain a dual pore structure,
however, requires a different approach. Some historical
background is in order, and a review of some early catalyst work
may prove helpful.

In the early 1950s, while involved in platinum on alumina
catalyst research studies at the laboratories of Sinclair Oil
(now a part of ARCO), I discovered that crystalline alumina
trihydrate was present in the amorphous pseudo-Boehmitelike
alumina gel used to prepare some new experimental reforming
catalysts. Further study showed the presence of several
crystalline alumina trihydrates, including a previously unknown
trihydrate that was dubbed "Randomite".(12) It was later
officially named Norstrandite in honor of Robert Van Norstrand,
who was then in charge of physical chemical studies at Sinclair
and who spearheaded elucidation of its structure. Next came
development work and some brilliant observations and deductions
by Marvin F. L. Johnson, then in charge of surface area and pore
volume studies of those laboratories. He showed that at an
optimum concentration of about 75% trihydrate in an extrudate, a
dual and even rather large triple-pore distribution structure
formed as trihydrate concentration reached a critical level.
This pore size distribution was shown to provide an optimum pore
structure for platinum reforming catalyst activity, selectivity
and catalyst life. This catalyst eventually was commercialized
and became the famous RD-150; still in use in only slightly
modified form.

In 1957 I transferred to Nalco Catalyst Division and became
Director of Research. At that time Nalco was faced with severe
competition to their synthetic silica-alumina gel cracking
catalyst by a relatively new and low cost natural clay-based
cracking catalyst containing Halloysite clay, introduced and
manufactured by Filtrol Corporation. In attempting to meet this
competition, we considered a number of alternatives. Among these
was the idea of incorporating some low-cost, high-purity Kaolin
(a platelet-type clay) as a low-cost diluent. If successful,
this would reduce the amount of costly silica-alumina gel
required. By reducing the cost, we might again make our catalyst
competitive.

As our experimental work proceeded, I realized that we were
dealing with a silica-alumina system (silica-alumina gel and
platelet crystalline silica-alumina Kaolin) that should be
similar to the alumina gel/alumina trihydrate crystal system of
RD-150. It seemed possible to achieve a similar pore diameter
spectrum structure here by judicious combination of crystals and
gel.

By achieving random dispersion of the Kaolin in the sodium
silicate solution prior to formation of the silica-alumina gel,
it was possible to disperse the clay crystals. They condensed
somewhat perpendicular to each other and were bound together by
silica-alumina gel. I therefore speculated that spray drying,
during which the gel system contracts, might create a dual
structure. An analogy would be a house built of cards (Kaolin),
cemented together with silica-alumina gel.

We varied the gel-forming parameters, the content of Kaolin clay, the crystal size, and the thickness-to-diameter ratio in a series of experiments. A dual structure began to appear at about 35-40% Kaolin. If the clay content was increased to too high a level, the microspheres became too weak and began to have poor attrition resistance. The cost of the various grades also affected our choice. Figure 9 shows a comparison of pore volume distribution for a typical synthetic versus a clay modified catalyst.

Kaolin had little or no cracking activity, and catalyst activity as tested in the laboratory was directly related to silica-alumina gel content. However, the catalyst performed much better in commercial tests than anticipated from laboratory testing. Undoubtedly, this open structure encountered much less severe conditions at the outer surface of the microsphere during regenerations and made internal catalytic surfaces more readily available. This first of the so-called "semisynthetics" was called Nalco 783, and the matrix is still used in many forms some 28 years later.(7,13) Today it is estimated that some 200,000 tons/yr. of kaolin clay is used for cracking catalyst manufacture as reported by Georgia Kaolin Corporation.(24) Figure 10 shows the pore volume distribution for Nalco 783 and two other commercial semisynthetics from that period.

This low cost matrix, with its unusual dual pore spectra and somewhat unexpected beneficial properties, became the matrix of choice for the next generation, the zeolite-containing catalysts. This approach continues to provide a pore structure that gives reactant molecules ready access to the zeolite crystals buried deeply within, while at the same time greatly reducing manufacturing costs.(23)

Kaolin is also an inexpensive ingredient, thus lowering raw material costs by replacing expensive sodium silicate, aluminum sulfate, and sodium aluminate, plus reducing use of neutralizing ammonia or acid. It generates much less waste effluent and reduces high-energy water evaporation spray drying requirements and final drying costs. This reduces energy costs while appreciably increasing manufacturing capacity.

The same approach was applied to enhance and extend resid catalyst technology. We gave considerable attention to specific grades of Kaolin to assure a very good pore structure and to keep costs down. For a combination of low cost, good open pore structure, low iron content, and low attrition, we preferred the smaller, spherical equivalent Kaolin crystals with a high diameter-to-thickness ratio.

DZ-40 has the properties of pore volume and pore diameter distribution listed in Table III.(11) Note the considerable pore volume in the 100-1000°Angstroms range (Figure 11). Figure 12 also shows some of our data indicating the benefit of a larger pore volume. It appeared to us that an optimum for catalysts in resid cracking occurs between 0.40 and 0.55 cc/gm.

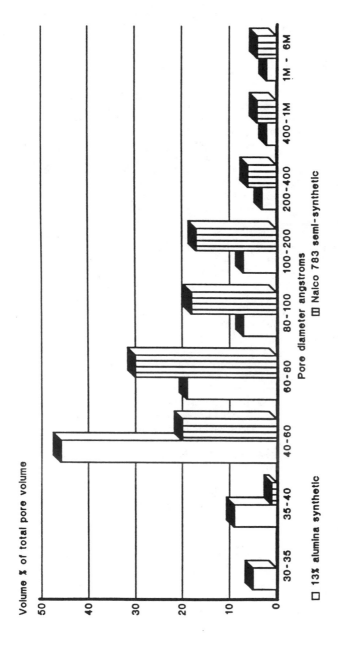

Figure 9. Distribution of Pore Volume vs. Pore Diameter –
Synthetic vs. Nalco 783 semisynthetic

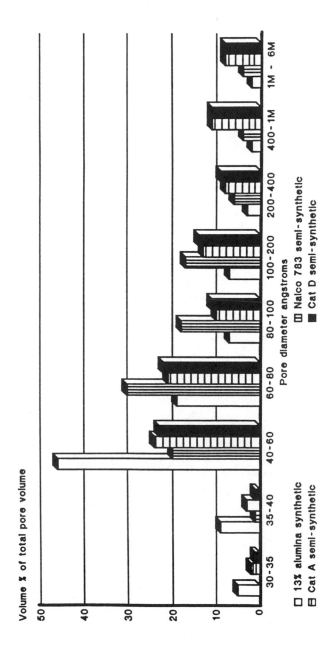

Figure 10. Distribution of Pore Volume vs. Pore Diameter – Synthetic vs. commercially-available 1958 semisynthetic

Table III. Pore Size Distribution cc/g
(% of Total Pore Volume)

6000A	0.03 cc/g (0%)
6000-1000A	0.09 cc/g (15%)
1000-400A	0.18 cc/g (31%)
400-200A	0.12 cc/g (21%)
400-100A	0.09 cc/g (16%)
100-80A	0.03 cc/g (5%)
80-60A	0.03 cc/g (6%)
60-20A	0.04 cc/g (6%)
Surface Area, m^2/g	198
Zeolite Area, m^2/g	99
External Area, m^2/g	108
Pore Volume, cc/g	0.59
Skeletal Density, g/cc	2.57
Apparent Bulk Density, g/cc	0.56

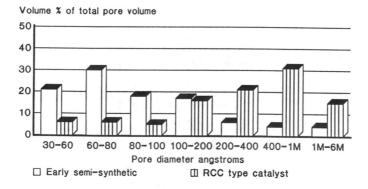

Figure 11. Distribution of Pore Volume vs. Pore Diameter - Early
semisynthetic vs. residuum (RCC) catalyst

Zeolite Acidity and Matrix Acidity

Resid cracking catalysts must deal with a feedstock of high-molecular-weight, high-boiling, and even nonboiling viscous molecules. This makes entrance into a zeolite structure questionable. On the other hand, much of it is in the FCC feed or gas oil portion of the reduced crude (600-1050°F), where zeolite cracking activity, selectivity, and stability are critically required. Furthermore, the severe environment for cracking and regeneration, also called for a zeolite with good performance in terms of resistance to high temperature and severe steam conditions.

We worked hard to evaluate structures such as rare earth stabilized versus Ultrastable hydrogen Y zeolites. H_2 transfer characteristics were also critical. With too much rare earth content, H_2 production increased with accompaning coke increase (Figure 11). Ultrastable Y sieves gave good product distribution, high octanes, and reduced hydrogen generation, but had lower activity and were more susceptible to metal deactivation and acidity neutralization. To enhance zeolite performance in the face of poisoning, asphaltene blockage, and coking, we tried to enhance portal surface area by grinding or breaking up sieve clusters to individual sieves and/or by producing very small sieves. Both approaches were requested of the manufacturer.

For the start-up of the RCC Unit DZ-40 was used. It was a combination of Ultrastable hydrogen Y, partially treated with rare earth, and ground to as fine a zeolite structure as commercially available and reasonable, and well dispersed in a specially developed silica-alumina cogel/Kaolin matrix. Table IV provides a typical analysis.

Matrix Acidity

Because we would be dealing with very large molecules, including some with long paraffin groups attached, we speculated that an acidic matrix would be desirable. At that time, generally the catalysts available from our suppliers had been stripped of matrix acidity, because commercial experience on FCC feedstocks had shown that zeolite acidity was generally quite adequate. However, we suspected that matrix acidity would provide optimum product distribution. Later operation of the 200 B/D demonstration unit and the RCC commercial unit established that acid matrix catalysts at constant conversion provided a lower 650°F+ yield and a higher middle distillate to 650°F end point ratio (see Figure 13). Note the decrease in heavy cycle oil at constant conversion for a catalyst with matrix acidity compared to a nonacidic matrix catalyst. More recently catalyst manufacturers have adopted this strategy of matrix acidity to deal with bottoms cracking. Titration techniques for isolating or defining zeolite and matrix acidity developed a relationship representing a balanced performance of the two acidities (see Table V).

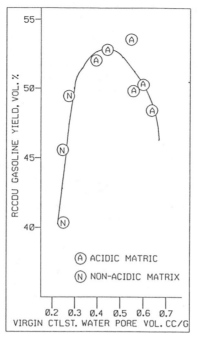

Figure 12. Effects of Pore Volume on RCCDS Gasoline Yield

Table IV.

Chemical Analyses	Typical Analysis, Wt.%
SiO_2	58.3
Al_2O_3	40.1
TiO_2	0.52
Fe_2O_3	0.43
Na_2O	0.42
RE_2O_3	1.29
La_2O_3	0.74
CeO_2	0.14
Nd_2O_3	0.31
Pr_6O_{11}	0.10
La_2O_3/CeO_2 Ratio	5.3
MgO	---

Phase Composition

Zeolite Type	USY
Zeolite Lattice K	24.58
Zeolite Content	
% Int./Na Y	8.8
Internal Std.	7.7
Nitrogen Method	15.0
Kaolinite	45.0

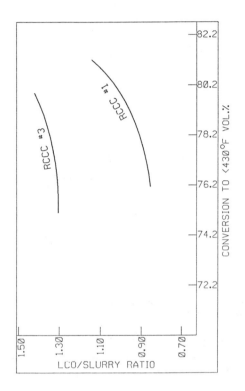

Figure 13. LCO/Slurry vs Conversion

Table V.

	n-butylamine Total Acidity in the Sieve	tridodecylamine Matrix Acidity	Ratio Matrix Acidity Sieve Acidity
RCC Catalyst #1	0.25	0.00	0.00
RCC Catalyst #3	0.22	0.22	1.00

Catalyst #3

n-butylamine acidity total catalyst	0.77 meg/gm
n-buytlamine acidity of contained sieve	0.22 meg/gm
tridoecylamine acidity	0.22 meg/gm
Total accessible acidity	0.44 meg/gm
Total micro porous acidity unaccounted for and evidently in the matrix	0.33 meg/gm

Silica-alumina gels containing 20-45% alumina provided the best combination of activity and activity stability. Therefore, we chose a gel with a composition in this range for binding the system together and as the matrix acidity ingredient.

Rare Earth Stabilization

Rare earth stabilization, as it relates to zeolite performance, has already been discussed. However, catalyst performance also varies depending on how the rare earths are deposited within the zeolite and the matrix, and also on how the ratio of individual species (such as lanthanum, cerium, and the other rare earths) are distributed. Yttrium can also be used to enhance zeolite catalyst performance and stability. These also seem to help mitigate the detrimental effect of vanadium, the most common and controversial contaminant.

We devoted much effort to exploring how much rare earth should be used in both the zeolite and the matrix, how it should be introduced or incorporated, and which ratio of rare earth elements was preferred. Figures 14 and 15 respectively show how activity and selectivity can be affected by rare earth content in just one catalyst preparation.

Metal Resistance

Anyone who is seriously involved in catalytic cracking, whether as an operator, a catalyst manufacturer, or a researcher, soon learns how severely sodium, vanadium, nickel, iron, and copper act as poisons. In the past, FCC feedstock preparation via vacuum distillation was to a considerable extent, determined by metal carryover. Generally, metal carryover to the fluid unit was limited to 0.1 ppm or less of each of these metals.

In the development of a process to crack reduced crude, it soon became evident that the metals levels encountered in these crudes would be considerably higher. Therefore, metals would be expected to manifest themselves in very unfavorable ways. Previously, nickel was considered the worst poison by far, in terms of H_2 and coke make, and poor product distribution. Vanadium was considered much less of a poison with about 1/5 the selectivity detriment of nickel. Iron, especially in the absence of sulfur, was considered even less of a poison. Copper and sodium were of little consequence if proper care was taken to avoid them in FCC feedstock preparation.

Nickel and vanadium carryover is mainly attributed to volatilization of porphyrins chemically combined with these two elements. Because volatility of the two species is roughly equivalent, carryover of nickel and vanadium are approximately equal. However, because the selectivity detriment of vanadium is so much lower, nickel has always generated the most concern.

With residuum processing, however, the situation changes. Metal levels rise dramatically. Figure 16 shows the metal distribution in a log/log scale plot of nickel versus vanadium for some 50 crudes. Obviously, many reduced crudes contain

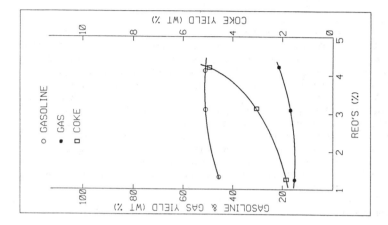

Figure 15. Rare Earth Exchanged
Effects on Product Yields at
Constant Conversion

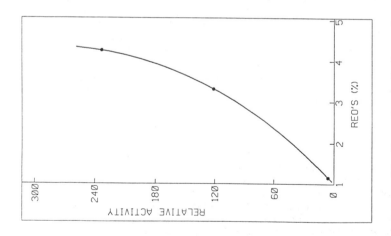

Figure 14. Rare Earth Exchanged
Effect on Activity

metals far beyond the 0.1 to 0.2 ppm metals levels of vacuum gas oil.

Not only do nickel and vanadium levels rise significantly, but vanadium content may greatly exceed nickel. Because of the absence of vacuum distillation, sodium, iron, copper, and other potential poisons can also appear at very high levels. These may have been present in the crude oil or added by contamination from corrosion, additives, or accidental carryover from desalting.

We knew the poisonous behavior of nickel, sodium, iron, and copper, and could anticipate the problems connected with them. However, vanadium appeared to offer some new problems. First of all, it appeared in our reduced crudes at one to three times the nickel level. It could be expected to show the same adverse product selectivity as at lower levels, but with much greater severity.

In addition, reports had been noted suggesting that vanadium in certain forms, and especially in the presence of sodium, had a low melting temperature. Therefore, its liquid form was likely to be harmful to catalyst performance. Thus we began a long and involved research program to determine how best to deal with these poisons, and especially with vanadium.

Early in our work, we had sought to achieve zeolite stability at high temperatures and in the presence of steam. We sought zeolites that could resist the extreme deactivating conditions of the RCC process.

In a series of experimental runs on virgin commercial catalysts and sieves then available and some of our experimental catalysts, we quickly learned that a catalyst impregnated with vanadium, and subjected to high temperatures in steam and air deactivated rapidly. Vanadium, especially in the +5 valence state, rapidly deactivated a catalyst by destroying zeolite crystallinity (Figure 17). In the presence of sodium, the deactivation rate of vanadium was even more severe. (14-17)

Catalyst replacement costs and yield loss costs can rise rapidly if poisoning occurs. Obviously, a high metals level must be dealt with appropriately. We accelerated our effort to discover a way to deal with vanadium poisoning.

Originally we evolved three basic approaches or strategies:

1. Search for an additive that would react with vanadium so as to immobilize and deactivate it. We dubbed these "vanadium immobilizers".

2. Seek to trap mobilized 5+ valence vanadium ions in sieves with small pores, such as A sieve, and thereby inactivate them. These were referred to as "vanadium traps".

3. Seek to divert vanadium to less harmful destructive activity by adding cheap and/or naturally occurring sieves. For these we proposed the term "sacrificial sieves".

We tried to exploit all three approaches. There was progress and some success in each case.

A review of the chemistry of lower valence vanadium oxides showed that they possessed much higher melting points than V_2O_5. Therefore, we developed a fourth approach, which has led to some patents and is presently a practical contributor to partial vanadium control. The procedure calls for maintaining a small but

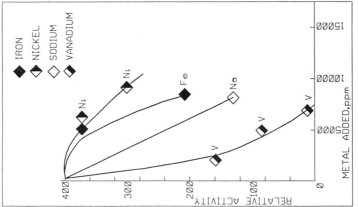

Figure 17. Catalyst Metal Torture Test Iron, Nickel, Sodium, Vanadium Effects

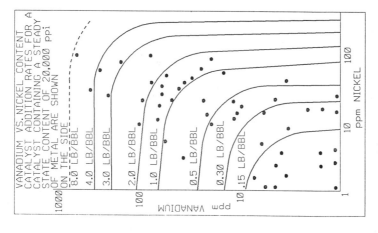

Figure 16. Reduced Crude Metal Content for 50 Representative Crudes

finite amount of coke on the regenerated catalyst to minimize oxidation beyond V_2O_4 to V_2O_5. In this manner, catalyst consumption due to vanadium-caused loss of catalyst activity has been somewhat reduced without significantly lowering regenerated catalyst activity due to the small amount of carbon remaining.

Efforts to control nickel proceeded along similar lines. Nickel aluminate, a spinel, has long been known to trap nickel. Metals like arsenic[19], antimony[20-21] and bismuth[20] are known to passivate transition elements and can be used to decrease H_2 and coke make. Sulfur is also a known inhibitor for nickel; therefore, higher sulfur-containing crudes may be a little less sensitive to nickel poisoning. In our work we also found that nickel at low concentrations is actually a slight promoter of the cracking reaction when incorporated into a molecular sieve (Figure 17).

Because of the high coke-forming tendencies of reduced crude, mainly due to a high concentration of Ramsbottom Carbon, the adverse effects of nickel appear to be somewhat moderated in the trip up the riser. Therefore, nickel does not appear to be quite as harmful as first anticipated.

We explored various possibilities in our efforts to control nickel. Catalysts high in alumina content, especially if a separate inclusion of alumina gel is utilized, did seem to show some improvement. It also appears that in severe conditions such as in the RCC operation, nickel tends to agglomerate, this reducing exposed surface and possibly also embeds in the matrix or zeolite.

We early noticed that the research octane number of RCC gasoline was high (see our early paper entitled "RCC Progress - An Inexpensive Route to High Octane Gasoline")[5], and we sought an explanation for this. One of the very earliest reforming catalysts, a nickel on steamed silica-alumina cracking catalyst, was developed by the late Frank Ciapetta.[18] We speculated that, in view of the high octane of RCC gasoline, its aromatic nature (Figure 18), and the abundance of hydrogen production without concurrent high coke formation, this high octane number may result from reforming reactions such as dehydrogenation, isomerization and dehydrocyclization resulting from the high nickel content on the acidic silica-alumina. This hypothesis, however, has not yet been proven. Pursuit of this possibility could open up a new area of cracking catalyst development.

RCC process catalysts with metals contents as high as 12,300 ppm nickel plus vanadium, plus 6,000 ppm of iron, have operated in the 200 B/D demonstration unit on feedstocks containing up to 84 ppm nickel plus vanadium.[4,5] Presently in our refinery, when metals levels are at still higher levels, the reduced crude is first processed in the Ashland ART unit, where some 85-95% of the metals and 75% of the Ramsbottom Carbon are removed.[6]

In normal operations, however, the RCC unit routinely runs at 6-9000 ppm nickel plus vanadium on feedstocks with as high as 35-75 ppm nickel plus vanadium content. Presently several commercial residuum-type catalysts are giving good performance at these levels. Catalyst manufacturers continue to seek further improvement in performance in terms of activity, selectivity, and catalyst life, while also trying to hold down or even reduce overall cost.

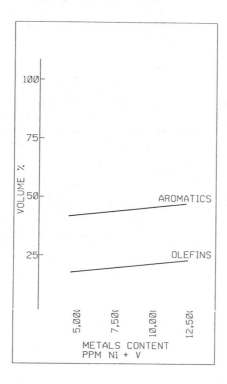

Figure 18.   Gasoline Composition versus Metals on Equilibrium
Catalyst

Other Catalyst Attributes

Resistance to High Temperature - High Steam Environments. Because
of the greater amount of coke deposited in and on a resid catalyst,
the nature of the coke, and the internal temperatures experienced
in connection with burning it off, early high-severity screening
tests were used to screen catalysts.(16,17) These tests consisted
of steaming and calcining at temperatures as high as 1400-1600°F
prior to testing. They were able to pinpoint preferred zeolites
and matrices for incorporation, where feasible, into the commercial
catalyst.

H_2 Production. The RCC operates with recycled gas, and we soon
recognized that recycled H_2 might serve to partially reverse coking
reactions and perhaps even to catalyze reforming reactions.(18)
Thus, hydrogen generation, in the absence of associated coke
formation, is not necessarily bad. Those of us who had worked on
fluid reforming in the early 1950s recognized that a very low, but
finite, H_2 partial pressure could induce reforming reactions
including dehydrocyclization.(19) Thus, we had mixed opinions
as to the benefits and detriments of H_2 production. Recycling of
high-H_2-containing gas is more difficult to achieve mechanically
because of the low molecular weight of the gas. On the other hand,
protection against catalyst coking and possible enhancement of
yield and high octane producing reforming reactions hold much
promise for even better results with higher H_2 recycle pressure.
Two schools of thought still abide on this unresolved issue. The
RCC unit operates with a significant H_2 partial pressure, gives
rather low coke yields in relationship to Ramsbottom Carbon in the
feed, and makes an unusually high research octane.(5)

Basic Nitrogen. Because of the high basic nitrogen content of
reduced crude, there was concern about how to handle such high
levels of basic nitrogen, which have been shown to poison acid
sites. The issue of constructing a catalyst with minimum
sensitivity to nitrogen has not yet been entirely resolved.
Personally, I am inclined to believe that the presence of an acidic
matrix tends to minimize the neutralization of zeolite acidity by
partial absorption on acidic sites along the walls of feeder pores.
Hence, matrix acidity may offer an additional benefit in catalyst
performance.

Asphaltenes. Asphaltenes are large polynuclear aromatic colloidal
particles that are rapidly and easily converted to coke in yields
of 50-70% or greater. Another asset of the large pore volume,
large feeder pore structure is that it may prevent plugging of
feeder pores to the zeolite by allowing the asphaltenes to deposit
on the walls of large pores, while allowing smaller molecules to
pass by on their way to the zeolite portal surface. See Figure 8,
which also seeks to depict overall catalyst structure and the role
of each ingredient in achieving a superior catalyst.

Normal Paraffins. Early in our work we noted that n-paraffins,
present in reduced crude, are known to be resistant to catalytic

cracking.(22) They would possibly cascade down into light gas oil,
which would give these gas oils a higher cloud and pour point.
While such data are not included in this report, our work has also
shown that in FCC operations the acidic matrix is able to better
crack and isomerize more n-paraffins, thus reducing the n-paraffin
content in middle distillate and thereby the characteristic high
cloud point associated with it, while also raising octane number by
removing or isomerizing n-paraffins in the gasoline fraction.

Burning Rates. The dual pore structure and large pore volume,
together with contaminated metals that are also oxidation
catalysts, very likely have a positive effect on burning rates.
     At any rate, the easy accessibility of oxygen to an
appreciable coke structure due to the open pore structure of these
residuum catalysts has undoubtedly helped regeneration and reduced
or eliminated pore sintering with accompanying catalyst collapse.
The presence of nickel and vanadium as burning promoters is also
helpful, especially when regeneration is accomplished in the quite
unique two-stage regenerator of the RCC process (Figure 19).
     Silica-magnesia matrices have not yet been properly evaluated
as an RCC catalyst matrix. However, such a matrix in conjunction
with stabilized zeolite might provide an attractive matrix with a
Kaolin-enhanced dual pore structure. Silica-magnesia matrices are
notorious for their poor regeneration characteristics. When
prepared by the dual pore Kaolin-enhanced method, they might be
easier to regenerate and, thereby, open up a new family of residuum
catalysts. Such catalysts have not yet been explored.

Catalyst Cost. Catalyst replacement cost represents a large
operating expenditure, in addition to the effect that catalyst
performance (good or bad) can have on yield and associated profit.
Therefore, in addition to all the other objectives, we continually
evaluated catalyst composition and method of manufacture as they
impacted on catalyst cost. Catalyst manufacturing modifications as
they impacted cost were always carefully reviewed and such review
was a key part of the catalyst development program.
     In retrospect, we envisioned a number of alternative catalyst
systems. Although some of them appeared quite promising, the cost
of raw materials, and/or the complexity of a process, or the
unavailability of specific manufacturing equipment or procedures
frequently militated against many attractive alternatives.

Summary

Research to develop a catalyst suitable for processing of residual
feedstocks has focused on the many faceted requirements of such a
catalyst.
     This work has shown that such a catalyst must possess very
high cracking activity that is stable in the presence of steam and
high temperature, but must have good selectivity as well. This has
been achieved by employing Ultrastable Y zeolite, partially
enhanced in activity by addition of a small amount of rare earth,
both in the zeolite and in the matrix.

Figure 19. Commercial RCC Process Unit Reactor and Regenerator

The catalyst must also have acidity in the matrix in order to reduce the molecular weight of molecules too large to enter the zeolite and in order to also convert heavy-cycle oil to light-cycle oil. Our studies have established that good balance in acidity between the matrix and the zeolite tends to enhance selectivity. A stable matrix acidity is also required, and here a high alumina silica-alumina cogel was selected due to its demonstrated stability in the pre-zeolite era. Certainly many other acidic matrices could probably be substituted.

Attrition resistant catalysts are required, but preferably should possess a pore volume in the 0.4 to 0.5 cc/gm range. This increased pore volume apparently helps in facilitating accessibility to the catalyst interior by heavy viscous liquids, and dual pore structures containing pores over 100 Angstroms in diameter also appear to facilitate accessibility to the zeolite while keeping feeder pores open. A porous system, yet attrition resistant and inexpensive, was achieved by incorporation of platelet kaolin clay.

Reduced crystallite size of the zeolite and/or breaking or grinding of clusters of zeolite crystals to individual crystals, also serves to enhance accessibility in the face of asphaltenes, nitrogen-containing molecules, destructive and harmful elements, and other molecular "clutter" associated with the bottom of the barrel.

Vanadium at high levels and in the +5 valence state has been shown to have highly destructive characteristics, while nickel at high levels continues to manifest its undesirable ability to increase H_2 and coke make. Much effort has been directed to controlling vanadium by several strategies including immobilization, trapping, offering sacrificial inexpensive sieves as zeolite substitutes, and finally by valence control. Here the efforts were only partially successful, and valence control through residual coke left on the catalyst to date appears to be the most successful. Antimony can help control nickel. While SO_x control is not a problem at Catlettsburg, due to the presence of a fluidized limestone bed combustor which captures effluent SOx, SO_x transfer capability might also be required in operations in other plants.

Cost is also a most important factor in developing a commercially acceptable catalyst, and includes consideration of both manufacturing and raw material costs. Many catalysts which could meet operating requirements were too costly. To keep costs low, both zeolite content as well as type and rare earth content had to be considered. Kaolin as a low cost extender and filler was of considerable help, but again had its limits.

In attempting to optimize a catalyst of this kind, many factors and parameters must be balanced one against another. Operating factors are also so complex that catalyst evaluation becomes extremely complex and costly. Literally hundreds of catalyst preparations and countless evaluations were undertaken before arriving at a final catalyst for manufacture.

A sound understanding of catalyst fundamentals and reaction mechanisms, an appreciation of catalyst manufacturing restrictions, and perhaps instinctive judgement are all required. Even so it

should be noted that there is still much additional profit to be
gained by further improvement in catalyst performance.

Notwithstanding these limitations, a very effective residual
cracking catalyst was developed, produced in large commercial
quantity and demonstrated to be very effective commercially.

Acknowledgements

In closing, I would like to take this opportunity to express my
appreciation to Ashland Oil for allowing publication of this paper,
and for the opportunity of participating in this exciting catalytic
development. I'd also like to recognize the outstanding contributions of Steve Kovach, Ron Kmecak, Wayne Beck, Ted Cornelius,
Patricia Doolin, Chuck Lochow, Jim Palmer, and all of the other
members of the catalyst research staff. My appreciation is also
extended to Dr. Maurice Mitchell and to Don Lee, Roger Benslay and
all of the members of the pilot plant staff for their untiring and
dedicated contributions. Dr. James Maselli and his staff at
Davison Chemical Company are also to be commended for their
valuable efforts on our behalf for this undertaking. In
particular, I'd like to cite the stimulating encouragement of
Messrs. Oliver Zandona, George Myers, John Hall, Robert Yancey,
Sr., and Robert Yancey, Jr. as being critical to the success of our
catalyst work and to the RCC process as well.

Literature Cited

1. Myers, G. D., U.S. Patent 4 332 673, 1982.
2. Myers, G. D.; Busch, L. E.; U.S. Patent 4 299 687, 1981.
3. Myers, G. D., et al; "Catalytic Conversion of Residual Stocks",
   1979 NPRA Annual Meeting, 1979.
4. Zandona, O. J.; Busch, L. E.; Hettinger, W. P., Jr. "Reduced
   Crude Conversion Symposium on Production, Characterization and
   Processing of Heavy Oils, Tar Sand Bitumens, Shale Oils and
   Coal-Derived Liquids", University of Utah, 1981.
5. Zandona, O. J.; Busch, L. E.; Hettinger, W. P., Jr. "Reduced
   Crude Conversion - An Inexpensive Route to High Octane
   Gasoline", 1982 NPRA Annual Meeting, 1982.
6. Hettinger, W. P., Jr.; Busch, L. E.; Krock, R. P. "Heavy Oil
   Processing Alternatives - The Ashland Approach", Electronics
   in Oil/World Oil and Gas Exhibition and Conference, 1984.
7. Hettinger, W. P., Jr.; Oleszko, T. J. Petroleum Refiner, 1959,
   38, 169.
8. Zandona, O. J.; Hettinger, W. P., Jr. "Reduced Crude Processing
   with Ashland's RCC Process", 47th Midyear API Meeting, 1982.
9. Zandona, O. J.; Busch, L. E.; Hettinger, W. P., Jr.; Krock, R.
   P., Oil & Gas Journal, March 22, 1982, 82-91.
10. Busch, L. E.; Hettinger, W. P., Jr.; Krock, R. P., Oil & Gas
    Journal, December 10, 1984, 79-84.
11. Beck, H. W.; Carruthers, J. D.; Cornelius, E. P.; Kmecak, R. A.;
    Kovach, S. M.; Hettinger, W. P., Jr. U.S. Patent 4 588 702,
    1986.
12. Van Nordstrand, R. A.; Hettinger, W. P., Jr.; Keith, C. D.
    Nature, 1956, 177, 713.

13. Hettinger, W. P., Jr.; Braithwaite, D. G.   U.S. Patent 3 034 994, and U.S. Patent 3 034 995, 1962.
14. Hettinger, W. P., Jr.; et al, U.S. Patent 4 377 470, 1983.
15. Beck, H. W.; et al, U.S. Patent 4 432 890, 1984.
16. Hettinger, W. P., Jr.; et al, Oil & Gas Journal, April 9, 1984, 102-111.
17. Hettinger, W. P., Jr.; et al, "Hydrothermal Screening of Reduced Crude Conversion Catalysts", ACS Meeting, Aug. 1983.
18. Hettinger, W. P., Jr., "Dr. Frank Ciapetta - Pioneer in Catalytic Chemistry", ACS Symposium, March, 1982.
19. Hettinger, W. P., Jr.; et al, I&EC, 1955, 47, 719.
20. Beckman, S.; Morrell, J. C.; Egloff, G.   Catalysis - Inorganic and Organic; Reinhold Pub. Corp.; New York; 1940; p 416.
21. Maxted, E. B.; Poisoning of Metallic Catalysts; Advances in Catalysis; Academic Press; New York, 1951; Vol. III.
22. Greensfelder, B. S.; Voge, H. H.; Goad, G. M., I&EC, 1949, 41 (11), 2573-2584.
23. Anonymous, "Refinery Catalysts are a Fluid Business", Chem. Week, 41, July 26, 1978.
24. Personal communication.

RECEIVED February 25, 1988

INDEXES

Author Index

Affiliation Index

Subject Index

Production and indexing by A. Maureen R. Rouhi
Jacket design by Amy Meyer Phifer

Elements typeset by Hot Type Ltd., Washington, DC
Printed and bound by Maple Press, York, PA